PHYSICS FOR POETS

Robert H. March
Associate Professor of Physics
University of Wisconsin

Physics for poets

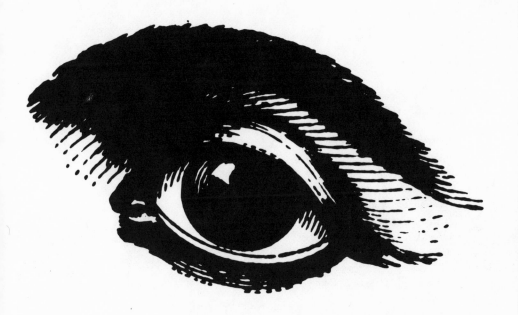

McGraw-Hill Book Company

New York
St. Louis
San Francisco
Düsseldorf
London
Mexico
Panama
Sydney
Toronto

PHYSICS FOR POETS

Library of Congress Catalog Card Number 75-96430

40241

1 2 3 4 5 6 7 8 9 0   MAMM   7 9 8 7 6 5 4 3 2 1 0

Copyrighted material quoted by permission of the publishers includes: "Fragment," by John Ciardi, copyright 1966, Saturday Review Inc.; excerpts from the poem "Excerpts from an Address to the Academy of Fine Ideas," by Wallace Stevens, and from "The Myth of Sisyphus," by Albert Camus, both copyright 1965, Alfred A. Knopf, Inc.

This book was set in Baskerville by The Maple Press Company, and printed on permanent paper and bound by The Maple Press Company. The designer was Merrill Haber; the drawings were done by BMA Associates, Inc. The editors were Bradford Bayne, David A. Beckwith, and Sonia Sheldon. Paul B. Poss supervised the production.

Preface

This book is the outgrowth of a course at the University of Wisconsin for students in the humanities and social sciences. No attempt is made to give a complete or balanced picture of physics as a body of knowledge. Instead, I hope to convey some sense of physics as a human activity, in the profound conviction that, viewed as such, it is neither as incomprehensible nor as removed from the general culture as is commonly thought.

In some ways, this book is more a personal testament than a textbook in the usual sense; my own prejudices have shaped both its style and its content. I believe that both for the general reader and for scientists themselves the specific content of a physical idea is far less important than the process by which it was born. Also, I consider the philosophical implications of an idea to be of more general interest than its applications to specific phenomena. Accordingly, I chose to cover a few topics in depth, rather than try to achieve the breadth of a conventional physics text.

The subject areas emphasized in this book are classical mechanics, special relativity, and the quantum theory, and even within these areas a highly restricted group of topics was chosen. Such traditional topics as geometrical optics and thermodynamics are neglected completely, and others, such as electromagnetism, are given only the skimpiest of treatments. Classical mechanics is covered for its value as a mature scientific theory, and because it deals with a level of reality accessible to the student's intuition. It also provides a basis for understanding the evolution of physics from classical to modern concepts. Otherwise, this book stresses twentieth-century physics. The type of person for whom this book is intended is insulted when he is told that while he can read modern literature, study contemporary art, and wrestle with the problems of modern society, contemporary physics is beyond his powers of understanding.

Classical mechanics offers such a wealth of topics that the selection required for a book of this type is bound to be somewhat arbitrary. The goal was a reasonably unified treatment, without loose ends, to illustrate the growth of mechanics from a simple descriptive science to a conceptual framework of staggering generality. The applications chosen for emphasis are circular motion and gravitation, the latter being one of the most dramatic examples of an intuitive leap that ties together disparate phenomena. Furthermore, it is instructive to realize that the success of this leap made believers of the whole scientific community, even though the empirical base for the claim that gravity was a "universal" force was decidedly suspect until the day of the Cavendish balance. This helps to show the student that science is not as naïvely empirical as is commonly supposed. But a different approach, with greater emphasis on such worthy material as simple harmonic motion or angular momentum conservation, might well have been taken.

No apology is offered, however, for the omission of the traditional treatments of friction and pulley-machines. These have always struck me as dull and artificial topics, revealing little of fundamental significance, and useful mainly to exercise fledgling physicists in skills that may be essential for them but are of little interest to others.

Though in organization this first section is historical rather than topical, it is by no means a history of mechanics. It represents a logically ordered sequence supported by modern interpretations and arguments, rather than an attempt to follow the actual mainstream of the development of mechanics. Only the chronology is historically exact.

The treatment of relativity is perhaps the most unconventional feature of this book. In particular, the reader will search in vain for any mention of the Lorentz transformation, and there is indeed little stress on the concept of "frames of reference." Physicists instinctively accept the notion that reality is described by functions of space-time variables, but untrained students find little meaning in anything so abstract. To teach them special relativity, it is necessary to break down deep-seated intuitive concepts of space and time. This is best accomplished by examples and *gedanken* experiments that illustrate the FitzGerald contraction, time dilation, and clock synchronization problems.   I have found that students taught by this flagrantly heuristic method can often think their way through problems that perplex graduate students in theoretical physics.   More rigorous treatments are available in a number of excellent paperbacks, and it has been the custom at Wisconsin to put at least one such text on the "recommended reading" list of the course.

The development of quantum mechanics is followed in fairly strict historical sequence.   This choice of treatment is natural to happenings recent enough for the student to relate them to the general intellectual history of his own time.   But it is to some extent a forced choice: without presupposing the mathematical training required to handle the Schrödinger equation or commutator brackets, it is almost impossible to treat the field as a unified, deductive scheme.   For the historical background of this subject, I am deeply indebted to Professor Max Jammer, whose truly remarkable volume *The Conceptual Development of Quantum Mechanics* (McGraw Hill, 1966) was a major resource in the preparation of this section.

In order to avoid interrupting the flow of the narrative, most of the numerical examples, derivations, and practical formulas have been confined to an appendix, along with study questions and exercises.   Extreme caution is urged in the use of this material, particularly the exercises.   Many of them will prove far too challenging, unless tutorial help or small-group problem sessions are provided.   Many of the exercises should be used as classroom examples, particularly in the case of relativity and quantum mechanics.

I would like to thank the American Institute of Physics and the editors of *Physics Today* for some of the photographs used in this book and for permission to reprint the quotations from Einstein used in Chapter 10.

Finally, I would like to express my gratitude to many who helped make this book possible: to the patient and imaginative staff of the College Division of McGraw-Hill for their sympathetic handling of this project; to my wife, Georgianna, for her manifold services as editor, secretary, patient critic, and pedagogical guinea pig; to colleagues who have made valuable contributions to my thinking on the material presented, particularly Professor Ugo Camerini and Dr. Bertram Schwarzschild; to my coworkers at Wisconsin and the CERN laboratory in Geneva, Switzerland, for their forbearance with a research collaborator who was pulling his oar at best fitfully during the writing of this book; but above all to the students, especially the irrepressible front-row critics who insisted that they could be taught physics if only their professor could be forced to make sense.

ROBERT H. MARCH

Contents

17

DOES GOD PLAY DICE?
219

18

WHATEVER BECAME OF REALITY?
233

Introduction

To the laboratory then I went.   What little
right men they were exactly!   Magicians
of the microsecond precisely wired
to what they cared to ask no questions of
but such as their computers clicked and hummed.

It was a white-smocked, glass, and lighted Hell.
And there Saint Particle the Septic sat
lost in his horn-rimmed thoughts.   A gentlest pose.
But in the frame of one lens as I passed
I saw an ogre's eye leap from his face.

—JOHN CIARDI, FRAGMENT
  Saturday Review, April 30, 1966

This book is devoted to physics for poets. As such it may fittingly be
opened with a poem, introduced as Exhibit A: evidence of the need for
a book entitled *Physics for Poets*. Not that this book will try to prove
that physicists are just like everyone else. Physicists are *not* regular fel-

1

lows—and neither are poets. Anyone engaged in an activity that makes considerable demands on both the intellect and the emotions is not unlikely to be a little bit odd.

Like many poets, the physicist feels he is looking for "truth." Of course, he defines truth by his own set of rules, and he doesn't think very much about what those rules are (until he gets old, when good physicists often turn into bad philosphers). Thus, he may be just as surprised as the poet to hear that some of those rules have to do with beauty. An idea must be more than right—it must also be pretty, if it is to create much excitement in the world of physics. Creativity in any field has an emotional dimension. This may seem surprising, in view of what we are always told about the rules of scientific objectivity. But these rules only concern the way in which an idea gets its final test. The way in which a new idea arises is usually quite the opposite of objective. And if the idea strikes the audience as beautiful, it is likely to be believed even in the absence of confirming evidence and clung to tenaciously until the evidence against it is overwhelming. The creator of an abstract scientific idea has as much of his personality in it as any artist.

In the current era of emphasis on science education, it has become a cliché to call scientific research a "great adventure." Well it may be; but the student approaching his first hard science course with this maxim in mind is in for a rude shock. Rarely does much of the sense of adventure manage to come through the hard work, for the subject matter often seems both difficult and dull. The student headed for a scientific career is usually told that he must face years of diligent drill before he can understand anything really profound.

But one wonders how many people would love music if they were required to master a good deal of piano technique before they were allowed to listen to, for example, the Beethoven sonatas. True, a concert pianist probably enjoys the sonatas on some levels denied to others, but a reasonably sensitive person with totally untrained fingers can appreciate their beauty. And the analogy with music may not be as farfetched as it seems. To carry it further, this book will let you listen to a bit of Bach and then see how you make out with Schönberg and Bartók.

Of course, we will have to give up something. What this book gives up is nothing less than a well-rounded view of physics. Much of what physicists traditionally consider important and interesting receives only passing mention or is omitted altogether. Heat, sound, optics, and electromagnetism are the principal victims. Instead, we will concentrate on classical mechanics, relativity, and the quantum theory.

Physics has seen two periods of rapid change. The word "revolution" has been much abused of late, but it is probably appropriate. The first revolution occupied most of the seventeenth century and was so complete that almost nothing preceding it can be recognized as physics at all, in modern terms.   The second occupied the first three decades of the current century, and it is not clear that we have seen the end of it.

It is convenient to regard the first revolution as beginning with Galileo and culminating with Newton (with some injustice to many worthwhile predecessors and contemporaries of these two heroes).   It created classical mechanics, probably the most successful scientific theory of all time.   For two centuries, this theory swept all before it, one phenomenon after another yielding to explanation in mechanical terms.   At the end of the nineteenth century, it seemed on the verge of absorbing optics and electromagnetism and achieving the final unity of all physics.   Indeed, to many scientists of that time, it appeared already to have done so, except for a few minor details.   But on these last details it ultimately failed—and failed catastrophically.

The triumph of Newton's mechanics had wide repercussions.   Leaving aside the legion of (mercifully) forgotten nineteenth-century theologians who came to look upon the Creator as a sort of master clockmaker, a number of intellectual trends developed in response to the success of mechanics.   To many of the nineteenth century's philosophers, and even to some of the more influential political thinkers, physics became the model for what an intellectually respectable theory should be.   This was probably unfortunate, for Newton's mechanics was in many respects unique.   There has never been another theory quite like it, in physics or elsewhere.

Indeed, it has nearly survived the second revolution—for Newton's most important concepts are still part of the language of modern physics.   But classical mechanics survives only in an embalmed state, for we now know that it can never again aspire to universality.   It rules supreme in a limited domain, but physics has passed it by and has struck out in new directions.

The second revolution has, in fact, compounded the confusion by striking out in *two* new directions: relativity and quantum mechanics.   The former was largely the creation of one man, Albert Einstein.   The latter grew from the contributions of many thinkers (including Einstein).   Relativity is popularly regarded as bizarre and abstruse, but the quantum theory is far more so.   Both theories were conceived, at least in part, in much the same spirit—that of critical evaluation of the process by which a physicist actually observes the world in which he lives.   Both deal mainly with phenomena that lie outside the realm of ordinary experience.   It is partly for this reason that they are so difficult to teach—the phenomena themselves are beyond our day-to-day experience.   Both theories contain startling concepts that seem absurd or paradoxical, for they conflict with basic intuitive feelings about space and time, cause and effect.

The realm of the quantum theory is the very small, while relativity deals with the very large or the very fast. Where they come together (in the very small very fast world of elementary particles), they have not gotten along too well. Attempts to combine them still have a bit of the appearance of a forced marriage, and it is not yet clear whether the marriage is doomed or merely slow to settle down. In this sense the revolution is incomplete; one tends to feel that these theories must be reconciled or else supplanted.

Part of the difficulty in teaching these new ideas, especially those of quantum mechanics, comes from the peculiar way in which they have developed. Time and again, over the current century, a remarkable pattern of discovery has repeated itself: a lucky guess based on shaky arguments and absurd ad hoc assumptions gives a formula that turns out to be right, though at first no one can see why on earth it should be. Gradually, physicists come to a more or less satisfying interpretation, at least one which satisfies a physicist. They may still feel uncomfortable, but meanwhile the formula cranks out predictions that turn out to be correct, and it is very hard to argue with that sort of success. An explanation clear enough to satisfy a layman may be a long time in coming. Many of these ideas simply have not yet had time to lose their bizarre quality, and physicists are as reluctant as modern painters to devote much effort to explanations of their work for people who seem naïve, philistine, or just not terribly interested. Like any artist, the creative scientist prefers to feel that his work speaks for itself.

Out of consideration for its intended audience, this book must regrettably work with rudimentary mathematics. Some of the beauty of physics is readily apparent only when it is written in its natural language, which is largely mathematical, and a lot of this beauty is unavoidably lost in translation. To ask a layman to study mathematics merely to appreciate physics is as unreasonable (or as reasonable) as asking him to study Italian merely to properly appreciate Dante. Of course, like Italian, mathematics is beautiful in itself and is likely to be useful for a variety of other purposes. A few of the required mathematical concepts are so indispensible that they will be developed as needed, in the text.

The worst possible attitude with which to approach the study of physics is one of awe. Like most successful human ventures, physics has prospered largely by sticking strictly to business. There are problems that lend themselves to the physicist's methods, and the solution of them can enrich the human experience, both materially and intellectually. But the scientific method, powerful as it is in its own domain, is neither universal nor magic. Most of what man values and holds significant must remain beyond its scope. If physicists have achieved much, it has been by limiting their ambitions to that which fell within their capabilities.

1

Falling Bodies and the Birth of Mechanics

SIMPLICIO: *Your discussion is really admirable; yet I do not find it easy to believe that a bird-shot falls as swiftly as a cannon-ball.*

SALVIATI: *Why not say a grain of sand as rapidly as a grind-stone? But, Simplicio, I trust you will not follow the example of many others who divert the discussion from its main intent. . . .*

—GALILEO, TWO NEW SCIENCES

It is not unreasonable to date "modern" physics from the publication, in 1636, of Galileo's *Two New Sciences*. The title refers to two studies, one on the strength of materials and the other on mechanics, the science of motion. In the case of mechanics, the outstanding achievement was a successful quantitative description of the motion of freely falling bodies. Not only was this description sophisticated and exact, but it also introduced the first quantitative concept for measuring change of state of motion, that of acceleration. Later, Sir Isaac Newton was to put this to good use.

In popular history, Galileo is often portrayed as a lone seer, the only objective observer in the midst of a pack of fools willing to trust the authority of ancient philosophers rather than the evidence of their own eyes. But were you to choose at random 10 reasonably portable objects from the room in which you are now sitting and cast them out the highest available window, the chances are that few of them would fall in a manner that much resembles the simple motion described by Galileo. His description of free fall was an idealization, an insight that neglected most of the complexity of the fall of real objects. His adversaries held to a description inherited from Aristotle. While this description had serious flaws, for many examples of fall it came closer to describing the phenomenon than did Galileo's. But Aristotle's insight was no more than a lucky empirical guess, a scientific dead end, while Galileo had taken a giant step toward a deep understanding of motion.

The First Modern Physicist

Galileo lived from 1564 to 1642, spanning the period from the death of Michelangelo to the birth of Newton and exactly contemporaneous with Shakespeare. He was born in Pisa to a somewhat notable but impecunious Tuscan family. His father, a musician and amateur scholar who wrote one of the first modern treatises on harmony, hoped his clever son might recoup the family's fortunes by means of a medical career. But at the university, Galileo's teachers diverted him into mathematics, then as now a far less lucrative profession.

Though he is a hero to all modern scientists, even his greatest admirers must admit that Galileo was often boorish, pugnacious, and petty. He was occasionally unscrupulous in seeking his own advancement, on several occasions claiming credit for the work of others. Tradition pictures him as a glutton and womanizer who lived with a bravura that charmed his friends but outraged his enemies. He had a remarkable gift for the written word and could not resist the temptation to sprinkle his works with elegant insults to his opponents. In short, he was very much the late Renaissance man.

Like most present-day scientists, Galileo had his most productive years, in terms of originality of thought, when he was comparatively young. These coincided with his term as professor of mathematics at the University of Padua, a post he held from the age of 27 to 46. The liberal atmosphere of the Republic of Venice, of which Padua was the second city, was hospi-

Portrait of Galileo by Sustermans.
(*The Granger Collection.*)

7

table to thinkers of Galileo's style. His university and its neighbor in Bologna, the oldest two in Italy, were practically the only schools in the world where "natural philosophy," as the physical sciences were then called, was taken seriously. He had been forced to flee his native Pisa, where orthodoxy was more prized and insults to respected scholars were not tolerated. But in his middle years, he was lured back to Florence, the Tuscan capital, by the promise of a large increase in his already unprecedented salary and freedom from formal teaching duties; thus Galileo's academic career was every bit as modern as his scientific method.

Galileo's brashness proved a severe liability in the subtle politics of the Florentine court. Within 6 years his powerful enemies made good use of the hysterical response of the Roman church to the Protestant Reformation, securing an edict denouncing his work supporting Nicholaus Copernicus' heliocentric universe. But with a man of Galileo's towering reputation, the Church was reluctant to deal in a cavalier manner. The edict was little more than a nuisance, forcing him to treat the Copernican theory as a hypothesis to which he did not necessarily subscribe. With the accession to the papal throne of his longtime friend Cardinal Barberini (Urban VIII) in 1623, Galileo was emboldened. Here might be a chance to cap his career by forcing Church acquiescence to, if not actually adoption of, the heliocentric universe. Accordingly he published, in 1632, his *Dialogue on the Great World Systems*. The work was widely acclaimed almost from the day of publication, and the tone was Galileo at his sardonic best. The book was cast as a Platonic dialogue, in itself an insult to the scholars of his time, who revered Aristotle and imitated his careful analytic style. Moreover, their best arguments were assigned to a character named "Simplico," a country bumpkin whom Galileo handled rather roughly.

Urban was in trouble himself over his personal ambitions and the failure of his military adventures. Setbacks in the Thirty Years' War had forced him to court alliances with Protestant princes. He was thus in no position to come to the aid of an old friend of questionable orthodoxy. Furthermore, Galileo's enemies whispered that Simplicio could be taken as a caricature of Urban himself. The Pope stepped aside and let the Inquisition do its work. Under threat of torture, Galileo recanted his "heretical" views. The last decade of his life was spent under the watchful eye of the Church, though his work continued to appear abroad in editions he was obliged to denounce. This period saw the publication of his greatest work, the *Two New Sciences*.

A present-day physicist reading the work of Galileo can hardly fail to recognize in him a colleague, one whose style of thought and argument are fully contemporary. Were a time machine to deposit Galileo in a twentieth-century university physics laboratory, it is easy to imagine him buckling down to work on the most interesting problems. More than likely, he would find university deans, foundation officials, and most of his fellow physicists as repugnant as he found their Florentine counterparts. His attitude toward the value of experiment, and his reluctance to bring up questions more general than demanded by the data on hand, are exactly those attitudes drilled into young researchers in the course of study for a Ph.D.

The era in which Galileo worked was quite hospitable to the emerging natural sciences. The late Renaissance had elevated the lay scholar to a high station in public life. The recent invention of the printing press had opened the way to wide, rapid dissemination of new ideas. This destroyed the monopoly of learning of the academies and monasteries, where close personal contact and isolation from lay support helped to keep heretical scholars in line. A worldly humanism, with an infinite faith in the power of man's reason, and a pagan love of life constituted the spirit of the times. Galileo had the effrontery to publish in the vernacular Italian rather than the Latin of a respectable scholar. His opponents could hardly overlook the implied insult; Galileo had left the narrow confines of established scholarly debate and taken his case to a public he regarded as more open-minded than the established authorities of the academies. Even today, a scholar whose ideas meet with a poor reception in academic circles will be in considerable trouble if he decides to promote his views in, for example, the science columns of the daily press.

But, repugnant as it may have been to the academic establishment, Galileo's style of work was well established by this time. A group of scholars with comparable methods of work had formed several nascent scientific organizations. Galileo was a member of one of these, the Academia dei Lincei, which had a kinship both with a learned society and a secret fraternity. Its members met to dine and debate, fostered scientific correspondence, and aided members and their protégés in securing publication of their works. Thinkers of this stripe had many places to turn to for financial help, partly because of the general intellectual atmosphere and partly because they were the first to bring the analytical tools of scholarship to bear on the practical problems of the artisan, thereby creating the modern ties between science and technology.

Galileo Takes On Aristotle

The central intellectual event of the early Renaissance had been the rediscovery of classical Greek philosophy, particularly the works of Aristotle. The Greek intellectual heritage had been preserved through the Middle Ages by the Arab civilization, which until at least the thirteenth century had every right to look down on Europe as a barbarous backwater. In the early stages of Europe's recovery, such scholars as St. Thomas Aquinas molded ideas taken from Greek thought, notably the work of Aristotle, into an all-encompassing world view known as *scholasticism.* The scholastics were most concerned with moral philosophy and theology and added little to the Greek achievements in physics. These had centered on static problems; the Greeks had made only a modest start in dealing with motion. Thus the scholastic philosophy of nature emphasized the static order of the universe, with every object in its proper place, revealing perforce the wisdom of the Creator. Motion was a temporary and possibly unnatural state, not totally unworthy of study, but certainly of secondary importance. A stone fell because it sought its natural place, on the ground; flames lept up to seek reunion with the divine fire of the stars. To inquire into the messy quantitative details of such processes, when their larger cosmic role was already well understood, was regarded as a sterile exercise. In the three centuries between Aquinas and Galileo, scholasticism had frozen into a dogma of almost scriptural rigidity. Its proponents felt smugly that it encompassed nearly all that was worth knowing, and respectable scholars spent their lives myopically working through the works of Aristotle.

But Aristotle had not completely ignored motion. In particular, he had formulated a quantitative description of the motion of falling objects. He asserted that if one compares bodies falling in the same medium, one will find that they fall with speeds proportional to their weights.

From the point of view of a physicist, this was a very good hypothesis, not because it was right, but because it could be either very right or very wrong. A quantitative statement of the sort Aristotle had made is valuable because it really commits a theory to a severe test. If I were merely to predict that the sun will rise tomorrow, the statement would hardly cause much excitement. But were I to predict that it would rise tomorrow exactly 1 minute and 32 seconds later than today, I would leave myself open to being proved wrong by a trivial check of a watch. It is a cardinal rule of the scientific method that a hypothesis is useful only if it can in principle be proved wrong. Speculations that are not testable are regarded as "unscientific."

Demolishing Aristotle's falling-body law took little effort on Galileo's part, because some of its predictions are so wrong that they can be easily refuted. Indeed, its falsity had been recognized at least as early as the sixth century by the philosopher John Philoponus. Thus, by adhering to every word of Aristotle as second only to the scriptures in authority, the scholastics left themselves open to demolition by appeal to everyday experience. In the following excerpt from *Two New Sciences,* Salviati, the author's spokesman, does exactly this with the hapless Simplicio and a third interlocutor, Sagredo, a reasonably intelligent practical-minded humanist much like those Galileo sought as an audience when he wrote in Italian.

SALVIATI: I greatly doubt that Aristotle ever tested by experiment whether it be true that two stones, one weighing ten times as much as the other, if allowed to fall, at the same instant, from a height of say, 100 cubits, would so differ in speed that when the heavier had reached the ground the other would not have fallen more than 10 cubits.

SIMPLICIO: His language would seem to indicate that he had performed the experiment, because he says: "We see the heavier": now the word *see* shows that he had made the experiment.

SAGREDO: But I, Simplicio, who have made the test can assure you that a cannon ball weighing one or two hundred pounds, or more, will not reach the ground by as much as a span ahead of a musket ball weighing only half a pound . . . .

The excerpt is an excellent example of Galileo's forensic style. Not content to merely demolish the Aristotelian theory, the author cannot resist the temptation to get in a dig at the methods of the classical scholar, by holding up to ridicule Simplicio's excessive concern for the exact meaning of every word in Aristotle's work. Unhappily, this particular form of scholarly nit-picking is not yet extinct, as any college student can testify.

Aristotle also stated that a falling body instantly acquires its speed of fall; an equally simple argument serves to dispose of this prediction:

SALVIATI: But tell me, gentlemen, is it not true that if a block be allowed to fall on a stake from a height of four cubits and drives it into the earth, say, four finger-breadths, that coming from a height of two cubits it will drive the stake a much less distance, and from the height of one cubit a still less distance; and finally if the block be lifted only a finger-breadth how much more will it accomplish than if merely laid on the stake without percussion . . . and since the effect of the blow depends on the velocity of the striking body, can any one doubt the motion is more than small whenever the effect is imperceptible?

Of course, the argument does depend on the unproved (but reasonable) assumption that the speed of the falling block is what determines its effectiveness as a pile driver, but how explain the phenomenon in Aristotle's terms, where the distance fallen should have no effect whatsoever?

However, tearing down is always easier than building up, and there had been many critics of Aristotle. Galileo earned his present place in scientific esteem by offering his own description of the motion of falling bodies: "In a medium totally devoid of resistance all bodies will fall at the same speed . . . [and] . . . during equal intervals of time [a falling body] receives equal increments of velocity. . . ."

The words "totally devoid of resistance" were crucial in this description; they represent the abstraction from nature that led to Galileo's success, and they provided a means of countering Simplicio's observation (see the heading of this chapter) that heavier bodies do indeed fall somewhat faster. Those words were a daring innovation, because "totally devoid of resistance" implies a *vacuum*. Not only was it impossible in practice to achieve a vacuum in Galileo's time, but the prevailing scientific thought regarded a vacuum as a most unnatural state: "nature abhors a vacuum." Furthermore, some ancient thinkers about motion regarded the medium in which a body moved as essential to supply the motive force; Simplicio at one point is depicted as expressing doubt that motion can even take place in a vacuum.

Nonetheless, Galileo could not cavalierly dismiss Simplicio's objections. Feathers indeed fall more slowly than cannonballs. Galileo was sure the effect was due to retardation by the medium, but it was beyond his powers to prove this conclusively. He was forced to offer arguments that merely made it seem plausible:

> Have you not observed that two bodies which fall in water, one with a speed a hundred times as great as that of the other, will fall in air with speeds so nearly equal that one will not surpass the other by as much as a hundredth part? Thus, for example, an egg made of marble will descend in water one hundred times more rapidly than a hen's egg, while in air falling from a height of twenty cubits, the one will fall short of the other by less than four finger-breadths.

In short, if the deviations from his law are far worse in dense media than thin ones, is it not reasonable to suppose they disappear if the medium is absent altogether?

Of course, it is always preferable to be able to account in a precise fashion for deviations from a proposed scientific statement, but failing this, an argument like that above is usually convincing enough. Science is far less absolute in its requirement of agreement with experiment than is commonly supposed, and nearly all contemporary scientific papers will contain at some point the sort of reasoning used by Galileo to deal with this case.

As a final touch, Galileo insisted, in a quite sophisticated fashion, that the question of the possibility or impossibility of a vacuum was quite irrelevant to the validity of his law. This is a very modern point of view, yet at the same time very ancient, dating from Plato and Socrates. It is possible to understand nature in terms of approximation to an ideal state, even if that state cannot possibly exist in nature.

But the acid test of Galileo's law lay in his assertion that speed increases with time of fall. To demonstrate this he had to invent some of the modern mathematical language to deal with motion. This is the real starting point of modern physics, so we must pause to develop the necessary concepts.

The Mathematical Language of Motion

Speed and *velocity* are terms familiar to anyone raised in the twentieth century. Actually, the two terms have distinct meanings in exact scientific parlance, which will be explained further in Chapter 3, but even physicists slip and use them interchangeably. Speed may be defined as follows:

$$\text{Average speed} = \frac{\text{distance moved}}{\text{time elapsed}}$$

The qualification "average" is necessary in recognition that the speed may not have been the same in all parts of the time interval. Expressed more concisely in conventional symbols, our definition becomes:

$$\bar{v} = \frac{\Delta s}{\Delta t} \tag{1}$$

Here the Greek capital delta (Δ) has been used to denote "change" or "interval," reminding us that the measurement compares two different positions at two different times. Of course, we could have used one-letter symbols for Δs and Δt, but this common device serves to jog the memory and more fully convey the significance of the formula. Similarly, the bar over the v is one of several conventional ways of saying "average value of" whatever symbol is found beneath. The use of s as a symbol for distance is conventional, for some obscure reason. Part of the role of mathematics in science is as an extension to the language, and notation is chosen for reasons of clarity.

If you were to use Equation (1) to compute the speed of your car in, say, ½-hour of city driving, taking odometer readings and the time on your watch, you might obtain 17 miles per hour. But this could conceal 5 minutes at a dead halt in a traffic jam and a few daring seconds at 70 mph. A lot of detail of the motion is obviously left out. To make the description more complete, you might further subdivide the trip into 1-min intervals, calculating the average speed for each interval. When must this process stop?

The physicist's answer is pragmatic, "When I have enough detail to answer the question at hand." As a rough guide to the harsh realities of modern city driving, your original measurement was probably pretty good. But suppose you want the kind of figures that enable you to tell how well your car performs? A physicist would reason as follows: A car can change its speed by perhaps 10 mph in 1 sec, when accelerating or braking hard. Thus, if I choose intervals of $\frac{1}{10}$ sec, the speed at the beginning of the interval will differ from that at the end by at most 1 mph. In

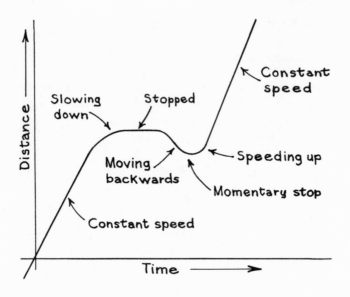

Figure 1

1 millisecond $(\frac{1}{1000}$ sec$)$ I can get a result good to within $\frac{1}{100}$ mph, and so on.

Figure 1 serves to illustrate graphically the problem. If an object is moving at constant speed, the relation between distance traveled and time elapsed is a straight line. The steeper this line, the greater the speed. The steepness of a graph is called its *slope*. When speed is changing, the slope is also changing. The distance-time graph of a motion at changing speed is thus a curved line.

When the speed is not constant, the measurement of an average speed leaves out much detail of the graph. In Figure 2 we see that measurements over smaller intervals more nearly represent the actual motion.

There are two tacit asumptions being made here. One is that no matter how small I make the time interval, the velocity measurement is still meaningful. The other and more subtle one is that no matter how precise a value I want, I can obtain it simply by choosing a sufficiently small time interval. Since we seem to be assuming that something called instantaneous speed exists, presumably measured over infinitesimal intervals, we might as well write down some symbols that enable us to talk about it in our new mathematical language of motion:

$$v = \frac{ds}{dt} \tag{2}$$

In this formula, a lowercase d replaces the delta to remind us that we're speaking of an interval so small that nothing changes significantly, and we've dropped the bar on the *v* because it is therefore no longer necessary to think of this as an average.   This equation is a statement in the mathematical language known as the *calculus*.   Read aloud by a physicist or mathematician, it becomes:

Speed is the derivative of position with respect to time.

The word "derivative" means almost the same thing as "rate of change of"; so completing the translation into ordinary English, Equation (2) is simply the sentence:

Speed is the rate of change of position with respect to time.

To one trained in the calculus, the formula is a clearer statement than the sentence and certainly easier to write.   This is why mathematically trained scientists find it difficult to converse without the aid of a blackboard.   It is like trying to speak in a foreign language that doesn't have "just the right word" for what you are trying to say.

Now that we have a definition of instantaneous speed, we can cope with motion at any instant without having to deal with a complex motion as a whole.   For the purposes of studying laws of motion, this idealized instantaneous velocity turns out to be far more useful than the average

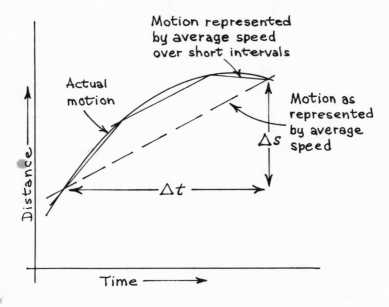

Figure 2

value. To a mathematician, the instantaneous speed is something qualitatively distinct from the average speed. To a physicist, who recognizes that any measurement takes place over a finite time, the derivative is merely a refinement of the concept of average. All that he needs is the assurance that by choosing a sufficiently small interval, he can obtain a *real* average measurement that is as close as he desires to the ideal instantaneous value.

The next step in the development of a mathematical language to describe motion is to obtain a means of describing the way in which a body changes its speed. Earlier we commented that an automobile can change its speed by 10 mph in 1 sec. It is exactly this kind of statement that best describes change of speed: how much does the speed change in how much time?

With the armament of the calculus, we can proceed to deal with this description by defining a new quantity, called *acceleration,* which is the change in speed divided by the time interval over which the change of speed took place:

$$a = \frac{dv}{dt} \tag{3}$$

Referring back to Figure 1, it is clear that when acceleration is present the line describing the motion must be curved. If the object is speeding up, the graph curves upward. If it is slowing down, it curves down.

Note that since speed is a derivative, acceleration is the derivative of a derivative, called a *second derivative.*

The concept of acceleration handles equally well processes of speeding up and slowing down. In the latter case the change in velocity (and therefore the acceleration) is negative. So we need no separate concept of "deceleration." And it should be noted that the first and second derivatives need not both be positive or negative. A car which is moving forward (positive speed) but slowing down (negative acceleration) has a positive first derivative and a negative second derivative.

One might imagine asking how acceleration itself changes: what is the significance of the third derivative? Interestingly, this proves to be not too important in the study of motion and does not even have a generally accepted name, though a few physicists have proposed calling it "jerk."

The units for expressing speed are familiar enough (miles per hour, feet per second, etc.). How about acceleration? Clearly, it is a unit change in speed divided by a unit of time. For example, we stated above that the acceleration of a car never exceeds about *10 miles per hour per second*. Physicists abhor such mixed units and would probably report studies of automobile acceleration in *feet per second per second,* using the same units for time in both speed and acceleration. This expression they

contract to *feet per second squared,* abbreviated ft/sec², to avoid the awkward phrasing (the word "square" refers in this case to repeating a process
of measurement, not to squaring as in arithmetic).

The Crucial Test

Galileo used the concepts developed above, though without the aid of the
full panoply of tools of the calculus, to derive an interesting result which
could be compared with experiment to test his theory.   He obtained the
relation between distance traversed and time elapsed for a uniformly accelerated body starting from rest.   His law of falling-body motion is nothing
more, in our new language, than the statement that "*a* is a universal constant for falling bodies."   That is to say, if we measure the acceleration
of a falling body, we will find it the same at all times during its fall,
and the same for all bodies.

When a body starts from rest with *a* constant, its average speedup
to any given moment must be one-half its present speed at that moment.
This can be seen by means of a little arithmetic on the numbers in the
second column of Table 1.   The numbers in the table represent a constant

TABLE 1

Time, sec	Speed, m/sec	Distance fallen, m
0	0	0
1	10	5
2	20	20
3	30	45
4	40	80
5	50	125
6	60	180
Average speed = 30 m/sec		

acceleration (note the equal speed changes in equal time intervals) of
10 meters per second per second, which happens to be very nearly that for
a freely falling body.   This result may be expressed as follows:

$$\bar{v} = \frac{v}{2} = \frac{at}{2}$$

which reads, "To find the average speed, multiply the acceleration by the
time to get the final speed and divide by 2," because the body was speeding
up and thus was going faster at the end than at all times earlier.   To

get the distance traveled in a time interval, we multiply the average speed by the time:

$$s = \bar{v}t = \frac{at}{2}t = \frac{at^2}{2}$$

In interpreting this formula, we should always remember that the factor $\frac{1}{2}$ comes from the fact that the average speed is half the final speed, and the time is squared because it enters in twice; it allows the body to speed up and also allows it to move farther at whatever speed it is going.

To demonstrate his proposition that falling bodies acquire equal velocity increments in equal times (which is tantamount to showing that the distance traveled varies as the square of the time), Galileo faced serious experimental difficulties. With the best time-measuring instruments of his era, he could scarcely measure intervals to a fraction of a second. Yet a heavy object dropped from a tower 150 ft high will reach the ground in only 3 sec!

To solve this problem, Galileo chose to study the roll of a ball down an inclined plane. By ingenious arguments he asserted that this would "dilute" the motion of a falling body (i.e., reduce the acceleration) without fundamentally altering its character. This assertion had to be taken somewhat on faith, because Galileo did not have a complete theory to show exactly what effect the inclined plane would have. But a new theory in physics is rarely complete as first presented; there are often large logical holes that must be filled in later.

Using a smooth board with a small tilt and a groove to guide the ball, Galileo was able to produce indoors a motion that took about 10 sec to complete. His timer was crude but adequate for this experiment: a vessel of water with a hole in the bottom that he closed by means of his finger. When the finger was removed, water flowed into a cup. Afterward, the cup was carefully weighed. The amount of water in the cup was a measure of the time. The results agreed with Galileo's prediction. To argue that this result had any bearing on the problem of free fall was of course a bit of a logical leap. But ideal experimental conditions are hard to come by, and indirect tests, supported by arguments that are plausible but not completely rigorous, play an important role in the development of a young science.

Was Aristotle So Wrong After All?

The scholastics might have fared better in arguments with Galileo had they a spokesman capable of using his style of argument. Let us explore the question of falling body motion as Galileo's adversary for a while. If we were actually to observe the fall of a body from a great height, measure its speed at all times, and present the results in a graph, we would obtain the curve shown in Figure 3. The reason for this curious behavior is very simple. As a body speeds up, the resistance of the air to its motion increases. Eventually, a speed is reached where the force resulting from the rush of air matches that pulling the object down, and no further acceleration takes place. This speed is called the *terminal velocity* of the object. Interestingly enough, if we compare bodies of the same size and shape, their terminal velocities are very nearly proportional to their weights, as in Aristotle's falling-body law. A heavy steel ball falling from an airplane might require thousands of feet to achieve terminal velocity; a human body acquires it in a few hundred feet—the secret of sky diving, which is a long fall at terminal velocity, followed by the opening of a parachute to lower the terminal velocity to a safe value for landing.

Now it is far easier to study the motion of a body with a low terminal velocity, for example, a light object falling in a dense medium, such as a golf ball in water. This kind of object is what Aristotle spent most of his time discussing. There is no a priori reason for assuming this approach to slowing down falling-body motion to a reasonable speed is any less legitimate than Galileo's choice of an inclined plane. An object can acquire terminal velocity in a fraction of a second in a dense medium, and a graph of its speed versus time might look like the curve in Figure 4.

The graphs look even more striking when we consider that actual measurements must of necessity be of *distance* and time. A real experiment, if made with instruments available in Galileo's time and with its results presented in graphical form, as is customary in scientific journals, might look something like Figure 5.

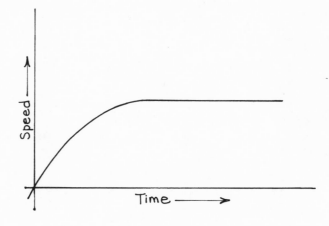

Figure 3

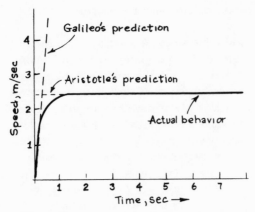

Figure 4

From these data a reasonable man might conclude that Aristotle was closer to the truth than Galileo. All we have to do is admit that the process of acquiring speed is not quite instantaneous, and Aristotle is out of the woods, with only a small modification of the original hypothesis. Add to this the notion from classical philosophy that the medium is in fact the source of motive power for the descent, and that the vacuum which Galileo regards as *his* ideal situation is a most unnatural state, and we might reasonably conclude that Aristotle must be dealing with the more fundamental situation, while Galileo has been led astray by his excessive

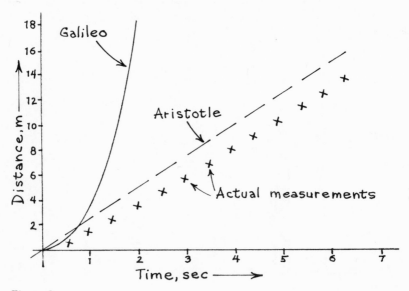

Figure 5

concern with a short-time phenomenon which goes away if we watch long enough. "Surely," we might tell Galileo, "you have allowed yourself to be misled by the fact that heavy objects falling in air for some reason take a long time to reach their natural speed. Besides, the only good data you have comes from the inclined plane, which may not be relevant to the problem of free fall."

But, it turns out, this quite reasonable point of view is wrong—not that it is a worse approximation to nature, but the regularity observed by Aristotle proves to have a far less fundamental significance than that observed by Galileo, viewed in the context of the subsequent development of the science of mechanics.

Indeed, Galileo described experiments with falling bodies in fluids and realized there was some value in Aristotle's work, though he was vain enough to attack him on a minor point—that Aristotle did not take into account the difference in weight between an object submerged and the same object in air, an effect discovered after Aristotle's time by Archimedes. With this correction, Aristotle's prediction would have worked out better, but Galileo, with his debater's instinct, insisted on holding Aristotle's latter-day followers to the original version, and they were too hidebound to strengthen their case by updating the theory.

Nonetheless, Galileo reasoned that the motion of falling bodies in fluids was sensitive to too many minor factors, such as the shape and the size of an object as well as its weight, to represent an important fundamental rule of nature. He found his *own* regularity, a universal speed and a uniform acceleration, far more appealing as a "law of nature," and subsequent developments bore out his insight. But it represented something more than mere observation and shows that the vaunted objectivity of science is not as naïve as it appears on the surface.

The message to be learned from this exercise in devil's advocacy is that there is nothing automatic about scientific progress. Suppose this particular problem were currently on the research frontier. A well-trained modern Ph.D. physicist might well receive a large research grant to study falling bodies, which he could use to acquire large quantities of data on falling objects in all possible combinations of shape, size, weight, medium, etc. He and his students would strive to refine their measurements, producing a deluge of papers for the scholarly journals. It is not inconceivable that, faced with the necessity for explaining all these data to a reasonable degree of accuracy without a complete theory, they would move toward a point of view like that of Aristotle and overlook Galileo's insight altogether. Science is more than a mere attempt to describe nature as accurately as possible. Frequently the real message is well hidden, and a law that gives a poor approximation to nature has more significance than one which works fairly well but is poisoned at the root.

2

Toward
a Science
of Mechanics

If I have seen farther than others, it has been by standing on the shoulders of giants.

—Isaac Newton

Mere description, no matter how precise, is only a primitive first step in the development of a science. Galileo understood this thoroughly when he dismissed his own work on falling bodies as merely "some superficial observations." Describing one form of motion, he realized, was of little value in dealing with the problem of motion in general. There was a clear need for general principles applicable to many or all forms of motion.

A few such principles had been proposed by Galileo's time, and he had the insight to choose the most significant, refine them, and finally demonstrate their power by solving the difficult problem of projectile motion. Then, a few decades later, the French philosopher René Descartes formulated a truly original law, the value of which was demonstrated in his treatment of collisions between objects. These two achievements are the topic of this chapter. They brought mechanics from the descriptive stage to the *phenomenological* phase of its development. When a science reaches this stage, general principles are used to find connections between a limited number of phenomena, but these principles do not yet constitute a complete theory. That latter step had to await the work of Isaac Newton, the hero of the next chapter.

Galileo's claims for his ideas on mechanics were modest, but they reveal a conceit that underlies the conservatism of the cautious empirical methods employed by all modern scientists: "There have been opened up to this vast and most excellent science, of which my work is only the beginning, ways and means by which other minds more acute than mine will explore its most remote corners."

Physicists tend to be wary of general speculation when they think it is premature, that is, when it goes beyond what is required to solve those problems which have been clearly formulated. They are of course interested in the ultimate goal of a beautiful and general theory, but are cautious about moving too far ahead of the solid base of empirical knowledge. This attitude often leads to misunderstandings between physical and social scientists. Many of the most celebrated social and economic thinkers appear, to a physicist, to be constructing sweeping general theories of society long before the simplest phenomena in their field are understood. Of course, the goals of social science are vastly different from those of physics. For the physicist, the theory is an end in itself, and he must have the patience to wait until the time is ripe for a general theory to emerge. A social theory that is only partly correct may still serve as a useful guide to social action.

Projectiles Follow Parabolas

Galileo used two simple principles in his analysis of projectile motion:

> The principle of inertia: *A body moving on a level surface will continue in the same direction at constant speed unless disturbed.*
>
> The principle of superposition: *If a body is subjected to two separate influences, each producing a characteristic type of motion, it responds to each without modifying its response to the other.*

The principle of inertia was, like the description of falling-body motion, a choice between two extreme ways of idealizing a complex phenomenon. The motions we observe in the real world all have some tendency to continue after the agent causing the motion is removed, but the motion persists only for a limited time. To cite two extreme examples, consider a stone dragged across rough ground, or a chunk of ice sliding across a frozen lake. Most ancient thinkers generalized from the former case and dismissed the persistence of motion as a temporary condition. By Galileo's time, however, the men who founded modern physics preferred the opposite generalization: motion has a natural tendency to persist unless the roughness of the surface interferes.

Each point of view had some appeal to the intuition, and there was no obvious basis for a choice between them. Once again, the most significant test in the final reckoning was not which idea more nearly described the motions ordinarily observed in nature, but which ultimately led to a deeper understanding of nature. Galileo's approach led straight to the triumphs of Newton, whereas the ancient picture had nowhere to go.

The acceptance of the principle of inertia completely changed the direction of speculation about motion. It brought a recognition that there was a certain kinship between an object at rest and an object in motion in a straight line at constant speed. This kinship is intuitively obvious to twentieth-century man, familiar with smoothly moving conveyances like airplanes and ocean liners; it is difficult to detect any signs of motion without looking out the window. But Galileo and his contemporaries had never had such an experience. Thus, it was quite a feat to come to the realization that it was not motion itself, but deviation from simple constant motion, for which a cause had to be sought. The essence of the experimental method is that when you finally get around to asking nature the right question, she will give you a simple answer; Galileo had indeed stumbled across the right question, even if the final answer was to prove a bit beyond his grasp.

To illustrate the application of Galileo's two principles, let us repeat his analysis of the motion of a projectile, as shown in Figure 1. He imagined this motion to be compounded of two independent, noninterfering components. One was a vertical motion—that of an object thrown straight up and returning to earth. The horizontal component was simply motion at constant speed. The principle of superposition tells us that if one were to run beneath a moving projectile at this constant speed and look up, the motion one would observe would be exactly the same as that of an object thrown straight up.

To describe the vertical motion, let us backtrack a bit and complete Galileo's picture by describing the motion of an object thrown upward. Such a body *diminishes* in speed in exactly the same fashion that one traveling downward increases its speed. In the upward portion of the motion, the effect of the acceleration is to reduce the velocity; in equal time intervals, the body *loses* rather than gains equal increments

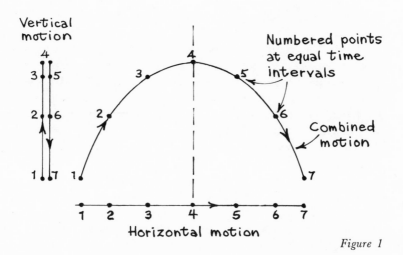

Figure 1

of speed. In any part of its upward travel, it loses exactly as much speed as it would gain in the corresponding downward portion. The ascent looks exactly like the descent would if it were photographed by a motion-picture camera and shown in reverse. The body rises and loses speed until it (instantaneously) comes to rest at the apex of its flight. In a time equal to that required for its rise, it falls back, hitting the ground with the same speed it had when it left the ground.

Now it is simple to analyze the combined motion. Let us choose as our objective predicting the horizontal distance it will land from its starting point. This distance is commonly called the *range,* for which we will use the symbol R. In order to use the principle of superposition, we must describe the projectile's motion as it leaves its source in terms of *two* speeds, one horizontal and one vertical. The horizontal speed V_h is the horizontal distance covered per unit time, ignoring the vertical motion. The vertical speed V_v is the height risen per unit time, ignoring the horizontal motion. We assume that somehow we know V_h and V_v. The principle of inertia tells us that V_h will not change. Horizontally, the body covers the same amount of ground in equal time intervals. Galileo's description of falling-body motion tells us what will happen to V_v; it will diminish proportionally to time, become zero at the apex of the flight, and ultimately become negative as the object falls. Both the horizontal and vertical parts of this complex motion are simple motions we already know how to describe.

To predict the range, we need know only two things: how fast the object is moving horizontally, and how long it is in flight before it hits. Call the horizontal speed V_h and the total flight time t. We then have the simple relation

$$R = V_h t \tag{1}$$

25

To obtain t we must deal with the vertical motion, for it is that component that determines how long the body will remain in flight. Our symbol t is the time required for the body to lose its original speed V_h, come to rest at the apex of its flight, and regain a downward speed of V_h. As we have shown, this is twice the time required for just the descending part of the trajectory. This change in speed is the result of the acceleration the body is undergoing, and the two are quantitatively related by

$$\Delta V = at$$

Thus, to calculate the time of flight, we need only divide the change in velocity by the acceleration and multiply by 2 to cover both the ascending and descending portion:

$$t = 2\frac{\Delta V}{a} = 2\frac{V_v}{a}$$

Now that we know t, we can make use of Equation (1), and we obtain the result we have been seeking:

$$R = V_h\frac{2V_v}{a} = \frac{2V_hV_v}{a} \tag{2}$$

Rather than measure V_v and V_h separately every time we want to predict the range of a projectile, it is simpler to measure the total speed V. This is convenient because a gun, for example, if loaded in the same way each time, will fire its projectile at very nearly the same speed each time. The well-known theorem of Pythagoras gives us a simple relation between the total speed and its components, apparent from Figure 2:

$$V = V_h{}^2 + V_v{}^2$$

This theorem is a useful adjunct of the principle of superposition: it tells us that, to find the *total* motion, compound two perpendicular components by means of the pythagorean theorem. With this step we are very near the concept of a *vector,* which will be developed further in Chapter 4.

Galileo used this analysis to construct a simple "artillery table," giving the range of a projectile in terms of the speed of the projectile and the angle at which the gun is pointed. The rulers of his time had as lively an interest in military technology as those of our day, but Galileo's table hardly qualifies as a practical example. Since his analysis ignores air resistance, the table is absolutely useless for any practical purpose. Air resistance could shorten the range of a cannonball of Galileo's time by hundreds

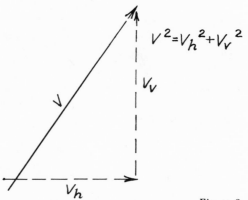

$$V^2 = V_h{}^2 + V_v{}^2$$

V_v

V

V_h

Figure 2

of yards. Besides, to make practical use of the table, the velocity of the projectile when it left the gun would have to be measured, which was out of the question with the instruments then available.

What was *most* significant to Galileo's contemporaries was that he proved the path of a projectile was a parabola, which we can easily demonstrate. Looking at the trajectory from the apex down, the vertical distance covered is, of course, proportional to the square of the time, since it is the motion of a body falling from rest, which we discussed in Chapter 1. Meanwhile, the horizontal motion is proportional to the time. Thus, the vertical distance fallen is proportional to the square of the horizontal distance covered. Since ancient times it had been known that this relation between vertical and horizontal distances from an apex is the unique property of a parabola. By the "motion picture in reverse" analogy, the rising portion of the trajectory looks the same. Even though no precise experimental test was then possible, it struck the geometrically minded philosophers of Galileo's time as so reasonable that it lent credence to his methods. After all, the parabola is one of the simplest curves known to mathematicians. Any reasonable observer can see that a projectile follows some curve, and a few had even guessed that it might possibly be a parabola. But until Galileo, nobody had been able to attack the problem from a theoretical point of view with anything like a convincing argument. Though the cardinal rule of modern physics, enunciated by Galileo himself, is that arguments are to be settled only by recourse to experiment, even when no experimental test is possible, a seemingly reasonable and pleasingly simple result will attract a lot of support to a theory, for everybody wants to see it come true.

Physicists commonly assume that nature is simple; Newton even later elucidated this credo in as many words, and nearly all physicists take it as an unstated article of faith.   But it is, in a sense, a self-confirming hypothesis.   If a problem turns out not to have a simple solution, a physicist will come to regard it as not fundamental.   When pressed to explain what he means by a "fundamental" law, a physicist is ultimately forced to invoke the essentially aesthetic criterion of *simplicity* or *elegance*.   Many physicists have been known to express surprise that elegant laws of nature do exist; it seems nature has been almost too helpful.   But physics, at least on its most fundamental level, is a science which has no obligations to the phenomena it studies.   If they prove too complex, they are usually dismissed as insufficiently fundamental and forgotten, unless a later generation finds them of practical value and takes the trouble to work through all the detail.   Thus, few physicists are even aware of the true path of a projectile, subject to air resistance.   It is a complicated curve mathematically difficult to describe, and thereby less "fundamental" than Galileo's parabola, even though the latter is a useless approximation to nature for nearly all practical purposes.   Indeed, the details of projectile motion in the air were not really worked out until our own century.

The history of physics contains many such examples of whole fields of study in which the original problem that served as the starting point was never fully solved, but was abandoned after it had served its purpose.

Descartes and Momentum Conservation

The next major contribution to the development of mechanics came from the French philosopher René Descartes, born one generation after Galileo.   While Galileo had made a good start at building mechanics from the bottom up, Descartes tried to work from the top down.   His goal was to construct a general philosophy, as a replacement for that of the scholastics, by means of his own meditations and analytical methods that placed great emphasis on the discovery and use of "first principles."   Having only the piecemeal education of a young man of the lower gentry trained for a military career, he disdained scholarship and erudition, placing little stock in the work of others.   For example, there is no indication that he was even acquainted with the works of Galileo.

In terms of goals and methods, he was in many respects more nearly akin to the ancient philosophers than Galileo, whose style was entirely modern.   To this day, French academic training encourages the use of the cartesian style of argument, in which a basic principle is isolated and then followed by impeccable deduction to conclusions of truly astonishing and often infuriating scope, a practice that does not always sit well with more empirically minded scientists in other lands.

The achievements of Descartes' mechanics fell far short of his projected goals, but he left two indelible marks on the history of physics. First, he directed attention to the problem of the interaction of two moving objects, an emphasis Newton was to turn to great advantage. Second, in the process of studying this problem, Descartes demonstrated the power of a remarkable format for constructing a law of nature, the *conservation law*.

A conservation law might be called the scientific equivalent of the familiar French aphorism, *plus ça change, plus c'est la même chose* (the more things change, the more they remain the same). Applied to a complex process in which things are constantly changing, a conservation law is an assertion that some simple quantity remains the same. The true power of this kind of law was not fully realized until well after Newton's time. Present-day physicists are so accustomed to thinking in terms of conservation laws that many attempts to formulate new basic laws of physics are phrased in this form.

A conservation law rarely provides a complete description of a process, for in spirit it implies that the details need not be considered—they will work themselves out. Herein lies its power, for it is exempt at the outset from the necessity of dealing with a phenomenon in all its complexity. To make an analogy with the social sciences, it is as if a political scientist worked out a means of predicting the exact electoral vote of a presidential candidate without being able to tell which way any particular state would go.

The law that Descartes used to analyze the simple problem of the collision of two bodies was that of the *conservation of momentum*. Momentum, to Descartes, was the product of the weight of a moving body and its velocity. Newton later made the minor but significant substitution of *mass* for weight, a distinction which need not concern us at this point. The law asserts that when two bodies collide, the sum of their momenta will not change. It is best illustrated by means of an example. (See Figure 3.)

Imagine two bodies free to move on one of the "frictionless" surfaces beloved to writers of physics texts. One is stationary and weighs 3 kilograms (abbreviated 3 kg), while the other is moving at 10 m/sec and weighs 2 kg. (From this point on we shall be very cartesian and employ the highly rational metric system of units, eschewing the English system, which is after all merely a modern patchwork codification of several sets of nearly unrelated medieval trade units, designed to minimize the social dislocation involved in adopting new units, a practice the French might call typically Anglo-Saxon.) Before collision, the total momentum is

$$p = (10 \times 2) + (0 \times 3) = 20 \text{ kg-m/sec}$$

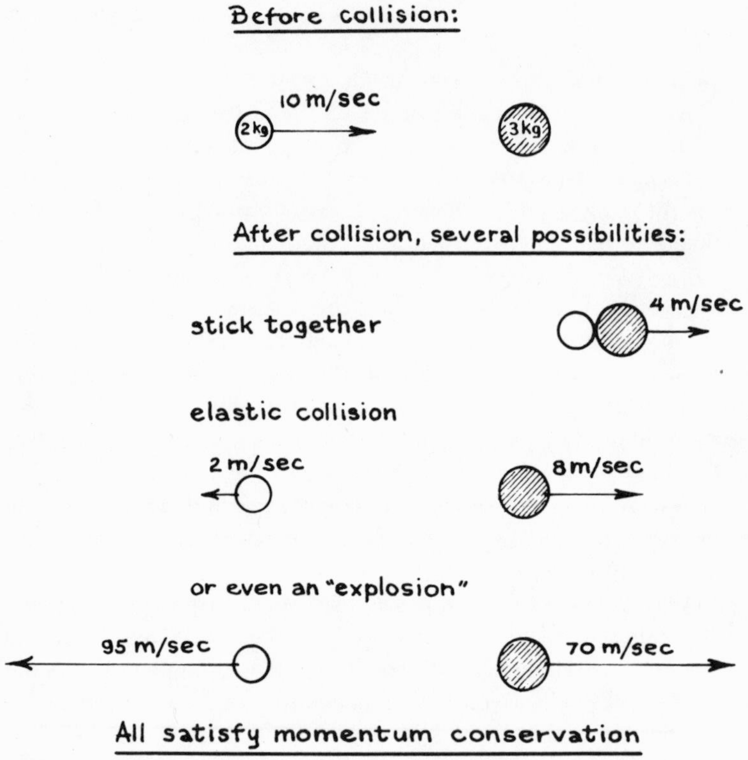

10 m/sec

(2 kg) ⟶   (3 kg)

After collision, several possibilities:

stick together   4 m/sec

○◍⟶

elastic collision

2 m/sec   8 m/sec

◀─○   ◍⟶

or even an "explosion"

◀────── 95 m/sec ○   ◍ 70 m/sec ──────▶

All satisfy momentum conservation

Figure 3

The use of p for momentum is another peculiar tradition, and the unit kg-m/sec unfortunately has no name of its own. ·

The law says that after the collision this sum will be the same. That is all it says. It does not pretend to assert what speed either body will have. Further information is necessary to settle that question.

The simplest case comes if the additional information is merely the qualitative assertion that "the bodies get stuck to each other." Then we have a combined body of weight 5 kg. In order to have a momentum of 20 kg-m/sec, the same as before the collision, this body must have a speed of

$$20 \div 5 = 4 \text{ m/sec}$$

To give another example, the additional information could be a measurement of the speed of one body after the collision. For example, we might find that the struck body is moving at 8 m/sec after the collision, in the original direction of motion of the moving body. Its momentum is then

$$3 \times 8 = 24 \text{ kg-m/sec}$$

Since this exceeds the original momentum, the 2-kg body must have *negative* momentum; it must be moving back along its path with a momentum of —4 kg-m/sec. Thus its velocity must be —4 ÷ 2 = —2 m/sec. This is in fact what would happen in an "elastic" collision, such as that between two hard balls; but we need either the measurement described above or another law separate from that of momentum conservation that tells us what happens in elastic collisions in order to predict what will happen. Elastic collisions are those which leave the *relative* velocity of the two bodies unchanged.

The law of momentum conservation also covers the situation in which the 2-kg body is moving 95 m/sec backward, while its partner moves 70 m/sec forward, and so on through any combination that gives the right total momentum.

Indeed, we have already oversimplified the problem by assuming that the collision is "head on," and that the bodies move along the original line of motion after collision. If we consider motion in two dimensions, like the balls on a billiard table, a wide variety of possibilities is opened, and both the analysis and the amount of information needed to describe the process completely become more complex. And if we were to go into the question of what is going on during the instant the two bodies are actually in contact, we would have to deal with a highly complex motion. These are among the many details the law has chosen to sweep under the rug.

But in this very incompleteness lies the value of the law. A whole host of different processes are covered by the same quantitative statement. Though it describes no single process in detail, it permits us, for example, to tell exactly what happens to one body after the collision by means of measurements made solely on its partner, which in itself no mean accomplishment.

It is characteristic of the lofty ambitions of Descartes' philosophy that conservation of momentum appears not as a statement confined to the simple two-body collision. Momentum, Descartes felt, was the Creator's own measure of the "quantity of motion," and the amount of momentum in the *universe as a whole* was eternal and unchanging, a demonstration of His rationality and omnipresence. This sweeping point of view brought Descartes into a somewhat pointless debate with Leibnitz as to what constituted a proper measure of the quantity of motion. Galileo might well have been more conservative and avoided the debate. But Descartes' conjecture, though far beyond the scope of any problem he could analyze in detail, is now regarded as correct. Furthermore, it set physics on the path of analyzing the universe by breaking it down into the interaction of objects taken in pairs, a simplification physicists have never been able to abandon with any great success.

An Amusing Result: The Center of Mass Doesn't Move

To close this chapter, we derive an amusing side result of the law of momentum conservation. It is of no great significance in itself, but it provides a good example of the application of the law. Furthermore, it will prove useful later in the development of the theory of relativity. The theorem in question is the statement that if the center of mass of a group of objects is stationary, no interaction among the objects can cause it to move.

The concept of "center of mass" was familiar to the ancient Greeks, and is equally familiar to any child who has played on a seesaw, for the "center of mass" is nothing but a modern term for the "balance point." Few readers are unaware that if a 90-lb child wishes to balance his 45-lb younger sister on a seesaw, he must sit half as far from the center as she does. Stated somewhat more mathematically, a seesaw is in balance if the product of *weight* and *distance* is the same for both

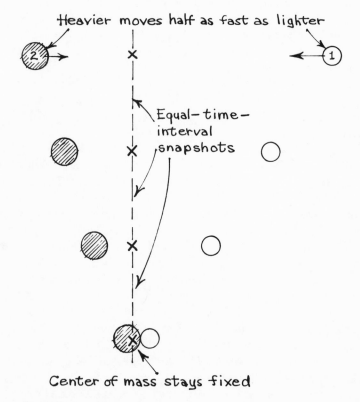

Figure 4

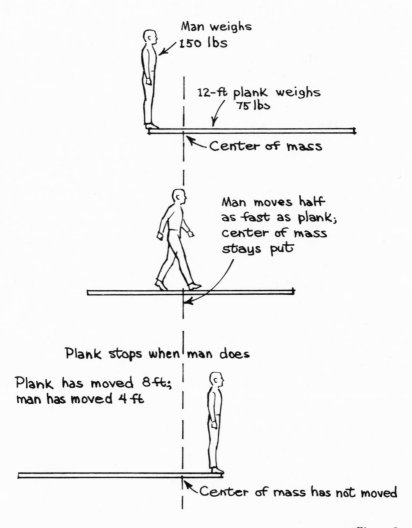

Man weighs
150 lbs

12-ft plank weighs
75 lbs

Center of mass

Man moves half
as fast as plank;
center of mass
stays put

Plank stops when man does

Plank has moved 8 ft;
man has moved 4 ft

Center of mass has not moved

Figure 5

riders. A child weighing 10 percent more need be only 10 percent closer to the center than his partner; if he weighs twice as much, he must sit half as far out.

If we consider the somewhat more difficult case of two *moving* objects, it is clear that if the center of mass is to stay put, the heavier must move more slowly than the lighter. If a 90-lb object and a 45-lb one are approaching one another, as long as the heavier one moves half as fast the center of mass, the balance point, stays put.

But from Descartes' point of view, this is merely the situation where the *total momentum is zero.* Two objects approach (or recede from) each other, the heavier at the proportionally slower speed. Their momenta remain equal and opposite. As long as no external influences come into play, the total momentum will remain zero.

Thus, if two cannonballs are fired at one another, and one is twice as heavy but moving half as fast, if they stick together they will be at a dead halt; and at all times in their motion, the center of mass will be two-thirds of the way between, closer to the heavier object, as shown in Figure 4.

As another example, imagine a tug-of-war between two people on roller skates. The heavier will move less, and they will ultimately collide at their center of mass, closer to the heavier one.

As a final example, consider Figure 5, in which a 150-lb man is standing at one end of a 75-lb plank set on the ice so that it moves freely. As he starts to walk to the other end, he pushes the plank back. Since it weighs half as much, momentum conservation dictates it must move twice as fast. If the plank was 12 ft long, the man actually moves 4 ft, while the plank slides back 8. When he gets to the other end and stops, the plank stops too. Since he has moved half as far as the plank, which weighs half as much, the center of mass has not moved.

3

The Denouement: Newton's Laws

*He has so clearly laid open and set before our eyes
the most beautiful frame of the System of the World,
that if King Alphonse were now alive he would not
complain for want of the graces of simplicity or of
harmony in it.*

—ROBERT COATES, PREFACE TO THE PRINCIPIA
second edition, 1713

In 1665, a scant 33 years after the publication of *Two New Sciences*, a young Fellow of Trinity College at Cambridge sat in a farmhouse in the obscure Lincolnshire village of Woolsthorpe and put the finishing touches on Galileo's "vast and most excellent science." Driven from the crowded university town by the Great Plague, Isaac Newton made remarkable use of his period of forced isolation from the intellectual environment he had adopted, returning to the small freehold on which he had been born only 23 years before.

A comparison of Galileo and Newton provides an interesting study in contrasts. Galileo's worldliness and arrogance could hardly be more remote from Newton's polite and almost mystical reserve. Galileo thought on his feet and was fond of public controversy; Newton was moody and introspective and left his friends to fight most of his battles for him. Where the former could hide his skepticism behind a formal capitulation to the Inquisition without unduly burdening his conscience, the latter remained throughout his life a convinced, if not fanatical, Puritan. Galileo's family hoped his studies would restore him to the elevated rank they regarded as the proper family station in life, while it seems likely that Newton's parents would have been content to see him succeed them as a simple dirt farmer.

England in the latter half of the seventeenth century was also a far cry from Galileo's Italy, especially for a physicist, or "natural philosopher," as they were then called. Galileo fought his way to celebrity through controversy and continually had to face personal vilification. Newton eased into prominence in the English intellectual establishment by the time he was 27, when Isaac Barrow resigned the illustrious post of Lucasian Professor of Mathematics at Cambridge in his favor, calling his successor a man of "unparalleled genius." It would be pleasant to report that, like Galileo's departure from Padua to Florence, Barrow's magnanimity had created a tradition followed by many of his scientific descendants. Unfortunately, the history of physics, and indeed of academic life in general, knows few comparable examples of altruism. Contrast also Galileo's irregular Academia dei Lincei with the robust, established Royal Society of Newton's time. When Newton was elected to membership in 1672, at 30 years of age, the society was only 12 years old, but it had enjoyed from its inception the favor and patronage of the crown, the respect of the leading scholars of England, and the support of many members of the British aristocracy and mercantile class.

But there is no set scenario for success, no one perfect personality type, no one most hospitable environment for a phenomenon as ephemeral as scientific creativity. Out of strife Galileo marshaled the nerve to defy his enemies and ask the right questions; Newton's carefully nurtured talents achieved the depth to come up with the right answers for a world receptive to his point of view.

Newton's Laws

Newton's complete theory of motion, one so perfect that it remains nearly intact to this day, was based in the main on two key insights:

1 The central problem in mechanics is that of change of state of motion, i.e., deviation from the behavior described in the principle of inertia.

2 Such a deviation can result only from the interaction of two objects, both of which have their motion altered in the process.

In order to treat the problem quantitatively, Newton needed three concepts—acceleration, force, and mass. Acceleration, as defined originally by Galileo, he took as the quantitative measure of the rate of change of state of motion. Force, as a measure of the strength of the agent causing the change, was a concept already prevalent in his time. Mass was in great part in his own invention, an index of the capacity of a body to resist a change in its state of motion. Newton regarded it, in fact, as the true measure of the "quantity of matter" in a body. In his great work, *Philosophiae Naturalis Principia Mathematica* (commonly known as the *Principia,* published in 1686), he defined mass as follows:

> The quantity of matter is the measure of the same, arising from its density and bulk cojointly.

This definition has been justly criticized as being of little practical value, as it gives us no indication of how we can determine quantity of matter for any particular object. Later in this chapter we shall see its value.

Next, consider Newton's definition of "quantity of motion," which is none other than Descartes' momentum:

> The quantity of motion is the measure of the same, arising from velocity and quantity of matter cojointly.

The language is archaic; in mathematical terms, it reads:

$$\text{Momentum} = \text{mass} \times \text{velocity}$$

Armed with these definitions, we are prepared to present Newton's celebrated laws of motion, again in his own words:

> Law I: *Every body continues in its state of rest, or of uniform motion in a right [straight] line, unless it is compelled to change that state by a force impressed on it.*
>
> Law II: *The change in motion [rate of change of momentum] is proportional to the motive force impressed; and is made in the direction of the right line in which that force is impressed.*
>
> Law III: *To every action there is always opposed an equal reaction; or, the mutual actions of two bodies are always equal, and directed to contrary parts.*

The meaning is somewhat obscured by Newton's choice of language, which was designed to appeal to an age in which Euclid's geometry remained the finest intellectual monument. The first law we recognize as Galileo's principle of inertia. The second is usually restated as the equation

$$F = ma \tag{1}$$

As we shall shortly see, this equation can be made to serve as the quantitative definition of both mass and force. But to make any further progress, it is necessary to understand the key role played by the third law.

The Third Law Is the Key

At first sight, Law III might appear the least significant of the three. Few of us have escaped introduction to it in grade school science class, with the recoil of a gun or the perils of stepping from a boat to a dock cited as vivid examples. But the third law is the offspring of the second key insight mentioned at the start of this section and represents the culmination of the line of investigation opened by Descartes' analysis of the problem of transfer of motion between colliding bodies. To fully appreciate its significance, let us reconstruct a chain of reasoning (not necessarily Newton's own) leading to it.

1 We start by observing that a change of state of motion requires the mutual influence of two or more bodies; let us give this influence the name *force*.

2 We take due note of the fact that the two interacting bodies are not usually equally affected; in particular, the lighter of the two seems to come off much the worse.

3 Nonetheless, let us make the following gamble: let us define the force as the same on both objects and try to formulate the laws of motion in such a way that it is the difference in some attribute of the objects, rather than in the force, that is responsible for the difference in their behavior. If all the differences can be accounted for quantitatively in this fashion, our gamble will have worked.

Behind this explicit statement lies a momentous implication: we have removed from mechanics the distinction between *active* and *passive* partners in motion. *Force* has been defined as an *interaction* between partners, between which no qualitative distinction can be made. The "action" and "reaction" are the inseparable components of a *single* interaction, which we give the name *force*. In most examples of motion, the active-passive distinction seems a natural one: imagine a horse pulling a cart, a boy throwing a ball, or a moving object striking a stationary one. Like falling-body motion and the principle of inertia, we must see beyond that first intuition.

Thus, according to Newton, when you walk along the ground you are pushing back against the earth, which gives you an equal push in the opposite (forward) direction, impelling you forward. That the earth moves backward you must take on faith; no instrument available can detect the tiny acceleration imparted by the puny force of a human leg to a mass as immense as that of the earth. But if you walk instead on a tread-mill, which has far less mass than the earth, the truth of the third law seems far more reasonable.

This discussion presents us with the opportunity for a brief digression into an exercise in a rather sophisticated form of argument fashionable in twentieth-century physics, called the *argument from symmetry,* or some-times the *principle of insufficient reason.* Such arguments are simple in concept, but represent a reasoning process uncommon in everyday life. You may have to read this paragraph several times before you get the point. By means of such an argument, we maintain that once the active-passive dis-tinction is removed, it is almost inevitable that the action and reaction must act in opposite directions, for that is the simplest way to avoid making a distinction between the two objects. This argument is illustrated in Figure 1. In cases *a* and *b*, the forces on the two bodies are oppositely

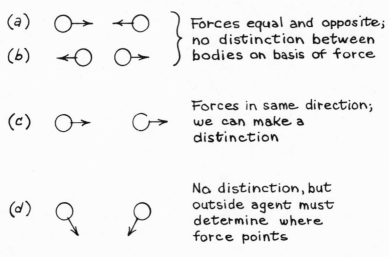

(a) Forces equal and opposite;
(b) no distinction between bodies on basis of force

(c) Forces in same direction; we can make a distinction

(d) No distinction, but outside agent must determine where force points

Figure 1

directed, and no distinction between the two objects can be made by looking at the forces. Case *c* shows both forces in the same direction, and we can make such a distinction; for example, we could say that we define as "active" that body that the reaction acts *toward*. We can avoid such a distinction by means of some peculiar contrivance such as that of case *d*, in which the forces remain symmetric, not pointing more toward one object or the other, yet not opposite either. But then we must introduce some outside agent, a *deus ex machina* that tells us in just what directions those forces will act; for only if the forces lie along the line joining the bodies will the positions of the bodies themselves be sufficient to indicate the direction of the force.

The argument is by no means rigorous, and indeed arguments from symmetry seldom are. But they serve as a guide to what is "reasonable" within the structure of a simple theory and are particularly useful in the early stages of formation of theoretical ideas.

The Logical Consistency of Newton's Laws

Now we are ready to turn to the problem of providing operational definitions of force and mass—definitions that will tell us how to determine the mass of a given object or the force on it. To do this, we follow a scheme proposed in the late nineteenth century by the physicist-philosopher Ernst Mach. By the time Mach wrote, physicists had been using Newton's three laws with great success for two centuries, without worrying too much about their logical consistency. Mach's treatment rejects Newton's definition of mass as "quantity of matter" as useless for all intents and purposes, since it gives us no way to measure the mass of an object without having some other definition of "quantity of matter," and Newton has provided no such definition. True, Newton speaks of density and bulk (volume), but there is no other definition of density than mass per unit volume, so the reasoning is circular. Mach saw in the second law the proper way to define mass.

To start with, we assume that we can measure time and distance with the aid of clocks and rulers. To this day, physicists have no better definitions for these two basic entities: time is what clocks measure, and distance is what rulers measure. Given time and distance, it is possible to measure speed and acceleration, using the definitions in Chapter 1.

Next we must choose some object as a standard of mass. This is no hypothetical step for there is a real standard mass: the standard kilogram that resides, well protected, in the International Bureau of Weights and Measures in Paris. It is the world's only standard mass. No standard pound exists; both the United States and Britain define a pound as

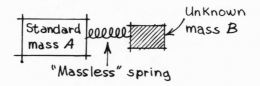

When spring released, measure speeds:

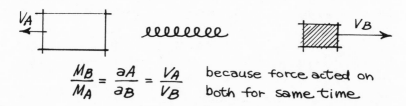

$$\frac{M_B}{M_A} = \frac{a_A}{a_B} = \frac{V_A}{V_B}$$

because force acted on both for same time

Figure 2   "Practical" definition of mass.

0.4535924 kg and trust the French to take care of the kilogram. On rare occasions, in order to standardize the measurement of mass everywhere, the standard is hauled out and compared by careful weighing on a sensitive balance with its "stand-ins" that travel around the world. Of course, for most purposes, nobody bothers with either the standard or its stand-ins; there are plenty of weights around that are good enough, unless you are terribly fussy.

Even though we have not yet defined force, we have the third law to reassure us that there is one situation in which we know that the force on two objects has the same value; namely, when they are interacting with one another, and no other bodies are involved. We can compare any object of unknown mass with our standard by letting them interact and comparing the accelerations produced. For example, we could let them collide or we could use the setup depicted in Figure 2, where they are tied together, separated by a compressed spring. When released, they will fly apart, subject to the force exerted by the spring. (We have exercised the physicist's prerogative of assuming that we can produce a spring whose own mass is too small to be of any significance in the measurement.) Since the third law assures us that we are dealing with the same force on each body, any difference in acceleration results solely from the difference in mass. We can use Equation (1) to equate the product of mass and acceleration for the two bodies, eliminating all mention of the force:

$$ma = MA$$

41

which, with a minimum of algebra, we can rewrite as

$$m = M \frac{A}{a} \qquad (2)$$

This equation is our definition of mass. We now have our prescription for determining the mass of an object, and we can perform the experiment pictured in Figure 2. If, for example, the unknown mass experiences twice the acceleration of our standard mass, we know its mass is one-half that of the standard.

The definition of force now follows free of charge—it is merely Equation (1). Now that we have a way to determine the mass of an object without actually measuring the force on it, we can measure any force by measuring the acceleration it produces on an object of known mass. The force is then the product of the mass and the acceleration. The unit of force is the unit of mass times the unit of acceleration; in the metric system, using the meter as the distance unit, the kilogram as the mass unit, and the second as the time unit (this is known as the MKS system of units), the unit of force is the kilogram-meter/second², or, appropriately, the *newton*. (Physicists customarily honor departed colleagues of particular eminence by naming units after them; they then insult them by refusing to capitalize the names of the units.)

At this point, I hope you are enraged and ready to challenge the circular reasoning in the last few paragraphs. For we have reduced Newton's laws to nothing but definitions, which in principle cannot be experimentally tested. To recap the argument, we first assumed the second law to hold in the experiment that defines mass, and then we used the same law to define force. It is as if we had written into the football rule book the additional rule that "the best team is the one that wins." That would end all arguments as to whether the best team had won, for the winner becomes best by definition. No experiment can show the second law to be false, for we cannot know what the force is until we have measured the acceleration it produces. Then what physical content do Newton's laws have? Is it really possible that Newton has constructed laws of nature by pure logic?

By no means; Mach's analysis of Newton's laws does indeed reduce the second law to the status of a definition. But in so doing, it shifts the essential physical content of the laws to the very definition of mass that he rejects at the outset. To see this, let us try to imagine how Newton's laws, as interpreted by Mach, can possibly fail, remembering that no physical theory is valuable unless it can be imagined to be wrong. It is easy to quote examples that, if true, would render Newton's laws entirely useless.

Suppose we found, for example, in repeating the experiment in Figure 2, that by compressing the spring a different amount or by using a different spring, we obtained a different ratio of accelerations and therefore a different "mass" for our unknown body.   Then the definition of mass would become useless; there could be a different mass for a body in every mechanical situation.   We could still use our definitions to measure a mass or a force, but we would have no assurance that the next time the object showed up it would have the same mass, or that the next time a force showed up it would have the same numerical value.   The laws would have no predictive value whatsoever.

To return to the football analogy, suppose Wisconsin beats Michigan, Michigan beats Army, and Army beats Wisconsin.   Are they *all* best?   We are forced by our definition to answer in the affirmative.   If our silly definition stands, it is of no value whatsoever.   It didn't help us to predict the result of the Army-Wisconsin game.

When Newton defined mass as quantity of matter, he implied by these words much more than he explicitly said.   He made it clear by the choice of words that he was referring to something which would be constant and unchanging; whenever two bodies interacted, whatever might be the nature of the force between them, you could count on their masses being always the same.   Unless this is true, the laws have no value.   The definition also implies that mass will have other useful properties, without which mechanics would become awfully complicated.   For example, it implies that identical objects must have identical masses, that the combined mass of two objects fastened together will be the sum of their individual masses, and so on.   Mach recognized this value, although he did not give it quite the emphasis it deserves, and, as a practical scientist, he also recognized the emotional value of Newton's belief in his definition of mass.

The definition of force also turns out to correspond to some previously existing notions of force; for example, the force exerted by a spring proves to be proportional to how much the spring is stretched.   Thus, though Newton's laws require a new definition of force and a new concept called mass, force turns out to be an old friend, and mass is closely related to another old friend, weight.   Though it is irrelevant to the purely logical underpinnings of the theory, such an intuitive base enormously enhances the value of an idea.

. It is rare indeed for the first version of a physical theory to be completely consistent in its logic.   It is far easier to achieve a neat logical structure in the leisure and safety of reexamination of a successful theory than in the original flash of creative insight.   Newton believed that he had found the *true* measure, perhaps even the *Divine* measure, of quantity of matter, and that it was the crucial element in determining how a body would behave in motion.   This belief was scientifically naïve, in the sense that the words "true" and "Divine" have no meaning in a scientific context, where one is concerned mainly with the prediction of the results of measurement. But without this belief, how likely does it seem that Newton would have been able to summon the intellectual power, or, if you will, the emotional resources, to see through the complex problem of all the diverse forms of motion found in nature to find a few simple rules that explained them all?

The history of science holds few examples of men who have made great strides without an emotional commitment to the value and significance of what they were doing. And since these emotions, these values, lie outside the pragmatic rules used to test scientific theories, they may seem on first inspection "unscientific." But, like chess, science is a far more complex game than its simple "rules" imply. In Chapter 5, when we study gravitation, we shall see how scientists often believe for centuries in a pretty theory that fits in with their general frame of reference, despite the absence of any confirming evidence.

Momentum Conservation as a Consequence of Newton's Laws

Having achieved the vantage point provided by Newton's laws, it is instructive to look back at the work of his predecessors, Galileo and Descartes. To begin with, Descartes' law of conservation of momentum is certainly contained in Newton's laws. This is quite easy to demonstrate.

The rate of change of the momentum of a body is identical with the force on it, as Newton said in his original statement of the second law. When two bodies are interacting, the third law assures us that the forces on the two are the same, but in opposite directions. Thus the changes in momentum are also opposite in sign. The changes in momentum cancel each other, and the *combined* momentum of the two bodies always remains the same.

Newton's laws even support Descartes' stronger claim for his law of momentum conservation: that the law applies to the universe as a whole. This extension contains a hidden assumption, however. If Newton's laws are *complete,* meaning that there is no form of motion that they cannot describe, it must be that any motion involving many bodies can be broken down and analyzed in terms of their "pair-wise" interactions; a complex motion is simply the sum of the motions produced by the interaction of bodies, taken two at a time. This is merely another example of the principle of superposition, which we can take as "Newton's fourth law." The assumption has been retained throughout the subsequent history of physics. It is by no means a trivial one, nor is it self-evident that it will necessarily work. There are severe mathematical difficulties in deal-ing with even the motion of three bodies all exerting forces on one another.

One should not be misled into thinking that Newton's laws are noth-ing more than cartesian mechanics in new words. As we saw in the last chapter, Descartes' law finds its greatest utility in its very incomplete-ness. Regardless of the complication of any form of motion, it is always possible to ignore the messy details. The law of conservation of momentum gives a "thumbnail sketch" of what happens in an encounter between two moving bodies. But the concept of force in Newton's mechanics demands more effort and promises a more complete reward. If the forces between two bodies are completely understood, it is possible to specify *all details of their motion at all times,* a task impossible in Descartes' scheme. This single overwhelming fact set the tone of Newton's own subsequent work and that of most of his successors, and had profound philosophical repercussions.

Falling Bodies in Newton's Scheme

The examination of Galileo's work on falling bodies in terms of Newton's laws provides an excellent example of how the internal logic of Newton's theory forced him to seek a deeper understanding than had his predecessors. To Galileo, the descent of a falling body was merely one example of motion, and once he had found a correct description there was nowhere else to go: the result did not necessarily have further implica-tions. But if we imagine Newton trying to make sense out of Galileo's findings, we find ourselves led down a remarkable path from which it is extremely difficult to turn back.

To start with, since a falling body undergoes accelerated motion, Newton was forced to conclude that there must be a force acting on it—a very peculiar force, indeed, because since the acceleration is constant, the force is constant. Wherever the body is, whatever its speed, this force apparently does not change.

Furthermore, the acceleration is the same for all falling bodies. This is a most astonishing feature. There is only one way to account for it: the force must be proportional to the mass of the object. Then, in com-paring two objects, if one is twice as massive as the other it will also have twice the force on it. The two effects compensate, and the accelera-tion remains the same.

This is the reason for the necessity of making a distinction between the *mass* of an object and its *weight.* The latter is our mysterious force that causes bodies to fall. By some fantastic coincidence, it seems to be proportional to the mass, but even in the absence of this force, or when responding to other forces or moving horizontally, a body still displays mass. Indeed, we find, when sufficiently careful measurements are made, that the *weight* of a body is slightly different in different parts of the world, but its *mass* never changes. Newton correctly emphasized the distinction between the intrinsic, universal property of *mass* and the peculiar phenomenon of a force related to mass, *weight*.

Numerically, the weight of an object is its mass times the acceleration due to gravity:

$$w = mg$$

Thus, an object that has a mass of 1 kg *weighs* about 9.8 newtons, according to a physicist. This causes some confusion between the language of physics and common usage, where mass units (gram, kilogram) are referred to as *weight*. Of course, what is being referred to in common parlance as weight is most nearly akin to the physicist's concept of mass. Just because a kilo of gold weighs somewhat less at the equator than at the pole does not mean there is any less gold there.

But Newton was not free to stop at this point in his analysis. One must not forget the third law. It is not sufficient simply to say that a falling body has this peculiar force on it. Some other body must be interacting with it, and the identity of this body is by no means obvious. But Newton had no choice: either he could ignore the whole phenomenon, or he could account for this mysterious force and find the partner demanded by the third law. Thus, in a sense he was forced by the logic of his own theory to invent the law of gravity! That he succeeded in doing so was a triumph, for the combination of his laws of mechanics with the law of gravity enabled him to explain the motions of the planets in the solar system in terms of laws that could be tested and forces that could be measured right on the surface of the earth.

This was the achievement that caught the imagination of Newton's generation and won him universal acclaim; in one stroke he removed the ancient distinction between Divine celestial motions and the common movements encountered in daily life. He brought the heavens down to earth, and, in his own age at least, even the poets thanked him for it. Newton had no need for the fabled chance encounter with an apple to inspire the theory of gravitation. He was committed by his own logic to a difficult course—one could hardly take his theory seriously unless it could account in some reasonable way for Galileo's celebrated result. In the end, Newton was forced to go all the way to his greatest triumph.

4

Vectors, Circles, and the Problem of Direction

It would be pleasant at this point not to interrupt the story, to move directly to the concept of gravitation. But first we must finally come to grips in a systematic fashion with the problems raised by the fact that little can be said about motion without talking about *direction*. To deal with this problem, in this chapter we will introduce the concept of a *vector*, which both helps in visualizing the problem and provides a mathematical shorthand for referring to it. We shall then use this concept to analyze a simple form of motion, that of an object moving in a circle.

Arrows

There is no more vivid way to put across the notion of direction than to draw an arrow. In doing so, we can take advantage of a long cultural conditioning to the arrow as an indicator of direction.

The simplest instance in which direction must be specified is that of position, although it applies equally well to velocity or acceleration. In any event, the easiest way to designate a direction is simply to point to it by drawing an arrow:

But an arrow can say a lot more than direction, for we can draw an arrow of any length; the length of the arrow can be used to indicate how far or how fast. For example, if the arrow above designates "one mile northeast," the one below can be used to say "two miles west":

Or equally well, we might use the length of the arrow to represent speed, with our first arrow standing for 10 m/sec and the second for 20 m/sec, or the first for 800 m/sec and the second for 1,600, as we are perfectly free to choose our own scale. Following a standard terminology, we will refer to the length of the arrow as its *magnitude,* for the word "length" has specific implications of *distance* that are inappropriate when talking of, for example, velocity or force. This is the source of the distinction between speed and velocity mentioned earlier: *velocity* is a vector, and *speed* is its magnitude, without referring to direction.

This combination of magnitude and direction is spoken of as a *vector.* As stated above, any physical quantity, such as position or distance, velocity, force, or acceleration, can be considered a vector. Quantities that do not involve direction, such as mass or time, are called *scalars.* A scalar can be represented by one number, and then we have said all we can say about it.

Now that we have taken the road sign designer's arrow and made a big thing out of its length, we will go much further and invent a number of interesting mathematical operations to perform with vectors, which turn out to correspond with situations that arise in the "real" world.

Comparing Vectors in the Same Direction

The simplest thing we can do with a vector is to *multiply it by a scalar.* In plain language, multiplying a vector by a scalar, let us say 1.5, means "make another vector 1.5 times as long *in the same direction.*" One way to represent this symbolically would be to essentially combine a picture and an equation:

$$\nearrow \;=\; 1.5 \times \;\nearrow$$

This way of symbolizing the multiplication of a vector by a scalar is about as convenient as writing it in Egyptian hieroglyphics, and thus it is never done—it was merely invented by the author as a horrible example. Instead, it is possible to refer to vectors abstractly, without actually drawing an arrow on paper. We use a letter or symbol to stand for a vector, just as we use one to stand for a number. To set it apart from scalars, we designate it by drawing an arrow over the symbol. The above operation can then be expresssed:

$$\vec{A} = 1.5\vec{B}$$

where $\vec{A}$ refers to the vector on the left and $\vec{B}$ to that on the right. Of course, it is equally possible to *divide* by a scalar, in the same fashion. $\vec{A} = \vec{B}/2$ means that $\vec{A}$ is half as long as $\vec{B}$ and in the same direction.

This mere process of stretching is the least important example of multiplication of vectors by scalars. Much more important is its use in physics to convert one type of physical quantity represented by a vector into another one. The second law is an example of this. Both force and acceleration are vectors, and Newton took great pains to specify that the force and acceleration were in the same direction. We can write the second law in our new vector notation:

$$\vec{F} = m\vec{a}$$

Now the directional statement in Newton's law is also expressed in our equation, for mass is a scalar (no arrow on the m), and a scalar times a vector produces another vector in the same direction. It would not be as convenient to express this relation by drawing arrows, because force and acceleration are different kinds of quantities; we have to choose a separate scale for each when drawing our arrows.

Adding Vectors

The most important operation performed with vectors is that of *addition*. To visualize this, let us return to our arrows. Let us represent the following position by the vectors in Figure 1—"3 miles east (vector $\vec{A}$) and two miles north (vector $\vec{B}$)." Of course, it is only the resulting position that counts, and that can be represented by the single vector $\vec{C}$. This process of laying vectors head to head and drawing the resulting

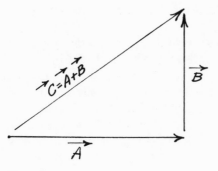

Figure 1

vector from the foot of the first to the head of the second is called *vector addition,* and we can represent Figure 1 symbolically by the equation:

$$\vec{A} + \vec{B} = \vec{C}$$

One illustration of the use of vector addition comes in figuring the When used in physics, we must be careful to add only vectors of the same type; the sum of, for example, a force and a velocity has no meaning. effect of wind on the motion of an airplane; in Figure 2 we see an example of this. The plane, traveling as it is in the air, has two things influencing its motion with respect to the ground. First, it moves with respect to the air, and second, the air moves with respect to the ground. A moment's reflection will serve to show that our "vector sum" is the proper way to combine these effects. The plane in Figure 2 flies at 400 knots airspeed,

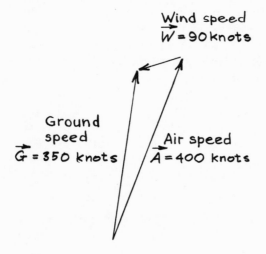

Figure 2

represented by the vector $\vec{A}$, and the wind, $\vec{W}$, is 90 knots in the direction shown. The resulting speed and direction relative to the ground are given by the direction and magnitude of the vector $\vec{G}$. The symbolic expression is, again:

$$\vec{G} = \vec{A} + \vec{W}$$

Another way to look at this is to think of the vectors $\vec{A}$ and $\vec{W}$ as representing the distances traveled by the plane and the air in an hour. At the end of this time, the plane has reached the point *in the air* represented by the head of the arrow $\vec{A}$. But in the meantime this point in the air has moved to a new position over the ground, represented by the end of the arrow $\vec{W}$.

If vectors can be added, they can also be *subtracted* by a similar process. What is the meaning of the expression

$$\vec{A} - \vec{B}$$

It becomes clearer if we write it as

$$\vec{A} + (-\vec{B})$$

Then all we need do is define the *negative* of a vector, and we can use the same rule as we did in adding vectors. The obvious way to define the negative of a vector is as *a vector of the same length pointing in the opposite direction*. Figure 3 shows an example of vector subtraction. $\vec{A} - \vec{B}$ is obtained by adding $\vec{A}$ to $(-\vec{B})$, a vector opposite in direction and equal in magnitude to $\vec{B}$. The reader can easily satisfy himself that this definition of subtraction agrees with some of the simple notions about subtraction from ordinary arithmetic. For example,

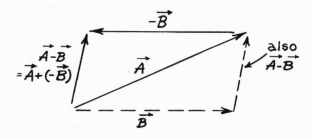

Figure 3

$\vec{B} - \vec{B} = \vec{0}$; subtracting a vector from itself produces a vector of zero length, or, if you prefer, no vector at all, for which we use the symbol $\vec{0}$. (The distinction between the vector $\vec{0}$ and the scalar 0 is obviously rather obscure.)

Examination of Figure 3 will serve to verify the following simple geometric rule for vector subtraction: $\vec{A} - \vec{B}$ *is the vector formed by laying* $\vec{A}$ *and* $\vec{B}$ *tail to tail and drawing the arrow from the end of* $\vec{B}$ *to the end of* $\vec{A}$.

It is also simple to extend our concept of *derivative* to apply to a vector. For example, consider acceleration: It is the change in velocity divided by the time interval in which the change takes place. Now the *change* in velocity is the difference between the velocities before and after the time interval; this could involve a pure change in magnitude, as shown below:

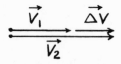

or a pure change in direction:

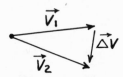

or a change in both. In any event, the acceleration is the change in velocity divided by the change in time, which is a scalar quantity. Thus, it lies in the same direction as the change in velocity. In the case of a pure change of direction, even though the speed does not change, it is obvious that the velocity has—some force must have intervened to deflect the object from its original course.

A Vector Picture of Projectile Motion

To illustrate the use of these concepts, let us recast Galileo's description of projectile motion in vector terms. This is depicted in Figure 4. The *horizontal* portion of the motion is represented by a horizontal vector. It never changes in magnitude. The vertical motion is represented by a verti-

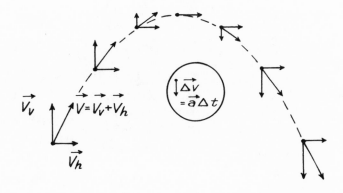

$$\vec{V_v} \qquad \vec{V} = \vec{V_v} + \vec{V_h} \qquad \left(\begin{array}{c}\uparrow \vec{\Delta v} \\ = \vec{a} \Delta t\end{array}\right)$$

$$\vec{V_h}$$

Figure 4

cal vector which *does* change in magnitude. The combined motion at any instant is the vector sum of the two.

The change in the vertical motion between any of the points depicted, which are at equal time intervals, is the change-in-velocity vector $\vec{\Delta V}$, which is obtained by multiplying the acceleration vector $\vec{a}$ by the scalar time interval Δt between measurements. The magnitude and direction of this change-in-velocity vector remain, by Galileo's law of falling bodies, always the same. Thus, in equal time intervals equal downward-pointing arrows are added to the velocity vector. As the body ascends, since its velocity vector points up, its speed is thereby diminished. On the way down, the added downward-pointing vector increases the speed.

Note also that the combined velocity vector is drawn as always *tangent* to the parabola. It is easy to see that it must be so, for this vector depicts the motion of the body at any given instant, which is of course always along the path.

Motion in a Circle

This brings us to the newtonian analysis of motion at constant speed in a circle. It is obvious, from the point of view of Newton's laws, that an acceleration has to be taking place. For example, if we wait for an object to travel half-way around a circle, we find it going with the *same* speed in the *opposite* direction—clearly a significant change!

To determine the direction of the acceleration involved, we must compare the velocities at two times close together. This is done in Figure 5. Note that, since the vectors $\vec{V_1}$ and $\vec{V_2}$ are of the same length and nearly parallel, the small difference ΔV is nearly perpendicular to them both; the smaller we make the time interval, the more nearly perpendicular

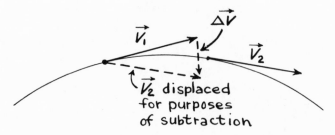

$\vec{V_1}$ $\Delta\vec{V}$ $\vec{V_2}$

$\vec{V_2}$ displaced
for purposes
of subtraction

Figure 5

$\Delta\vec{V}$ is to them. Thus, we conclude that in circular motion at constant speed the change in velocity, and therefore the acceleration, is a vector that points perpendicularly to the velocity—that is, *toward the center of the circle.* Applying the second law, we conclude, with Newton, that circular motion at constant speed requires a force pointing toward the center of the circle. Since the change $\Delta\vec{V}$ has the same magnitude in the same time interval anywhere on the circle, the magnitude of the acceleration must always remain the same. Since the acceleration changes direction constantly, remaining always perpendicular to the motion, it cannot change the speed of the motion.

It now remains to determine this magnitude of the acceleration produced. It turns out that this acceleration has the magnitude V^2/R, where V is the (constant) magnitude of the velocity $\vec{V}$. That the formula V^2/R is *reasonable* can be established without going through the details of a rigorous argument. Consider again Figure 5. How large will $\Delta\vec{V}$ be? This depends on two factors: the size of the *angle* between $\vec{V_1}$ and $\vec{V_2}$ and the magnitude V of $\vec{V_1}$ and $\vec{V_2}$. Consider the angle. Since the object moves at constant speed, the angle increases with time constantly at a rate that is greater the greater is V; thus, it must be proportional to both V and the time interval Δt. On the other hand, the larger the radius of the circle, the slower the angle changes. Thus, the angle is also inversely proportional to R, the radius of the circle. In total, the angle is thus proportional to the quantity $V\,\Delta t/R$.

Since ΔV is proportional both to V and to this angle, it must be proportional to $V^2\,\Delta t/R$. Dividing by Δt to obtain the acceleration, we have:

$$\frac{\Delta V}{\Delta t} \propto \frac{V^2 \Delta t}{R\,\Delta t} = \frac{V^2}{R}$$

(That this proportionality is actually an equality will be apparent to any reader familiar with radian measure of angles.)

54

It is also instructive to now compare circular motion and the motion of a projectile. In the latter case, the acceleration does not change direction as the projectile moves; it remains always in the same direction. Only at the apex is it perpendicular to the motion, opposing it slightly on the ascent and helping it slightly on the descent. The speed does not remain constant; it is greatest when the body starts, reaches its lowest value at the apex, and is restored to its original value by the end of the descent. Therefore, it was far simpler to consider the horizontal and vertical portions of the motion separately.

At this point, let us state two general rules that should have become apparent from the foregoing discussions:

1 *When acceleration is* parallel *(or antiparallel) to the direction of motion, a pure change in speed results, with no change of direction.* The mathematics used in this case is exactly that used in previous chapters.

2 *When acceleration is* perpendicular *to the motion, a pure change in direction results, with no change in speed.*

Because of these rules, in the case of a complex motion it is always simplest to consider separately the portions of the motion perpendicular and parallel to the acceleration, as was the case with the problem of the projectile. Later, in the chapter on energy, we will make more of the distinction.

If you have had difficulty following this section, it may have occurred to you that motion in a circle at constant speed is actually a rather simple process, understood by any child riding a merry-go-round. Surely the physicists have overcomplicated the problem, with all these changing vectors spinning madly about. What then of the physicist's claim to seek *simple* descriptions of nature?

The answer is that the simplicity of Newton's laws lies in the economy of the equations in which they are stated, in the concepts behind these equations, and also in the universality with which they can be applied, but not necessarily in their application to any particular situation. Applying Newton's laws to even a simple motion often proves very complex indeed. In the case of circular motion, it seems far more complex than the phenomenon itself. Nonetheless, no single simple law describing circular motion can be also describe projectiles, objects moving in a straight line, etc. Newton's laws claim to apply to all forms of motion, and three centuries of study have shown this claim to be upheld, with small modifications. In the next chapter we shall see how Newton dared extend this claim to the heavens.

5

The Moon Is Falling

He lives below the senseless stars and writes his
meanings in them.

—THOMAS WOLFE

Newton's laws of motion proved to be the most enduring achievement
in the history of physics, dominating the science for two centuries. With
some modifications, they remain the basis of the study of motion to this
day. But in Newton's own time and the generations immediately to follow,
more excitement was generated by the law of universal gravitation.

There were both emotional and scientific reasons for the reaction
to the law of gravity. The emotional reasons hardly need explanation:
to the common experience, nothing could be more striking than the distinction between the earth and the skies. The motions of the points of light
in the heavens are perfectly regular and unchanging. Nearly all of the

56

world's religions, and most of its philosophies, had assigned to the heavens an existence completely separate from that of earth, partaking in some measure of the essence of divinity. Many even made the sun, the stars, and the planets themselves gods. Eternal, beyond human influence, it could hardly be imagined that they were subject to the same laws that governed motion on earth.

The scientific reason was simply that, by virtue of their regularity and the ease of observation, the motions of heavenly bodies had, by Newton's time, long been studied and charted to a remarkable precision. The phenomena are inherently easy to observe and presented no experimental difficulties. It was simply a matter of slowly perfecting the instruments and accumulating the data, a process begun with the earliest civilizations. The reasons for these studies were obscure and varied. Many had been taken by and for astrologers (the separation of astronomy from fortune-telling was by no means complete even in Newton's era). Others were taken out of pure curiosity, or in hopes of finding some regularity of philosophical importance. Such a regularity had indeed been discovered by Johannes Kepler and provided an important foundation for Newton's work.

The Law of Universal Gravitation

The best way to grasp the significance of the law of universal gravitation is first to state it and then analyze it in detail. In Newton's words, all bodies are attracted toward one another by a force proportional to the product of their masses and also inversely proportional to the square of the distance separating them. In mathematical language:

$$F = \mathcal{G} \frac{Mm}{R^2} \tag{1}$$

where M and m are the masses of the objects concerned, R is the distance separating them,* and $\mathcal{G}$ is a universal constant that determines the strength of the force.

The beginning of the chain of reasoning leading to this law has already been outlined at the end of Chapter 3. Newton was forced from the outset, in order to explain the motion of falling bodies, to postulate a force proportional to the mass of the falling body. By what means could

---

* One might legitimately ask what is meant by distance of separation for objects of extensive size. Newton was able to show by difficult geometric arguments that for spherical objects, at least, a mass acts as if concentrated at its own center.

such a force act? After Galileo had argued convincingly that falling bodies moved as well, indeed, even more perfectly, in a vacuum as in the air, Newton could hardly revert to earlier ideas and ascribe this action to the medium. Thus Newton's thought was directed inevitably to the concept of an "action at a distance," an action that takes place between two objects not in contact. To most of his scientific peers, and indeed to Newton himself, this was the most disturbing feature of the law of gravity. But, building on the achievements of Galileo, he hardly had a choice.

The next problem is uncovering the identity of the "other body" demanded by the third law. Again, there appears one most logical candidate. Once we visualize our spinning ball of an earth, with "down" miraculously always toward its center, it becomes the obvious choice.

At this point, the third law intervenes decisively. It makes no distinction between the earth and a falling apple. The force on each is the same. The immense disparity of their masses is what is responsible for the fact that the apple falls, while the earth moves only imperceptibly. Then why make the distinction between the two bodies in the law of force itself? If the force must of necessity be proportional to the mass of the apple, why is it not also proportional to the mass of the earth?

This is not a question of logical necessity; it is one of style. The universal laws of motion, which apply to all objects, all forces, make no distinction between the two partners in the interaction given the name *force*. But there is no logical reason why some *particular* force cannot make this distinction. For example, when a spring pushes on a ball, it is the characteristics of the *spring*, not the *ball*, that determine the force between them, though the force is the same on each, and their individual reactions to it are determined solely by their masses. Why not a similar distinction in the case of gravity? Newton chose another route—to preserve the uniqueness of his system, the beauty of a perfectly symmetric theory—by introducing the mass of the earth, at the time unmeasurable, as a variable in his theory.

Besides, a theory ignoring the mass of the earth would be unaesthetic; if the force of gravity depends only on the arbitrary mass of the particular falling body, it is the *earth itself* that has a passive role, hardly the appropriate choice if one must choose active and passive partners. Once again, as so many times before and since, the search for harmony, for beauty, was a guiding force in the choice of a hypothesis. But aesthetic considerations are not enough; the theory must also explain the facts.

The numerator of Equation (1), the term *Mm,* is at this stage of the argument completely determined. For the only way a force can at the same time be proportional to the mass of the earth and to that of a falling body is to be proportional to the product of the two.

How Far Does the Force Act?

Newton might well have chosen to stop at this point, feeling that his speculation had gone as far as the information available to him could justify. But in that case, the unmeasurable mass of the earth would remain a purely superfluous element of his theory. So he reached out for further confirmation. He had his force; it acted at a distance. There is no sign that gravity ends anywhere within the limit of human experience—why not extend it right to the skies themselves?

In the context of a twentieth-century education, it is difficult to visualize how daring it was in Newton's day to think of the moon as a material object possessing no attribute exempting it from the laws applicable to a falling stone. Having once made this step, an extension to the whole solar system was natural. But once Newton dared this venture, a few simple calculations easily demonstrated that the moon was experiencing an acceleration far more feeble than that of a falling stone on the earth, and likewise that the planets closest to the sun were accelerated far more than those more remote. The force he had postulated might well extend to great distances, but it was clear that its effect diminished with distance. This was hardly an unnatural idea, but to discover the exact nature of this dependence on distance was a very difficult mathematical labor.

Fortunately for Newton, the quantitative details of the motion of the planets had already been admirably dealt with by Johannes Kepler, a contemporary of Galileo. This work played such a crucial role in Newton's arguments, establishing the dependence of gravity on distance, that it is necessary to break the discussion at this point to analyze Kepler's achievements in detail.

Kepler Charts the Motions of the Planets

Kepler started with no physical principles to guide him, since before Newton the heavens were not yet in the domain of physics, but he had a belief in the basic correctness of a heliocentric (*sun*-centered) planetary system, as proposed by Copernicus.

Carefully studying detailed, long-term, precise records of the apparent positions of the planets as seen from earth, most of them "inherited" from the celebrated Danish astronomer Tycho Brahe, he obtained three fairly simple laws describing the motion of the planets and accounting perfectly for the observations. Before stating these laws, it may be instructive to comment on the labor that went into obtaining them.

Like Galileo's work on falling-body motion, Kepler's laws were a feat of purely descriptive science. But these two contemporaneous efforts were very different in character. Galileo worked in an active milieu and in frequent contact with other scholars. He used half-formulated principles to lead him to what was in part a lucky guess confirmed by fairly crude experiments. He could well have been wrong. Kepler carried out a solitary labor of years, finally uncovering a simple order hidden in a veritable mountain of data of exceptionally high precision. If such an enormous quantity of information could be summarized in three simple laws, these laws were very likely to have some basic significance, even though their discovery was, in a sense, accidental.

This form of scientific labor, the search for a "magic formula" to summarize a vast body of data on a phenomenon to which no known principles apply, has been repeated many times in the history of physics and other sciences. It is increasingly important today, when far more scientists are producing far more data, which is widely available in the scientific literature. Electronic computers are a significant aid in the search. If Kepler's triumph had taken place in the 1960s, it might have gone something like this: a few days' labor by a hired keypunch girl would serve to put Tycho's observations on IBM cards. A search of the literature could add much more data to this "library." With a few weeks' effort, Kepler could have written a computer program designed to perform the necessary calculations to test whether any proposed "law" could account for the data. Then a few minutes (or, at most, hours) of computer time would suffice to tell whether any particular idea would work or not. A lot of wrong guesses could be quickly dismissed en route to the correct answer.

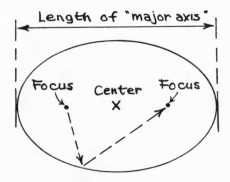

Figure 1 Structure of an ellipse. If it were lined with a mirror, any light ray from one focus would reach the other; hence the term focus.

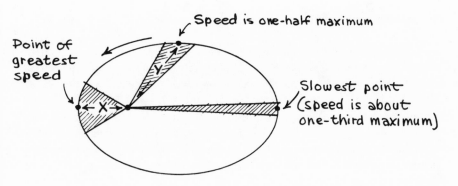

Figure 2   Areas swept out in equal times are equal.

Such methods are ideal for today's era of giant research institutes. They have the added advantage that the talents of quite ordinary men can be brought to bear on very complex problems, for the tasks of collecting precise data and trying empirical formulas may require training and experience, but they make little demand on the imagination. Yet to find the meaning behind the magic formula requires a different breed of man. What Kepler achieved so cleverly might today be duplicated by a drudge with a machine; but it hardly seems likely that we can automate the insight of a Newton.

Kepler's three laws describing the motions of the planets can be restated in modern terms as follows:

1   The planets travel in ellipses with the sun at one focus. Figure 1 explains the terms used to describe an ellipse, indicating the *focus.*

2   The area swept out by a line drawn from the sun to a planet is the same in equal time intervals. Figure 2 illustrates this. Each planet moves fastest when it is nearest the sun, slowest when it is farthest away. If its farthest point is twice as far as it nearest point, for example, it will go half as fast at the one as at the other.

3   The square of the length of each planet's year is proportional to the cube of the major axis of its orbit. Figure 1 shows the *major axis,* the largest dimension of the ellipse. This law implies that the outer planets move more slowly in their orbits than the inner ones, and thus the length of the year increases more rapidly than the size of the orbit.

Though Kepler describes the orbits as "ellipses," the orbits of the planets are very near to being circles. The laws are based on observation of almost imperceptible deviations from the simple behavior they would exhibit if the orbits were perfect circles. But these deviations are important, because they enabled Newton to demonstrate the inverse-square character of the force.

A major portion of Newton's *Principia* is devoted to detailed, complex geometric arguments designed to explain the significance of these three laws.   First, he showed that Kepler's second law is evidence that the planets move subject to a force directed toward the sun—*any* force of this type would produce the observed variation of velocity.   For Newton's purposes, this was quite important, because it demonstrated that if the behavior of the planets can be accounted for in mechanical terms, that is to say, by a force, it must be a force directed toward the sun.

Angular Momentum

Today Kepler's second law is recognized as the accidental discovery of a very important physical principle: the conservation of angular momentum.   The physical quantity, for which the symbol L is commonly used, is defined as the product of the distance of an object from a center and the component of ordinary momentum perpendicular to the line from the center:

$$L = rp_\perp = rmv_\perp$$

Motion toward or away from the center does not contribute to the angular momentum; it is only the *tangent* component of the motion that

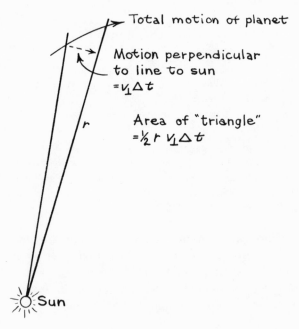

Total motion of planet

Motion perpendicular
to line to sun
$= v_\perp \Delta t$

Area of "triangle"
$= \frac{1}{2} r\, v_\perp \Delta t$

r

Sun

Figure 3

counts.   That Kepler's law follows from the conservation of this quantity is easy to show.   In a small time interval Δt the area swept out is a triangle, as shown in Figure 3.   The long *base* of this triangle is r.   Its *altitude* is $v_\perp \, \Delta t$.   Thus, the area swept out is $\frac{1}{2} r v_\perp \, \Delta t$.   Since m stays constant, angular momentum conservation ensures that $r v_\perp$ also stays constant.

Angular momentum conservation can be proved from Newton's laws whenever the force is directed toward (or away from) a center.   But today it is regarded as far more significant than Newton's laws themselves.   It will play a very crucial role later in the story of the quantum theory.

The Role of Kepler's First and Third Laws

Newton then demonstrated that Kepler's first and third laws were possible *only* for a force that varied inversely as the square of the distance.   To emphasize this point, he found the comparable laws for a number of other types of forces.   For example, a force proportional to the distance would still produce elliptical orbits, but the sun would be at their center, rather than at a focus.   And since such a force increases with distance, the outer planets would have to move faster than the inner ones to have greater acceleration, and all planets would turn out to have the same length of year.

It is interesting that Newton, after inventing the calculus, which enormously simplifies computations of the type required to interpret Kepler's laws, made little use of it in this connection.   He fell back on intricate geometric arguments, and much of the *Principia* reads like a somewhat old-fashioned, very advanced high school geometry text.   This was in response to the fashions of a time in which Euclid's geometry remained the highest achievement in mathematics.   The use of his new methods might confuse his readers, and in any event they would have found arguments based on the calculus less convincing.

The Moon Is the Link

But Kepler's laws spoke only of *relative* speeds of motion of different planets or of the same planet at different points in its orbit.   Not knowing the magnitude of the force on the planets, knowing neither the mass of the sun nor the $\mathcal{G}$ in his formula, there was no way to complete the analysis; Newton had demonstrated that his law could account for the fact that Mars's year is nearly twice as long as the earth's, but the length of either year in itself could not be accounted for.   Merely accounting for Kepler's laws could not destroy the dichotomy between terrestrial and celestial phenomena.

Fortunately for Newton, our earth has a moon. Since it is the same earth that is responsible for the acceleration of a falling stone and of the moon in its orbit, the only difference between the two phenomena is that the moon is farther from the center of the earth, and the resulting reduction in the force of gravity can easily be calculated. From the measurement of the acceleration of a stone on earth, he could calculate the acceleration the moon must have if subject to no force other than the earth's gravity. Would the calculation agree with the observed motion of the moon? Here was Newton's opportunity for a direct *quantitative* confirmation that the same force responsible for the stone's motion could account for the moon's.

Already in Newton's time the distance to the moon was known, for it is quite easy to measure. It is 380,000 kilometers, which is 60 times as great as the earth's radius. Thus, the acceleration resulting from the earth's gravity, at the moon's orbit, must be less than that at the earth's surface by a factor of $(60)^2$, that is,

$$a = \frac{9.78 \text{ m/sec}^2}{(60)^2} = \frac{9.78}{3,600} = 0.00272 \text{ m/sec}^2$$

If we assume the moon's motion to be simply that of a material object, with no force acting upon it other than the earth's gravity, this must be its acceleration as it travels in its orbit. This is Newton's "leap to the stars"—a prediction about the moon based on the behavior of falling bodies on the earth.

There now remains only to calculate the observed acceleration of the moon, using the formula obtained in the preceding chapter. The speed of the moon in its orbit is 1,016 m/sec.* Thus, its acceleration is

$$a = \frac{V^2}{r} = \frac{(1,016)^2}{380,000,000} = 0.00271 \text{ m/sec}$$

Considering the fact that the moon's orbit is not quite circular, but very slightly elliptical, the agreement is remarkably good.

Just to be sure we have not lost the train of the argument while worrying about the arithmetic, let us recap. We started by assuming that the moon is a material object subject to the same laws that apply on

---

* This figure is obtained by the circumference of the moon's orbit, $2\pi \times 380,000$ km, converting it to meters, and dividing it by the length of the lunar month, 27.32 days, converted into seconds (86,400 sec per day). The reader will please forgive us for leaving this trivial step out of the main text. He may verify the calculation for himself, if he is enough of a zealot.

earth. We find that the acceleration of the moon is smaller than that of a falling body on the earth by exactly the square of the ratio of their distances from the center of the earth.

The result was electrifying. Of course, a single such success can turn out to be a coincidence, and final confirmation waited upon more detailed calculations of other phenomena. Yet this calculation was the clincher, a quantitative correlation between an earthbound and a heavenly phenomenon. It provided the first link between a phenomenon on earth and one in the skies.

But the boldest aspect in the theory remained untested: its claim to represent a universal force that acted between all bodies proportional to the product of their masses. An inverse-square force exerted by the sun could be seen to account for the motions of the planets (including the earth itself). A similar force exerted by the earth could account for the motions of both falling bodies and the moon. Not knowing the masses of either the sun or the earth, Newton had feeble grounds for claiming the force was proportional to the mass of the large "central" object in each case. And he had no grounds whatsoever for assuming it would act between, for example, two rocks except for the negative evidence that since they are far smaller than the earth, the rocks would not exert on one another a force sufficient to measure. Nonetheless, so convincing were the theory's successes, and so well did it fit into the general spirit of Newtonian physics, that few physicists seriously doubted the claim to universality from the date of its publication. It was not directly confirmed until a century and a half later, when Henry Cavendish developed an instrument to measure the feeble force between two objects in the laboratory. By then the faith in Newton's law of gravitation was so great that Cavendish did not describe his experiment as a "confirmation of the law of universal gravitation," but instead called it "weighing the earth," a title that rested on the also unproved claim that the force of the earth's gravity on a stone was proportional to the mass of the earth, as well as to that of the stone. Since he had measured the force between two objects both of known mass, Cavendish was the first to have all the information necessary to measure the constant g in Newton's formula. Once this constant is known, the weight of a known mass on earth can be used to calculate the mass of the earth, since all the other factors in the formula for the force on it are known.

For at least a century after the publication of the *Principia,* caluculations of the motions of the planets remained the most important application and confirmation of both Newton's laws of mechanics and his law of gravity. It was not until well into the nineteenth century that the design of machinery, for example, ceased to be a trial-and-error process, and Newton's laws of motion received their first practical application.

But the ability to perform precise computations of the motions of the planets appealed very much to the spirit of the age of enlightenment, the eighteenth century. It was to this period that France owed its claim to be the center of European civilization, and physics was by no means an exception to this domination. A succession of brilliant French mathematicians developed techniques to carry out the ultimate refinements of an analysis of the solar system in the framework of Newton's laws. Miniscule deviations from Kepler's laws, resulting from such insignificant effects as the tiny forces exerted by the planets on each other, were analyzed in detail, while astronomers struggled to perfect their measurements to the point where such minor effects could be seen. Far from appealing to a small intellectual elite, these achievements were closely followed by fashionable French society, in much the way that art movements and literary prizes are followed today. The publication of *Traité de Mécanique Céleste* made its author, Laplace, the darling of Paris drawing-room society. Rarely before or since has abstract science enjoyed such social prestige.

But the root of this immense flower should not be forgotten. Newton may have been a bold and original thinker, but he was also a prolific one and a cautious expositor. By the time the *Principia* was published, decades after he had originated the ideas on which it was based, Newton had worked out so many examples to strengthen his case that there was little left to say about mechanics. At least two generations of physicists devoted themselves primarily to refining the confirmation of his findings by observation. Furthermore, mechanics and the law of gravity were not the only monuments he left behind: for example, he made many of the first important discoveries in the study of light.

But the story of Newton ends strangely. The last years of his life were spent wrapped in a rather naïve form of mysticism, a fruitless pursuit of evidence in the quantitative details of the physical universe for the existence of God. Many theologians in later generations were content to see in Newton's laws themselves ample evidence for divine guidance of the universe. Yet this solitary thinker let himself be misled into ascribing supernatural significance to some of the numerical accidents in the structure of the universe. Like many of his successors, Newton rewrote the laws of nature from inspirations developed in the fire of his youth and rounded out by the skill and experience of his maturity; in his old age, his powers betrayed him.

Energy: What Is It?

If you asked a physicist, "What is the single most fundamental law of physics?" he would probably answer, after some grumbling about stupid, unanswerable questions, "The law of conservation of energy." If you then asked him what energy *is*, anyhow, he probably would refuse to answer—and rightly so, as we shall see in this chapter.

Energy has a long history, and the concept has evolved with each step in the development of physics. Originally conceived as a nondirectional measure of quantity of motion, a competitor to Descartes' and Newton's momentum, it has come to have a significance transcending that of motion itself. One can almost characterize each era in the history of physics in terms of the state of development of the energy concept. Similarly, the history of man's conquest of his material environment can be written as the story of the mastery of energy. This single concept is probably the foremost bridge between the abstract world of physical theory and the practical one in which men try to get things done.

We will trace the history of the law of energy conservation from its humble origin as an approximate mechanical law. But the true power of energy conservation comes precisely from the fact that it is not a purely mechanical law. It can only be established as a general law by forming a bridge between mechanics and other fields of physics. It was the link that enabled mechanics in the nineteenth century to reach out and absorb nearly all physical knowledge. This drive was so spectacularly successful that by the 1880s, many physicists believed that the job was done; physics was complete and final, and there was nothing left for future generations of physicists to do but round out the quantitative details, refining their measurements to complete the catalog of a completely understood universe.

How Do We "Pay" for a Force?

Up to this point, we have held to a strictly Newtonian view of motion. A force produces a change in momentum. This may be a change in speed, but it may also be a mere change in direction. Newton's laws themselves make no distinction.

But this is merely because Newton's laws take a force as given, without asking what it takes to generate that force. If we do ask where the force comes from, there is a considerable distinction between forces that merely change direction and those that also change speed. A force that produces a change in direction only can be a more "passive" force, in the sense that nothing need be expended to maintain it.

Consider, for example, two possible uses of a spring. In one case it is used to hold a mass in circular motion. The spring is stretched the amount required to produce enough force to hold the object in its circular path. It can remain that way indefinitely, the body moving at constant speed, the spring remaining the same length.

But if we use the same spring to speed up a body, as in the "gun" of a pinball machine, we must first compress it and then release it. This is a one-shot process. The spring cannot be used to impart further speed to the body, or impart speed to another body, unless we intervene by once more compressing it.

Similarly, to turn a car around a curve at constant speed, a small pull on the steering wheel will suffice. The motor can even be turned off. But to produce an acceleration of equal magnitude in the forward direction, speeding up the car, the motor must intervene. The puny effect of the hands on the steering wheel would never come close to doing the job, even though the force is the same in both cases.

In Chapter 4, it was shown that the distinction between forces that produce changes in speed and those that merely change direction lay in the relative direction of the force and the motion. A force perpendicular to the line of motion produces no change in speed, while one along the line of motion does. We need not "pay" for the former kind of force, while we must pay for the latter. And the amount we must pay must be somehow related to the amount of motion along the line of force. We thus have to seek a relationship between this part of the motion and the change in speed, one that is independent of the directional character of the motion.

Work and Kinetic Energy

The relationship between motion along the line of force and change in speed proves to be a simple one; it can be derived from Newton's laws. The relationship is

The product of the force along the line of motion and the distance moved while the force is acting is equal to the change in the quantity $\frac{1}{2}mv^2$.

Stated as an equation:

$$Fs = \Delta \left(\tfrac{1}{2}mv^2\right) \tag{1}$$

This is *not* a vector relationship. Here we insist that the F on the left-hand side of the equation is merely that component of the force along the line of motion. If there is also a perpendicular component we ignore it, for it has no effect on the speed. Similarly, v^2 is the square of the *speed,* ignoring direction.

The proof of this relationship is simple. (Those unduly disturbed by mathematical arguments may skip this section and take Equation (1) on faith.) Assume the body starts out with speed v_1. After traveling a distance s, its speed has changed to v_2. Then the force along the line of motion must have been, from Newton's second law and the definition of acceleration,

$$F = ma = \frac{m(v_2 - v_1)}{t} \tag{2}$$

The distance s traveled is obtained directly from the definition of speed, noting that the average speed is halfway between v_1 and v_2:

$$s = vt = \frac{v_1 + v_2}{2} t \tag{3}$$

We can combine these two equations to obtain the product Fs:

$$Fs = \frac{m(v_2 - v_1)}{t} \times \frac{(v_1 + v_2)}{2} t$$
$$= \tfrac{1}{2}m(v_2 - v_1)(v_2 + v_1)$$
$$= \tfrac{1}{2}m(v_2{}^2 - v_1{}^2) = \Delta\left(\tfrac{1}{2}mv^2\right)$$

The quantity on the left side, Fs, has been given the name *work*. This is one of many examples of a scientific term which is confusing not because it is an obscure Latin or Greek construction, but because it has a host of meanings in the ordinary language and a precise one in its scientific context. The quantity $\tfrac{1}{2}mv^2$ is called *kinetic energy*, that is to say, energy of motion. Work is our measure of how much we have to pay for a change in speed. The unit of energy in the metric system has been named the *joule*. It is the work done by a force of one newton over a distance of one meter.

So far, we have defined work as the product of the total distance traveled and the force along the line of motion. We might just as well have called it the product of the total force and the net motion along the line of force. In either case, the result is the same, whether we take the product of the diminished portion of the force along the line of motion and the total motion, or the diminished portion of the motion along the line of force and the total force. In each case, the diminution is given by the cosine of the angle between the force and the line of motion, which is 1 if they are parallel and 0 if they are perpendicular.

The reason for dwelling on this point is that frequently a motion follows a complex curved path while the force remains in the same direction. This is the case with, for example, a roller coaster, which will be treated later in this chapter. In such a case it is easier to refer to motion along the unchanging line of force, rather than constantly follow the component of force along the changing line of motion.

As an example of the application of this law, we derive the following well-known result:

> *The speed acquired by a body on an inclined plane is the same as that acquired by a freely falling body dropping the same vertical distance.*

Using the concept of work, the result follows easily. We count only the vertical part of the motion, which is parallel to the force of gravity. Then the work done is the same in both cases, because the horizontal motion of the ball contributes nothing to the work. The total work is mgh in either case, where h is the height of the plane, and mg is the weight of the body. To prove the same result from Newton's laws, we would have to show that the diminished acceleration of the body on the inclined plane was exactly offset by the greater time it spent picking up speed on the longer inclined path. But even though the process takes longer on the inclined plane, and the final direction is different, the speed turns out the same in both cases.

Can We Get Our Money Back?

The difference between the Newton's-law view of motion and that obtained from the concept of work can be made clearer by considering the simple process of lifting a stone by means of a hoist, as shown in Figure 1. From the newtonian point of view, hardly anything is happening, for through most of its rise the stone is moving at constant speed, its weight exactly balanced by the force exerted by the rope. To set it in motion there had to be a brief instant when the force exceeded its weight, but from

Figure 1

then on the motion is not accelerated. In terms of Newton's laws, the stone might as well be standing still. Yet from the point of view of the person pulling on the crank, there is a considerable difference. He is really working up a sweat. Were the stone standing still, he could set a brake on the hoist and go away; but no such simple process will raise the stone. He is putting work into the process, exerting a force on an object that moves. The work is the product of the weight of the stone, mg, and the distance h he raises it. Yet this work does not go into increasing the stone's kinetic energy; the counterbalancing force of gravity takes it right out again. Is that work lost forever?

The answer, of course, is no. If he cuts the rope, the stone will fall. Gravity will then work on the stone, and it will reach the ground with a kinetic energy equal to the work done by gravity. Since the distance moved was the same as that covered in the hoisting process, and the force again is the weight of the stone, he has gotten back exactly the amount of work he put in. The stone reaches the ground moving at the same speed it would have acquired if he had done the same amount of work without gravity opposing his efforts.

Thus, gravity seems to be an "honest" force; work done overcoming its effect, even if that work produces no immediate reward in the form of motion, can be recovered later. Not all forces have this nice property; the work done dragging a stone across rough ground is forever lost.

Energy "stored" in this form is called *potential energy*. The sense of the word is self-explanatory. By raising the stone we have created a situation which has the potential of creating motion. Allowing the stone to return to its starting point will convert that potential to an actual motion.

The process of converting the potential energy to kinetic energy is a gradual one. When the stone has fallen only one-tenth of the way to the ground, gravity has done only one-tenth of the work it will finally do; one-tenth of the energy has become kinetic, the other nine-tenths remain potential. As the stone continues its fall, the potential energy is gradually used up, and the kinetic energy increases. When the stone reaches the ground, the potential energy has all been converted, and the work originally put into raising the stone appears as kinetic energy.

These relationships can be expressed mathematically in the form:

Kinetic energy + remaining potential energy = work done in hoisting

or, in conventional symbols,

$$\tfrac{1}{2}mv^2 + mgh = mgH \tag{4}$$

where h is the height of the falling stone, and H was its height when it started its fall. With the aid of this formula, for any height h we can calculate the speed of the stone, for its kinetic energy is the difference between mgh and mgH.

But Galileo could have done the same thing without introducing all these new concepts. If Equation (4) were applicable only to a falling stone, it would hardly be worth the trouble to write it down. But consider the roller coaster depicted in Figure 2. The formula applies equally well to it. Once it is hoisted to the top of the first rise and released, it moves subject to only two forces: gravity and the support provided it by the rails. But the latter is perpendicular to the motion, and therefore does no work. The speed acquired in dropping a certain vertical distance is the same as for a freely falling body, just as on an inclined plane.

Here we see a more complex process. Just as the roller coaster draws on its supply of potential energy as it falls, it "puts it back" as it rises, slowing down but increasing its potential energy. Equation (4) tells us that anywhere on the roller coaster's track, its speed depends solely on how high it is above the ground.

Equation (4) is still too specific to deserve the name "energy conservation law." For the case of our roller coaster, it ignores the fact that part of the work done in raising the coaster may not have wound up as potential energy. Ordinarily, the coaster is cut loose at the first rise with some forward motion. To account for this, we would have to add to the right-hand side of Equation (4) the kinetic energy it has by virtue of this motion. Furthermore, there is no reason why the station from which the initial host began need be at ground level; the coaster could (and usually does) start somewhat higher. Thus, the mgH need not represent the actual work done in hoisting the coaster, but merely the work that would have been done had it started from the ground. Once it gets to the top of

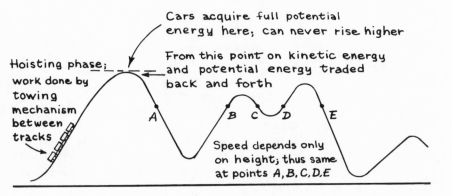

Figure 2

the first rise, it has the same potential energy, regardless of whether we actually lifted it all the way. A stone dropped off a cliff acquires the same speed of fall regardless of whether we carried it up or found it already there.

To express this fact, we rewrite Equation (4) in a more general form:

$$\tfrac{1}{2}mv^2 + mgh = E \tag{5}$$

We call E the *total energy*. The prescription for using the formula is as follows: at some point, preferably but not necessarily the first rise, measure the speed of the roller coaster and its height above some reference level (which need not be the ground, after all). Then Equation (5) can be used to compute E. The important point is that this need be done only once, for at all times in the future E will remain the same. We can use the formula to compute the speed at any point on its path; we need only know the height of that point above the reference level to compute mgh and subtract it from E. The remainder of the energy is the kinetic energy of the roller coaster.

Of course, the exact value of E is somewhat arbitrary, as it depends on our choice of level from which to measure h. If we had chosen a higher point than the ground, E would be smaller. But so would mgh; the difference would remain the same. So the physically "real" effect, the kinetic energy, remains unaffected by our choice of reference level, even though the numbers in the formula will turn out to be slightly different.

Other Forms of Energy

Equation (5) is still applicable only to the force of gravity. Were gravity the only force that could store energy, the concept of potential energy would hardly seem worth the effort we have gone through. Fortunately, there are other forces that can store energy. For example, a spring or a rubber ball stores energy as it is compressed, and this fact can be expressed in a formula:

$$\text{Potential energy} = \tfrac{1}{2}kx^2$$

where k is a constant that tells how "stiff" the spring or ball is, and x is the distance it is compressed. k is the ratio between the force and the distance that a spring or ball is compressed. A ball bouncing on a floor has two kinds of potential energy, gravitational and the kind stored in the ball when it is dented by contact with the floor:

$$\tfrac{1}{2}mv^2 + mgh + \tfrac{1}{2}kx^2 = E$$

The graph in Figure 3 shows how energy converts between these *three* forms as the ball bounces. For this graph we take $h = 0$ at the point the ball is just touching the floor. x is then "negative h," in the sense that the center of the ball does get lower than $h = 0$ as the ball is compressed.

There are many other forces that have this property of storing energy; for each one it is possible to find a formula for the potential energy, and for each force the formula is different.

Unfortunately, not all forces are so generous. If we drop a stone on soft ground it will not bounce; the energy is lost. Even a very good rubber ball loses a bit of energy, rising a bit less each bounce. The roller coaster can't quite top a rise as high as its first one, for a bit of energy is lost as it moves on its rails. For most real motions, energy conservation is at best a poor approximation. This is as far as one can go within the domain of mechanics itself.

The great discovery of the nineteenth century was that whenever energy disappears there is some observable change in the world, and by patient study this change can be quantitatively related to the amount of energy lost. For example, when a rock falls on soft ground, it leaves a

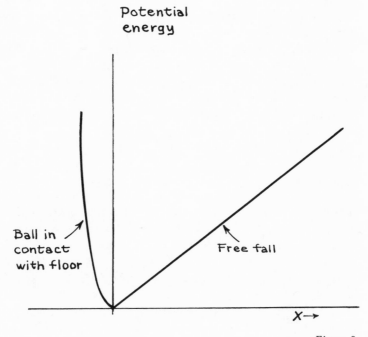

Figure 3

dent; it also makes some sound; and finally, a very good thermometer would disclose that both the rock and the ground near the dent were slightly warmer after the rock hit.   With some study, it would be possible to come up with formulas relating the energy lost because of deformation of the ground to the size of the dent, that lost in the form of the sound to its loudness, and the heat energy to the change in temperature.

Heat Becomes a Mechanical Phenomenon

The most common way for mechanical energy to be lost is through the production of heat.   Physicists began to realize this late in the eighteenth century.   Who it was that first attempted to quantitatively relate the energy lost to the heat produced is subject to some debate, but certainly one of the more dramatic early efforts was that of a rather picaresque eighteenth-century American, Benjamin Thompson, better known under his acquired title of Count Rumford.   Rumford was an energetic and ambitious Tory who fled America (deserting a wife and family) during the War of Independence.   Entering a career in the British civil service, he pursued some rather practically oriented chemical studies that earned him appointment as a Fellow of the Royal Society only three years after his arrival in Britain.   When a political turnover threatened his career, he decided   to   seek   his   fortune   abroad,   traveling   extensively   on   the Continent.   He settled for some years in Bavaria, where he played various political and military roles as an advisor in the court of the Elector Maximillian.   It was from this sovereign that he received his title.

In the late 1790s, using the facilities of Maximillian's royal arsenal, Rumford employed a cannon-boring machine to obtain a crude quantitative estimate of how much heat is produced by expending a known amount of work.

This was one of the first steps toward a new science called *thermodynamics,* the study of the transformation of mechanical energy to heat and, of more practical interest, the reverse process.   The industrial revolution was in full swing, and its symbol was the steam engine, which reverses Rumford's cannon-borer; heat is converted into mechanical energy.   The practical demands of technology provided a strong motive for theoretical studies of this process.   Much of the time, however, technology led science, rather than vice versa; practical men made improvements in steam engines, and the scientists came along later to explain why they worked.   The relation of science to technology is a complex one, and the view that science is the starting point, with technology the follower, is a naïve one.   The reverse is often the case.   Even today, in an era when basic scientific research is fairly generously supported in nearly all the developed countries, it is still common for a new gadget to come on the market long before scientists fully understand the principles by which it operates.

Energy exists in and can be transferred to many other forms, for example, electrical and chemical. Thus, a complete law of energy conservation would read:

$$\begin{bmatrix} \text{Kinetic} \\ \text{energy} \end{bmatrix} + \begin{bmatrix} \text{potential energy} \\ \text{of various types} \end{bmatrix} + [\text{heat}] + \cdots + [\quad] + [\quad] = \text{const} \quad (6)$$

In each of the brackets of this equation, the formula for energy is different. We have already seen two formulas for potential energy; for heat, the formula involves the temperature, amount of material, and a constant called the *heat capacity* which is related to the properties of the material containing the heat. Another example of one of the formulas that might be found in the brackets would be one relating the loudness of a sound, as recorded by a microphone, to the energy carried by the sound.

Thus, the law of energy conservation is a very peculiar beast indeed; it provides a quantitative relation between a number of seemingly unrelated quantities, some mechanical, others not. The celebrated American theoretical physicist Richard Feynman has emphasized this by means of an amusing parable which the student is strongly urged to read.* A mother gives her child a number of blocks. Later, going through his playroom, she finds that, from time to time, some of them are missing. By such devices as weighing his toy box, measuring the level of the dirty water in a washstand, etc., she is ultimately able to account for all the blocks. The punch line of Feynman's story is that the analogy with energy conservation is perfect, except that in the case of energy conservation *there are no blocks*. By that he means that we can't say which of the various forms in which energy manifests itself represents what energy "really" is. This represents one stage in the development of the concept.

Energy and Atoms

When one looks below the surface of Equation (6), the law of energy conservation once again achieves a sort of unity. One of the greatest accomplishments of later nineteenth-century physics was the discovery that if matter is regarded as being composed of atoms, all the laws of thermodynamics can be understood by assuming that heat is nothing more or less than the energy of motion of these atoms. Imagine, as in Figure 4,

* The parable may be found in Feynman, Leighton, and Sands, *The Feynman Lectures on Physics,* vol. 1, chap. 4, Addison-Wesley, Reading, Mass., 1964.

a collision between two balls of soft clay of equal mass, heading toward one another at equal speed; after the collision they will be stuck together and standing still. Without even bothering to look into the internal structure of the clay balls, we find that total momentum is conserved, for momentum conservation holds without exception in mechanics, regardless of the level at which a system is observed. But the energy of motion is lost. Yet if we examine things on a deeper level, we find that the energy of motion has merely been transferred into motion of the atoms of which the clay balls are composed; this can be observed by noting the increase in temperature of the clay balls, for temperature is nothing more than a measure of the average energy of these atoms, as will be seen in Chapter 13. This motion is complex, chaotic, and random, and there is no way to reverse the process; to get all the atoms of a clay ball moving in one direction to restore the original energy of gross motion would be impossible. Momentum conservation also holds for this random motion, but there is no need

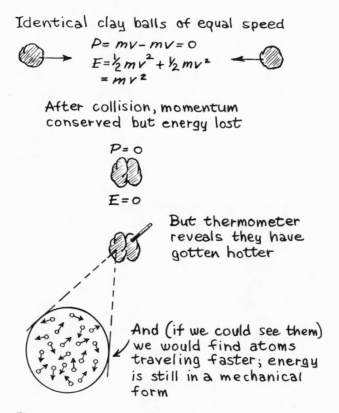

Identical clay balls of equal speed

$$P = mv - mv = 0$$
$$E = \frac{1}{2}mv^2 + \frac{1}{2}mv^2$$
$$= mv^2$$

After collision, momentum conserved but energy lost

$$P = 0$$

$$E = 0$$

But thermometer reveals they have gotten hotter

And (if we could see them) we would find atoms traveling faster; energy is still in a mechanical form

Figure 4

to go into such details to establish that the total momentum of the clay balls has been conserved.

When we go from the macroscopic world of the clay balls to the microscopic one of the atoms of which the balls are composed, the law of conservation of energy regains its mechanical character to some extent. Not only does heat yield to this analysis; chemical energy can be seen as potential energy of the forces that bind atoms together. This was the source of the power of the concept to unify physics, for it led to a hope that all natural phenomena might ultimately yield to a mechanical interpretation, if only their microscopic details could be understood. On this scale, the ultimate forces of the universe would all conserve energy. The existence of forces that do not is merely a result of ignoring the microcosm.

The example of the clay balls points up another advantage of the concept of energy. From the point of view of total momentum alone, there is no distinction made between the clay balls before and after the collision, or between an elastic collision and one with clay balls. Energy does provide such a distinction—it provides a measure of motion that is independent of its directional properties. Indeed, the laws of elastic collision are derived from assuming momentum and energy are simultaneously conserved. Applied together, the concepts of energy and momentum permit a more complete description of moving objects than either concept can by itself.

Binding Energy

The potential energy concept is a very useful tool for describing situations in which objects are bound together by forces of attraction. The earth and moon are bound in this fashion, as the earth and its sister planets are bound to the sun. In the microworld of the atom, the electrons are bound to their atoms by electrical attraction.

From the energy viewpoint, such objects are bound because they do not have enough energy to get away from one another. To move the moon away from the earth, one would have to put in energy in the form of work against the force of attraction.

For example, if an object leaves the earth's surface with a speed greater than about 11 km/sec, it is free to "escape" the earth's gravity. It still slows down as it moves out, but gravity can never do enough work to bring it to a halt. No matter how far it goes, there will still be some energy left. This is the meaning of the term "escape velocity" heard so often since sending objects out into space became a commonplace. Escape would not be possible were it not for the fact that the force of gravity drops off as the square of the distance. Were the force to remain constant, for example, one could do sufficient work to stop the object and bring it back simply by going far enough. The formulas used earlier in the chapter, in which the dropoff of gravity with distance is ignored, are useful only on a terrestrial scale of distances, where vertical travel is small compared to the earth's radius.

In situations like this, it becomes convenient and logical to choose our arbitrary zero-point of potential energy in such a way that an object just free to escape has zero total energy. For a force like gravity, this is tantamount to taking as a reference point an infinite distance from the earth. If you find this notion disturbing, just satisfy yourself by substituting some great distance beyond which you regard the force as too small to be worth mentioning.

When this convention is adopted, all potential energies become negative. An object *gains* kinetic energy as it moves inward in response to an attractive force. Thus, its potential energy must decrease. If potential energy is considered zero at remote distances, it must become increasingly negative as the object moves in.

This becomes a convenient scheme for classifying the motion of objects under attractive forces. If the total energy is positive, that is to say the positive kinetic energy is greater in magnitude than the negative potential energy, the object is free to escape. If the total energy is negative, it is bound. There is a distance at which the potential energy itself is equal to the negative total energy of the object. Since kinetic energy cannot be negative, it can never go beyond this point.

As an example, consider the lunar orbit mission flown by the Apollo 8 astronauts in 1968. They approached the moon from a great distance; with respect to its gravity, they had positive total energy. To become bound to the moon in a lunar orbit, they had to slow down by firing their rockets in reverse, "giving away" energy. Had they not done this, having come from a position where they were not bound by the moon's gravity, they would have left it. The maneuver was not undertaken without some trepidation; once they had thus obtained negative total energy with regard to the moon, they could not escape it without putting energy in. Had their rockets been unable to restart and boost them to a positive energy with regard to the moon, they would have been trapped forever.

Stars, Planets, and Life

If the notion of defining potential energy in such a way that it is always negative seems unaesthetic, consider that it accurately represents the process of creating a bound pair of objects. Were we to try to build the solar system, starting with the earth and the sun at a remote distance from one another, we would have to take energy *out* of the system to put the earth in its close-in bound orbit. Otherwise it would be free to return to its original remote location. Since it is reasonable to regard objects so remote from one another that they exert no significant forces as having no energy due to interaction, when energy is taken out to bind them, it is reasonable to regard them as having negative energy. When we study relativity, we shall see that this negative energy takes on a more concrete manifestation, a defect in mass.

This analysis is the basis of one of the more popular theories of how stars and planetary systems are formed. One starts with an immense, diffuse cloud of cool gas. As it collapses toward its center under its own gravity, potential energy is converted to motion of its molecules, or heat. Eventually, at the center, the temperature becomes high enough to kindle thermonuclear reactions, and a star is born.

As for the planets, suppose the cloud initially has a very slow rotation. It then has a quite substantial angular momentum. At great distances this involves very small speeds, but as the cloud collapses, it must turn more and more rapidly, just as a skater or dancer spins more rapidly as she pulls in her arms. By the time one reaches the comparatively small dimensions of a star, the spin may be too fast to allow it to hold together. Some of the material is spun off, or perhaps never reaches the center. It coalesces in smaller centers further out which have too little potential energy to reach thermonuclear temperatures, so cooler planets are formed. Though the planets are small, they are so far out compared to the diameter of the star that they carry most of the primal cloud's angular momentum. The fact that all the planets in our solar system move in orbits in the same direction, and the sun itself rotates in this direction, lends credence to this speculation.

Of course, one might expect that a planet might be formed big enough to become a thermonuclear star in its own right. This proves in fact to be rather common. A substantial fraction of the nearer stars in the sky can be seen, through a powerful telescope, to consist of double stars bound in orbits. Even when one of the partners is too small to be seen by its own light, its effect on the motion of its senior partner can reveal its presence. In many of these cases, it is probably far more reasonable to regard the unseen partner as a planet.

Even after man accepted the blow to his pride of finding the earth no longer the center of the universe, he still held out some hope that the solar system might be unique, perhaps the result of some cataclysmic cosmic accident. But today it seems far more likely that planets are the rule, rather than the exception. Among the myriad stars and galaxies of stars, there must be countless planets as hospitable to life as our own. It would be foolish in the extreme to let our human pride delude us into thinking that life is confined to our poor corner of the universe, or even that the mystery of consciousness is reserved to us alone.

Energy and Force

In succeeding chapters, the concept of potential energy, at first introduced in such an arbitrary and artificial fashion, will come to appear more real as the energy stored by a force comes to be associated with a *field*. Let us close this chapter with a remark on one simple but important mathematical property of potential energy.

We begin by inquiring what significance should be attached to the rate of change or *derivative* of the potential energy. Intuitively, it is not hard to see that the stronger a force is, the more rapidly the energy of a body changes as it moves. Going through the formalities, we calculate the derivative *with respect to distance* of gravitational potential energy:

$$\frac{\Delta\,(mgh)}{\Delta h}$$

for very small Δh. Since m is constant and g essentially constant when we speak on a terrestrial scale of distances,

$$\Delta\,(mgh) = mg\,\Delta h$$

i.e., all change in the potential energy comes from the change in height directly, not from changes in m or g. Thus, the derivative becomes

$$\frac{mg\,\Delta h}{\Delta h} = mg$$

which is nothing other than the *force* of gravity on an object of mass m! This relation can be shown to hold for any force whatsoever, and we may state the following general rule:

> *The derivative with respect to distance of the potential energy is the force; and it points in the direction of most rapid change of the potential energy.*

This result is not offered just as a mathematical curiosity. It suggests that when dealing with the *fundamental* forces that conserve energy, it is enough to talk about them in terms of their potential energy. The force law, if desired, could always be obtained from the potential energy law by simple mathematics. Indeed, during the nineteenth century, methods were developed to solve complex mechanical problems directly from the potential energy, without ever explicitly mentioning forces at all. For example, the potential energy due to the inverse-square gravitational force has a particularly simple form:

$$PE = -g\frac{mM}{r} = -Fr$$

It differs from the force in that $1/r^2$ is replaced by $-1/r$. To show that $1/r^2$ is the derivative of $-1/r$ is trivial with the use of the calculus. Without this mathematical tool, the argument is laborious and unconvincing.

Describing a force by means of its potential energy actually seems a more basic approach than describing it by the force law, at least to present-day physicists. Newton's laws are of little direct utility in the world of atoms. But the great conservation laws, those of energy and momentum, survive intact.

7

Completing the Job: The Classical Physicist's "World View"

With Earth's first clay they did the last Man knead
And there of the Last Harvest sow'd the seed
And the first morning of creation wrote
What the last dawn of reckoning shall read.

—THE RUBAIYAT OF OMAR KHAYYAM

As was suggested in the preceding chapter, the concept of energy conservation shows its greatest power to unify physics when dealing with matter on the atomic level. By the latter part of the nineteenth century, physicists had a most enticing prospect open before them: it seemed likely that the universe was composed solely of atoms in motion. If all the forces between atoms could be understood, then *all natural phenomena* could be explained in terms of Newton's laws. All forms of energy might then prove ultimately to be mechanical in nature. Hopefully, there would prove to be a very small number of "fundamental" forces, like gravity, which might well have force laws nearly as simple as those for gravity. The story of this search, which nearly succeeded and still goes on today in a modified form, is the topic of this chapter.

Electricity and Magnetism

One such fundamental force is that of electricity. Electrical phenomena were studied extensively during the eighteenth century by physicists and a host of scientific amateurs, not the least of whom was Benjamin Franklin. Among Franklin's achievements were contributions to the understanding of electricity which range far beyond his celebrated (and personally risky) demonstration of the electrical nature of lightning. In Franklin's day, a certain amount of social prestige in polite society could come to a gentleman who dabbled in natural science. Electrical phenomena were perfect for this sort of amateur, and much of what passed for electrical research bore a strong resemblance to parlor magic. A few large sparks generated by a crude apparatus were bound to impress the guests at a fashionable *soirée,* and having the courage to tackle a "dread natural force" was bound to reflect favorably on the host's honor and virility.

Despite the confusion generated by this sleight-of-hand approach, by the end of the century a sufficient base of empirical knowledge had been built up to permit a really systematic attack on the law of electrical force.

In 1789, the French experimenter Charles A. Coulomb announced the discovery of such a law. Like many of his predecessors and successors, Coulomb owed his success as an experimenter in large measure to the patient development of a precision instrument, the torsion balance (see Figure 1), an ideal device for measuring small forces. With the aid of such a balance, Coulomb was able to perform a series of experiments to establish that electrical forces obey a law that remarkably resembles that for gravity:

$$F = \frac{q_1 q_2}{R^2}$$

The masses in Newton's gravitational law have merely been replaced by a new type of entity, "quantity of electricity" or "electrical charge," denoted by the symbol q. Note that this law does *not* contain a constant like the g in Newton's law of gravitation; that is because, there being no previously agreed-upon units for amount of electricity q, one can *define*

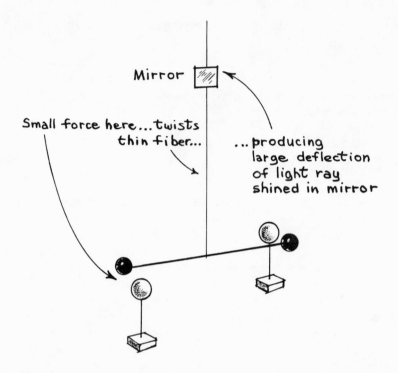

Mirror

Small force here...twists thin fiber...

...producing large deflection of light ray shined in mirror

Figure 1

the unit of electrical charge so that the constant comes out 1. The unit of charge, called the *electrostatic unit* or esu, is defined as whatever charge must be placed on two objects 1 cm apart to produce a force between them of 1 gm-cm/sec².* Indeed, in Coulomb's time, there was no more reliable absolute measurement of the quantity of electricity than to measure the force produced.

Another distinction from gravity is that electrical force can be either attractive or repulsive. Electrical charge, unlike mass, can be either *positive* or *negative;* charges of *like* sign repel, while those of *opposite* sign attract. The formula indicates this fact, too: if the charges are of the same sign, their product is positive; if opposite, the product is negative.

Electrical forces are immensely more powerful than gravitational ones; the particles making up atoms are bound together by electrical forces 10^{40} times greater than the gravitational ones between them, and 10^{40} is a fantastically large number.† Though Coulomb's crude torsion balance

---

* There are alternative sets of electrical units in which a constant *does* appear in Coulomb's law. Indeed, though all electrical units are based on the metric system, there are three separate sets, a situation that often provokes physicists to profanity when dealing with electrical computations.

† A convenient way of expressing very large or very small numbers is the *exponent notation,* in which a number is expressed in a reasonably sized form and multiplied

was adequate to establish the nature of electrical forces, it took two further decades of patient development before the English experimenter Henry Cavendish, as mentioned in Chapter 5, was able to perfect a sufficiently refined torsion balance to measure the feeble gravitational attraction between a pair of lead weights.   The purpose of the experiment, in Cavendish's view, was to establish the value of the constant $\mathcal{G}$ in Newton's gravitational formula, since in this case all the other quantities, the masses, distances, and force, were known.   Cavendish's instrument resembled Coulomb's much as a Boeing 707 resembles a Piper Cub.   Since knowing the value of $\mathcal{G}$ permits one to calculate the mass of the earth from the known weight of an object on earth, Cavendish styled his experiment as "weighing the earth."   (He might as well have said "weighing the sun," for from Kepler's description of planetary motion the accelerations of the planets are also known, and one can thus use the value of $\mathcal{G}$ to calculate the mass of the sun.)

The study of electrical forces was by no means completed with Coulomb's law.   The first half of the nineteenth century was a period of intensive study of electrical phenomena, in particular the intimate connection between electricity and magnetism.   By the end of this period, it had become clear that magnetism was merely an additional force between two electrically charged objects that appears when both are in motion.   It is a far more complex force than Coulomb's, for it is proportional not only to the electrical charge on the bodies but also to their velocities.   To make matters worse, it is not parallel to but perpendicular to the line joining the interacting bodies.   By 1800 the international community of scientists had become quite large, and its means of communication through journals and extensive systematic private correspondence were well established. Thus, it was possible for many physicists to contribute to the understanding of electromagnetic phenomena.   One name stands out above all the rest, however: that of Michael Faraday.

Faraday and the Concept of Field

In the same tradition as Newton, Faraday was of humble origins, the son of a blacksmith.   Unlike Newton, however, he never received the opportunity for a university education.   His scientific career began with a stroke

---

by 10 raised to some power. Thus, 10^{40} designates a 1 followed by 40 zeros. Other examples of this notation are:

$$524 = 5.24 \times 10^2$$
$$10{,}746{,}000 = 1.0746 \times 10^7$$
$$0.00000000000000029 = 2.9 \times 10^{-16}$$

When we reach the physics of the atom, where our ordinary scale of measurement is terribly inconvenient, this notation will be indispensable.

Faraday and his wife.
(*The Royal Institution*)

38

of luck of the sort that would appeal to a second-rate movie script-writer. While serving at age 21 as an apprentice bookbinder in London, he attended a series of popular lectures by the chemist Humphrey Davy, then the most celebrated scientist in England. He applied for a job as Davy's assistant, sending as credentials a careful set of notes on the lectures. They must have been good, for the unknown apprentice in fact landed the job. After only a few years under Davy's tutelage, it had become clear that despite his lack of formal education, Faraday was a talented researcher in his own right, and he began to work on his own, primarily in chemistry. By the age of 34 he was director of the Royal Institution, perhaps the first government research laboratory in the modern sense of the term. The turning point in Faraday's career, however, came in 1831, when he was 40. He began the series of electrical experiments that were to give him the reputation among physicists as possibly the greatest experimenter that ever lived.

Perhaps because of his lack of formal university training (those less charitable may prefer the word "brainwashing"), Faraday found it difficult to visualize electrical and magnetic forces in terms of "action at a distance." Instead he invented a graphical method for visualizing these forces, which was viewed by many of his contemporaries with the bemused toleration due to a mental crutch required by an obviously brilliant but uncouth thinker. Faraday visualized electrical charges as filling space with imaginary *lines of force,* as depicted in Figure 2. These lines represent the force in two ways: the *direction* of the force at any point in space is along the lines, and the *strength* of the force is greatest where the lines are closely spaced. The absolute number of imaginary lines is of course arbitrary, but the relative number in various places on the graph is important. Regarding one charge as fixed, the force any other charge introduced in the region can be deduced from the pattern of lines of force.

The power of this graphical device is not very evident when dealing with a single charge. In Figure 3, the lines of force produced by a system of two opposite charges is depicted, alongside a sketch indicating how the force on a third charge at one particular point is deduced by the more conventional method of vector addition. In this situation, one of the rules for drawing these lines of force is that each one begins on one charge and ends on the other. When even more complex arrangements are considered, it is obvious that the value of the lines of force as a means of visualization is very great.

Eventually Faraday came to think of the pattern of lines as representing an invisible entity, nowadays called a *field,* permeating all space. This implies a subtle change in thinking from Newton's idea of action at a distance. Instead of one body acting directly on another, Faraday visualized one charge or pattern of charges producing a *field,* and the field in

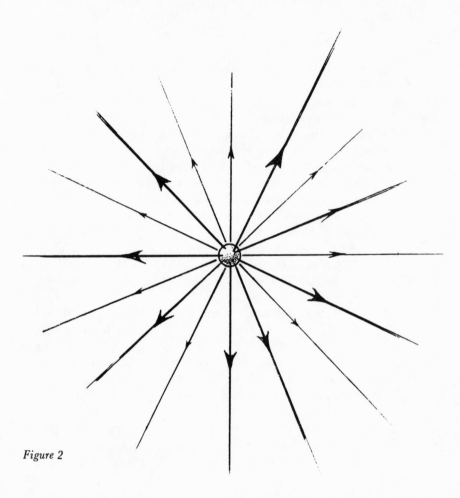

Figure 2

turn acting on another body with a force proportional to the charge on it.

Following this point of view, one should rewrite Coulomb's law as two equations:

$$E = \frac{q_1}{r^2} \qquad F = q_2\,E$$

Obviously, when dealing with the interaction of two charges, the distinction seems somewhat pedantic. But when dealing with the complex assemblages of many charges, the field E is formed from the vector sum of the fields generated by each individually.

It must be emphasized that the two points of view, field and action-at-a-distance, are completely equivalent *as long as the field is constant in time*. Thus, Faraday's approach was not taken very seriously until his work was refined and extended by a very sophisticated mathematical physicist, James Clerk Maxwell, who saw better than Faraday himself the vast implications of the concepts developed by Faraday as merely an aid to visualization.

Examining Faraday's discoveries concerning the interrelations of electrical and magnetic fields in order to put them on a sound mathematical basis, Maxwell discovered a startling implication: if the charges generating a field move or disappear, the effects of this change would *not* be communicated instantaneously to a remote charge. The change in the field instead moves out at a high but finite velocity, the velocity of *light*.

That this discovery makes it essential to assign some reality to the field itself is very easy to show. Consider two charges interacting, as depicted in Figure 4. Now let us displace charge *A* to the right. Since *A* is responding to the field of *B*, the force on it will continue to point

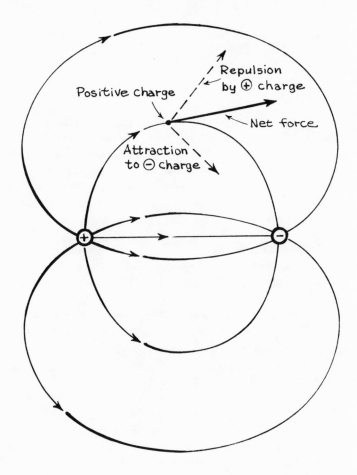

Figure 3

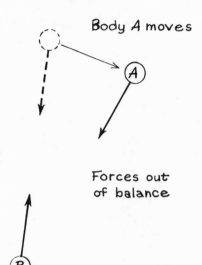

Body *A* moves

Forces out
of balance

Figure 4

to *B*. But *B* will be, for a brief period, "unaware" that *A* has moved; the force on *B* will continue to point to where *A* *was!*

Thus, we find the electrical force violating, at least temporarily, Newton's third law; the forces the two charged bodies are mutually exerting on one another are *not* opposite. As a further disastrous consequence, if the two charges are free to move, momentum is not conserved, since if the forces are not opposite there is a net increase in momentum to the right of the line joining the charges.

Must we therefore give up Newton's laws and momentum conservation when dealing with electric and magnetic fields? Not at all, for Maxwell and his successors were able to show that when an electric charge is moved an additional force is required above and beyond that needed to accelerate an inert mass. This force is the consequence of the interaction of the charge *with its own field,* regardless of whether or not other charges are present. In the process, forces are exerted on, and thus momentum is imparted to and work is done on, the field itself. This momentum and energy are transported at the velocity of light and may be recovered elsewhere by other charges. Figure 4 shows a violation of Newton's laws only if we consider space as containing only bodies *A* and *B*; the field is there, too, and it carries energy and momentum and exerts quite tangible forces on accelerated charges. If the interaction of each body with the field is considered in detail, it is found that Newton's laws, and also momentum and energy conservation, are preserved.

Another useful feature of the field concept is that it gives reality to the concept of potential energy, which we regarded as a mathematical fiction in the context of the preceding chapter. Maxwell showed that whenever a field exists, there is energy distributed throughout the region of space where it is present. It is this bank of energy on which an object "draws" when it converts potential energy to its kinetic form.

An Almost-final Unity

The capstone of Maxwell's achievement was the recognition that the speed of propagation of a changing electromagnetic field is the velocity of light. This Maxwell was able to deduce from the relative strength of electrical and magnetic forces, as measured by Faraday. At this point it seemed logical that light itself must be one such form of electromagnetic disturbance, produced by a charge in a regular, repetitive, accelerated motion so that a repeated "wave" of energy and momentum is generated. (This will be discussed further in Chapter 8.)

Maxwell's achievements, unifying electricity, magnetism, and light, were the high-water mark of classical physics, its last great triumph. His principal work, the *Treatise on Electricity and Magnetism* published in 1873, can be compared to Newton's *Principia* in significance. Like the *Principia,* Maxwell's *Treatise* is a work of synthesis, combining the efforts and thoughts of his predecessors and a few new ideas to form a complete and all-encompassing theory. Like Newton, Maxwell worked best in solitude, preferring his family's isolated estate in Scotland to university life.

Let us now examine where Maxwell's achievements left physics, for in a sense they mark a breaking point in the story that began with Galileo.

A physicist in the latter years of the nineteenth century could believe there was nothing in the universe but matter and a mysterious substance called electricity. Both of these generated *fields,* electrical and gravitational, which had a reality of a different order than that of matter. The fields produced forces which acted on matter in accordance with Newton's laws. The properties of matter derived from those of the atoms of which it was apparently composed, and once these were catalogued, all natural phenomena would be completely understood.

There seemed to be only two remaining tasks, each very well defined and even well on the way to completion, for subsequent generations of physicists. One was to complete the study of atoms, and the other was to cap the unity of physics with a purely mechanical explanation of the electromagnetic field. Maxwell believed, in fact, that he had actually achieved this explanation in the theory of the *Aether,* which will be dealt with in Chapter 9. Many of the finest scientific thinkers of the time were advising young men not to go into physics, as nature held no further secrets of importance in that realm. Man could at last dream of a final understanding of nature on its most fundamental level. It is a curious fact, and perhaps no coincidence, that this sentiment came during the late Victorian era, one of the most complacent times in modern European history, when the middle and upper classes in Europe felt they had created a nearly perfect society, likely to endure forever, with merely a few minor social problems remaining for reformers to clean up.

But, along with the "old order" that had supported it so well under royal patronage, with the material assistance of the bourgeoisie, classical physics was headed for a smashup. The study of atoms led to inquiries into their structure, which proved full of paradoxes unresolvable within the Newtonian framework, necessitating the development of the quantum theory. And Maxwell's Aether theory failed spectacularly in its most significant experimental test, a failure that was to force a reevaluation of such elementary concepts as space and time, leading to relativity. This is the story of the remainder of this book.

Epilogue: The Nightmare of Determinism

At several points in the exposition of classical mechanics, we have commented on how the thinking of physicists often shows signs of the influence of the spirit of the time in which they lived. That their ideas in turn influenced this spirit may seem surprising, in view of the abstract nature of physics and its near isolation from other fields outside the natural sciences. But through the medium of philosophy, physical thought does from time to time filter down into the general intellectual currents. It seems fitting to close the story of classical mechanics with some remarks about its impact on social thought.

The spectacular rise of physics in the two centuries leading up to the Victorian era led thinkers thoughout the intelligentsia to give considerable credit to its claims of universality. Given the classical physicist's "world view," it is reasonable to believe that everything that happens in the universe is no more than a manifestation of the motion and interaction of the constituent atoms of matter. This motion is governed by perfectly deterministic laws; the mathematical physicist Laplace speculated that, if one could only observe at some instant every atom in the universe and record its motion, both the future and the past would hold no secrets. Put another way, all of history was determined, down to the last detail, when the universe was set in motion. The rise and fall of empires, indeed, the heartbreak of every forgotten love affair, represent no more than the inevitable workings of the laws of physics; the universe marches on like a gigantic clockwork.

What room, then, for free will, for salvation and damnation, for love and hate, when the most trifling decision any human being can make was determined 10 billion years ago? It gave the ethical thinkers of the nineteenth century something to ponder. Admittedly, it is inconceivable that one could actually achieve the omniscience speculated on by Laplace. But the fact that it was possible in principle was viewed by materialist-oriented thinkers as a genuine nightmare.

Later we shall find that modern physics has at least partially resolved the dilemma by introducing an element of chance into the heart of the infernal clockwork, and by making the distinction between what can be known in principle and what is actually known by observation a crucial one at the core of the theory; thus, we shall return to this point again in the context of quantum mechanics.

But even those thinkers untroubled by this admittedly abstract nightmare felt the impact of physical thought. For the first time, man had succeeded in explaining all the details of a tremendous range of natural phenomena in terms of a remarkably small number of principles. Classical physics became the model of what human knowledge should be. Many of the social thinkers of the nineteenth century tried to emulate this universality and precision, seeking general laws to explain history and human behavior. Consider, for example, the writings of Karl Marx. Consider also the efforts of Freud to explain society in terms of his picture of the human mind.

This sort of "social determinism" is particularly reflected in the tactics of the celebrated defense attorney Clarence Darrow. Defending a client who was patently guilty of the offense as charged, Darrow would point to him as the prisoner of his own heredity, placed in an environment not of his own choosing. Under such circumstances, following from a chain of causes leading back to time immemorial, what was the meaning of "responsibility for one's actions?" And how could society presume to punish a man for a situation it had itself created, in which the victim was as powerless to modify his fate as the hands of a clock are to refuse to turn?

But, as we shall see, the twentieth century has taught physicists another lesson: as one moves from one level of reality to another in the study of nature, the laws and concepts used to describe it themselves must change. Though the laws describing the behavior of atoms are, at least in principle, the basis for the behavior of larger objects, it is inconvenient and perhaps even impossible to so use them in practice. On the basis of this, a physicist might well suspect that, for example, even if psychology were to become a perfectly exact science, it would be of little value in understanding society. Most problems in human knowledge must be solved on their own "natural" level, and to look to a "deeper" level may be instructive in itself, but rarely helps to solve the problem that started the inquiry.

8

Waves

With this chapter we finally drop the study of mechanics and devote a brief interlude to the motion of waves. One might well imagine that as long as the word "motion" is used, the subject is still mechanics, but the wave is a peculiar concept that appears in many guises. It is particularly ubiquitous in twentieth-century physics, so an understanding of the language of waves is essential to the remainder of this book.

Wave motion is not a mechanical phenomenon because a wave is not a material *object,* but a *form.* It cannot be assigned a mass, and the concept of acceleration is absolutely valueless for dealing with waves. The motion of a wave is vastly different from that undergone by the medium in which it travels; in fact, we can have a wave without any movement of matter at all. The wave follows its own laws, regardless of the underlying physics.

What, then, is a wave? It is a pattern, a form that moves. It can be a deformation of a material object, as in the case of a music string or waves on the surface of a body of water. It can also be a pattern in a field, such as light or radio waves. And these examples by no means come close to exhausting the roll of wave phenomena.

Moving Bumps

In this chapter we shall start with waves in their simplest form, single bumps or *wave pulses* traveling on a one-dimensional object, such as a string. We shall then move to continuous or repeated waves, and next to waves in two or three dimensions, building ultimately to the explanation of the experiment by which the wave nature of light was finally convincingly demonstrated.

There is no point to going any farther without introducing concrete examples, so we shall begin with the simplest, the single wave pulse. The easiest example to visualize is that of a bump on a taut string. Left to itself, such a string would remain straight. If some outside agent deforms the string, the tension will pull the bump down, as illustrated in Figure 1. But Newton's third law remains operative here; if the portion of the string to the right of the bump pulls it down, it must in turn be pulled up. By the time the original disturbance has been eliminated, a new one has been created to its right; this process continues, and the result is a bump that travels to the right. Note that it is the bump that travels, not the string, which experiences an outward deflection, followed by a return motion, actually perpendicular to the motion of the wave itself.

There is no need to dwell on the mechanical details of the process. True, a real motion of the string gives rise to a very different apparent motion of a bump. But we shall see that it is perfectly possible to understand the latter motion without troubling ourselves with the details

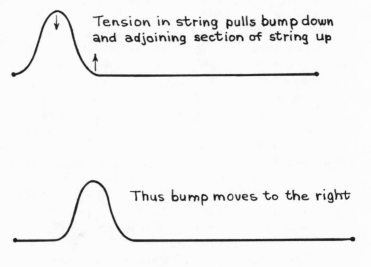

Tension in string pulls bump down and adjoining section of string up

Thus bump moves to the right

Figure 1

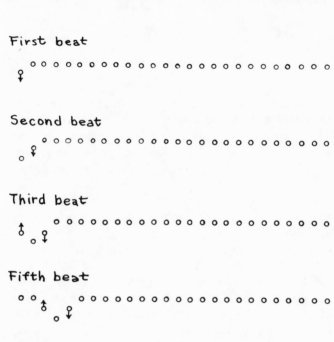

Figure 2

of the former. The motion of the medium can almost be ignored in the study of waves.

To make this point clearer, let us choose another example totally devoid of any connection with the laws of mechanics. Imagine a marching band formed up in a long single line. Each member of the band is given the instruction, "Watch the man on your right and do what he does one beat of the music later." We then go to the end of the line and ask the musician there to take two steps out, then two steps back.

The resulting effect is illustrated in Figure 2; viewed from above, a "bump" travels down the line of musicians from left to right, yet not one of them has moved either to *his* left or right. And this is by no means a mere analogy, but an actual wave phenomenon in the full meaning of the word, except that the "medium" is not continuous, as it is in most of the cases we will study. Nonetheless, wave laws can be applied in exactly the same way they are to more physical waves.

This gives us the opportunity to cite one important property of waves: they travel at a constant speed that depends on the nature of the medium, not that of the wave. The wave travels a distance of one interval between musicians for each beat of the music. This is because of the marching instructions, not the form of the wave. Had we asked the end man to take *three* steps out and back, a larger wave would have been formed, but it would still have traveled the same speed. In fact, the "elementary concept" in wave motion is that of a wave that travels at constant speed without changing its form. Any other kind of wave behavior must be expressed in these terms, by methods that will be shown. Thus there is no need to "prove" that this form of behavior holds true for the wave on the string. If it does not, it merely shows that the string is a poor example. As it happens, a tightly stretched string is an excellent wave medium. If the tension is high or the string light, the acceleration of the string in returning from a distorted condition is great, and the wave moves fast. If the string is heavy or the tension weak, the wave moves more slowly.

There do exist cases in which waves do not have this property. In light waves in transparent substances and water waves, the dimensions of a wave do affect its speed somewhat; but usually the effects are small, and the simpler wave laws need to be modified very little.

Superposition

There is one universal law that has a crucial role in the study of wave motion, however, a role comparable to that of Newton's laws in mechanics. This law is called the *principle of superposition.* It is similar in spirit to the law of the same name in mechanics, but should not be confused with it. It rests on the fact that the presence of one wave does not alter the ability of the medium to transmit another wave. Thus, two waves can pass through one another on a medium without changing their form. A simple example for the case of opposite-traveling waves on a string is illustrated in Figure 3. The small wave merely appears as a bump on the big one as they pass.

Stated in quantitative terms, the principle of superposition ensures that *the displacement produced by two waves at the same point is merely the sum of the displacements produced by each alone.*

The results of this principle are most interesting when applied to waves of equal size. Figure 4 illustrates the application of the principle of superposition to two identical waves, first displaced in the same direction and then oppositely displaced. The second case, Figure 4*b,* is perhaps the most amusing. For a brief instant, the string is absolutely flat; but since the segment just left of the center was just an instant previously moving down, and that to the right moving up, this motion will persist, and the waves will be recreated. A little reflection will show that there is one point on the string, halfway between the waves as they approach,

Before meeting

When meeting

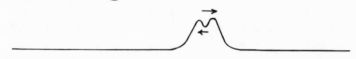

Afterward

Figure 3

that will never move at all. This is a significant point which will shortly be used to advantage.

The simultaneous presence of two waves at a single point is called *interference*. When the waves both act in the same direction, as in Figure 4*a*, the interference is called *constructive*. The phenomenon in Figure 4*b* is known as *destructive* interference.

The only connection between the mechanical and wave superposition laws is that when the origin of the wave is a mechanical process, as in waves on a string, the wave law can be proved as a consequence of the mechanical one. But many wave phenomena are nonmechanical, so it is best to regard the wave rule as standing independently.

The most interesting applications of the principle of superposition are the "backward" ones. These are the cases in which we analyze a wave and predict its future development by imagining it as the sum of two other waves, similar in spirit to the argument by which Galileo analyzed projectile motion, where he decomposed a complex curved motion into two simple ones.

100

As an example, let us ask what happens if we form a bump in the *middle* of a string. It is equally free to move in both directions, with no inherent tendency to go one way or the other. What will it do?

The question is easily answered if we take note of the fact that this situation is exactly that which exists for the instant the two waves in Figure 4*a* are exactly together. There is no difference in the appearance or motion of the string in the two situations. Even though in one case the bump formed as the fusion of two waves, and in the other we formed it artificially, there can be no difference in the subsequent behavior of the wave. We thus predict that the bump will split into two waves, each of half its height, moving off in opposite directions, and .observation verifies that this is the case.

For a more difficult example of this sort of reasoning, let us try

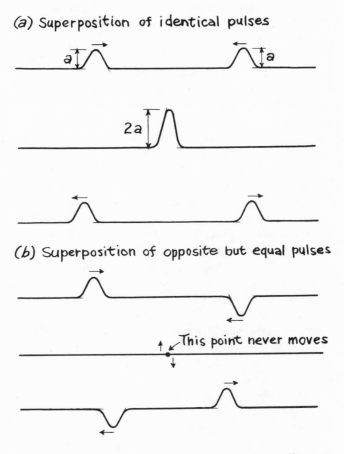

(a) Superposition of identical pulses

(b) Superposition of opposite but equal pulses

This point never moves

Figure 4

to answer the question of what happens when a wave pulse meets the fixed end of a string. Since this point cannot move, the wave must change its form as it approaches. Of course, we could throw up our hands and aver that the laws of wave motion must be invalidated by this situation, but since the string is continuous and uniform in its properties right up to the tied-down point, it is hard to say where we should draw the line.

Since the wave involves a real motion that carries energy, it is reasonable to assume it will somehow survive the encounter. After all, the end of the string is a fixed point. Since it cannot move, no work can be done on it, and thus the energy of the wave cannot leave the string. It must be reflected somehow. What form will the reflection take? And what form will the distorted wave have as it approaches the string end?

Both questions may be answered in one step, if we insist that the behavior of the wave near the end of the string be described as the interference of the wave *with its own reflection*. Since the wave has some width, there might be a time when both the wave and its reflection are present in the region near the end. Now refer back to Figure 4*b*, remembering that here, too, there is a point which never moves. It might therefore just as well be tied down, clamped between two sharp edges; since it never moves, this could not affect the waves in any way. No new forces are introduced, since unless the string tries to move, the clamp exerts no force on it.

On the other hand, there is no reason to suppose that when a wave reaches a tied-down point it matters one whit whether the string continues past this point or not. If the point cannot move, there is no way to transmit the wave beyond that point.

The only way to resolve this conflict is to conclude that when a wave reaches a tied-down point *it is reflected back as an identical but oppositely displaced wave*. Then it will not matter whether the fixed point in Figure 4*b* is actually clamped in place; the wave looks the same either way. In the tied-down case, we merely describe it as two waves simultaneously arriving at and being reflected from the same point. The simultaneous arrival gives the illusion of two opposite waves passing one another. The crucial insight is that the behavior of a wave reaching the clamped point should in no way be affected by the presence or absence of another wave coming from the other side. If they had not arrived simultaneously, we would have seen them individually reflected, each as a reversed wave.

Of course, when the two waves do arrive simultaneously, the clamp holding the string has nothing to do, since no force is required to hold in place a point that has no tendency to move. This is brought up to emphasize that it is meaningless to argue in this particular case whether the waves really *passed* or *were reflected*. The observed results are the same, and a wave, being merely an ephemeral moving bump, a shape rather than a material object, does not have an individual identity like that of the components of the string. As long as waves are nowhere near each other, we can think of them as independent entities. When they are in the same place, we must deal with the resulting combined wave.

Repeated Waves

The most important wave phenomena concern not individual wave pulses but trains of repeated, identical waves. These follow no laws different from those of individual wave pulses, so all we need add is a terminology to describe them. Figure 5 illustrates this terminology. The *wavelength,* for which the lowercase Greek letter lambda (λ) has become the conventional symbol, is the interval at which the pattern repeats. The *amplitude* measures the size of the displacement produced by the wave. One more word is required to complete the description: since the wave is moving, any point on the medium goes through a motion that repeats itself as each wavelength passes. The number of times per second this happens is called the *frequency,* usually denoted by the Greek letter nu (ν). Frequency is measured in units called *cycles per second,* recently renamed *hertz* (abbreviated Hz) in honor of the discoverer of radio waves.

Of course, the wavelength and frequency are not unrelated, since the wave does travel at a fixed speed. For example, if a wave has a frequency of 5 Hz, that is to say, if 5 complete cycles occur each second, and if each wave is 4 m long, the wave must be traveling 20 m/sec. This relationship can be summarized in the formula

$$c = \lambda \nu \qquad\qquad (1)$$

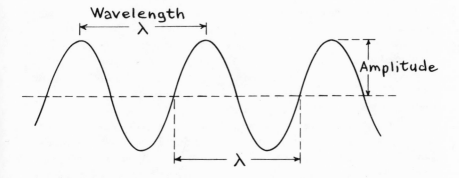

Figure 5

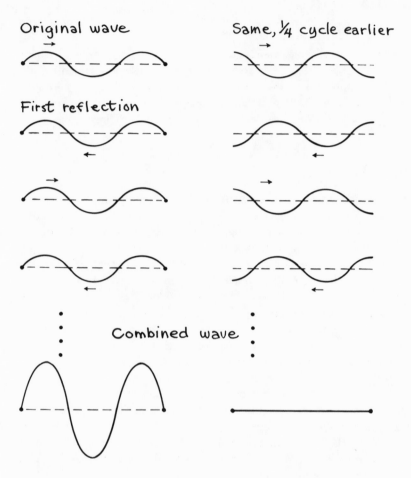

Figure 6

where c is the (also conventional) symbol for the wave velocity. This is not a physical law in the usual sense, but merely a relation that follows from the definitions of wavelength and frequency.

The only significant application of the principle of superposition to one-dimensional continuous waves, such as those on a string, is the case of *standing waves*. Not only is this phenomenon the basis of operation of every musical instrument that sounds a definite pitch, but it occupies a critical role in the modern description of the atom.

Consider what happens when a continuous wave generated at one end travels down a string fixed at both ends. If the wave continues, it soon finds itself jumbled with its own reflection, then the reflection of that reflection, and so on. After enough reflections, at any given point there are likely to be about as many waves passing with upward deflection as downward; the resulting wave will be jumbled and small in amplitude.

This is true with one exception: if the wavelength (or, to be exact, half a wavelength) fits evenly into the length of the string, then there is always a simple relation between the original wave and each of its reflections, as depicted in Figure 6. At one instant they are identical and exactly reinforce everywhere. One-quarter cycle later, the reflections traveling one way exactly oppose those travelling the other, giving a straight string. In another quarter of a cycle, the waves are again reinforcing. The resulting motion, a kind of "wave" which appears to be stationary, is shown in Figure 7. For those with musical training, the situation shown in Figures

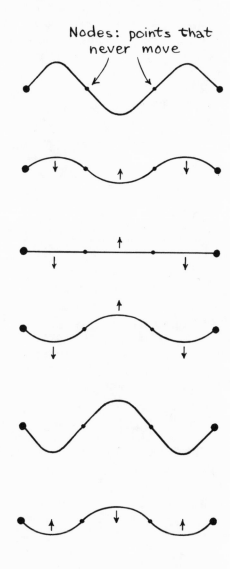

Figure 7

6 and 7 is a music string sounding the "second harmonic," where the string is $1\frac{1}{2}$ wavelengths long. Standing waves with the string $\frac{1}{2}$, 1, $1\frac{1}{2}$, 2, $2\frac{1}{2}$, . . . wavelengths can all be produced; no others can survive for more than the time required for a few reflections.

Water Waves and Such

So far we have considered only one-dimensional waves, that is, waves traveling on a string, a linear medium. The very earliest waves to come to man's attention were the two-dimensional water waves—bumps in the form of long ridges on a two-dimensional surface of a body of water. The

(a) Sectional view

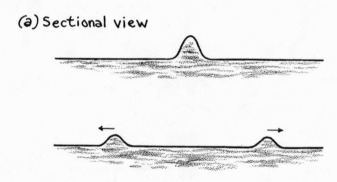

(b) View from above

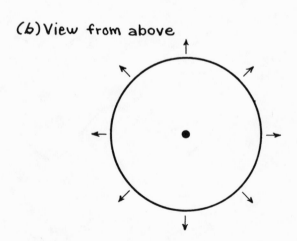

Figure 8

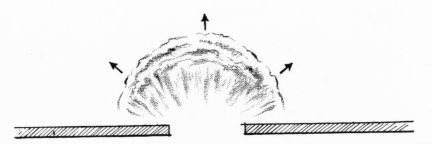

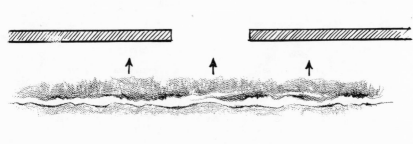

Figure 9

next step in the discussion of waves is to consider them in two or three dimensions. Again, no new physical principles are involved; the problem is simply one of description.

We will begin the treatment by reverting to the simple situation with which this chapter began—a single wave pulse. However, this time let it be a bump not on a string but on the surface of a pond. As the bump recedes under its own weight, adjoining regions are forced up by the increased pressure, beginning the propagation of a wave. A sectional view of the process is depicted in Figure 8*a*, and the logic of the situation is exactly that used when we considered the effects of a bump in the center of a string. But this time the wave is free to move in all directions, not just two linear ones. Having no reason to prefer one direction over another, it must move out in all directions. The result is the familiar expanding circle of the ripple on a quiet pond, Figure 8*b*.

Even more common to the ordinary experience is the case of continuous repeated *linear* waves, ones that take the form of long lines, such as the breakers rolling into a beach. One interesting property of waves of this type is the way they behave when they go through gaps in barriers, such as the opening in a breakwater. Figure 9 illustrates this case. If the opening is comparable to the length of the wave, each successive wave produces a "bump" in the opening, much like the source of the circular ripples of Figure 8. The result is a circular wave pattern inside the breakwater. This phenomenon is known as *diffraction*. If the width of the opening is much larger than a wavelength, this will not happen; instead the waves will continue through as linear waves, with a slight fanning out at the ends.

Waves can also exist in three dimensions. The most familiar example is that of sound waves. The crest of a sound wave is a region in which the air molecules are packed closer together. The analogue of Figure 8 for this case produces an expanding wave in the form of a *sphere;* similarly, just as *linear* water waves are observed, so are three-dimensional *plane* waves.

Both two- and three-dimensional waves exhibit a property called *refraction*. This is an effect that occurs when a wave passes a boundary from one medium to another in which it moves more slowly. The end of the wave inside the new medium is moving slower; therefore, since it remains connected to the faster-moving end in the old medium, it must

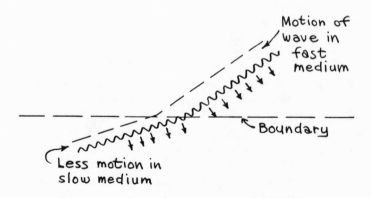

Figure 10

have turned, becoming more nearly parallel with the boundary, as shown in Figure 10. If the change in speed is gradual, so is the turn; this is why water waves nearly always strike a beach parallel to the water line, regardless of the direction they had in the open sea. As waves enter shallower water they slow down, and the resulting turn brings them straight into the beach.

How Light Was Shown to Be a Wave

We now have the tools to examine a very significant interference effect, the one used by Thomas Young in 1789 to settle a long-standing controversy as to the nature of light. This controversy dated from the time of Newton, who did extensive studies of optical effects, many of which began in the same plague-enforced absence from Cambridge that led ultimately to the *Principia*. Newton favored a theory that represented light as a hail of tiny particles. One of his contemporaries, the Dutch physicist Christian Huygens, favored a wave theory. Though the evidence available at the time to distinguish the two theories was skimpy, it must be admitted that even then Huygens' point of view seemed more plausible. But such was the prestige of Newton's name that few physicists dared finally discard the particle theory, despite mounting evidence for such effects as diffraction and constancy of speed, easy to account for in a wave theory but seemingly unnatural for particles.

Thomas Young, whose work represented the *coup de grâce* to Newton's point of view, was a man of truly protean talents. While still in his prime he resigned a physics professorship to carry on a medical practice, and a period during his later years was spent cracking the code of the Rosetta Stone, the key to the Egyptian hieroglyphics.

The experiment Young chose was that of *two-slit interference*. It is easiest to visualize in two dimensions, which brings us back to water waves and the hole-in-the-breakwater example of Figure 9. Only this time, imagine a breakwater with *two* small gaps. The waves striking the breakwater will produce two synchronized circular patterns inside, and in due course these will overlap, as shown in Figure 11.

At a point on the shore opposite and halfway between the two gaps, the waves always meet crest-to-crest, because this point is equidistant from both gaps; the waves from each gap arrive simultaneously, and the interference is constructive, giving a wave twice as high as that from one gap. As we move along the shore from this point, the synchronization is destroyed, for we are closer to one gap than to the other. Eventually we reach a point where the crests of the waves from one gap meet the troughs in the waves from the other. Here the interference is *destructive:*

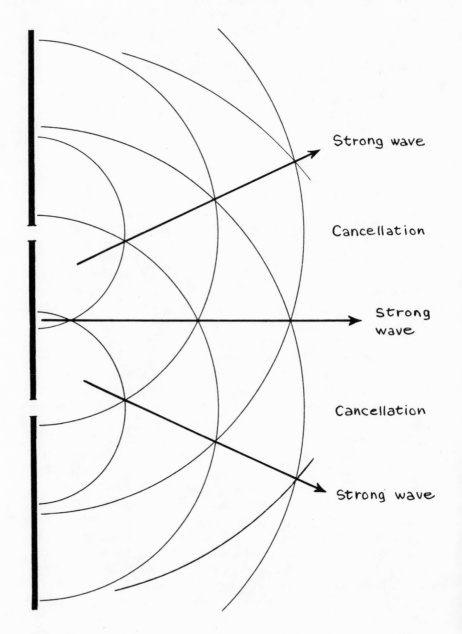

Figure 11

the waves are small or absent altogether. Moving further, we reach a point where the wave from the nearer gap meets the *preceding* wave from the farther gap. Once again the interference is constructive, and the waves are high. If we continue, we again reach a point of destructive interference, and so on. The rule is really quite simple: if the difference between

A two-slit interference pattern.

(Brian J. Thompson, The Institute of Optics, University of Rochester.)

the distance to one gap and the distance to the other is an integer (whole number) multiple of a wavelength, the interference is *constructive*. If it is $\frac{1}{2}$, $1\frac{1}{2}$, $2\frac{1}{2}$, $3\frac{1}{2}$, . . . wavelengths, *destructive* interference results.

Now to Young's experiment: replace the breakwater with an opaque screen, the gaps with narrow slits. On a sheet of paper well back from the slits, one observes a pattern of bright and dark bars parallel to the slits—a bright one in the center, dark ones to either side, and so on. If the spacing of these lines is measured, a little work with geometry enables one to calculate the wavelength of the light. The result is fantastically small: light waves have wavelengths which range from 0.00007 cm for red light to 0.00004 cm for blue light. The slits must be very narrow and close, and the viewing screen well back from the slits, to make the effect visible.

What Kind of Wave Is Light?

Young's experiment convinced the last of the doubters that light must indeed be a wave phenomenon. But the question still remained: what sort of wave? It was Maxwell who, by perceiving the relation between electromagnetism and light, provided the answer.

The picture Maxwell gave is illustrated in Figure 12. It rests on two facts, both discovered by Faraday: that whenever an electric field is changing it generates a magnetic field and that the magnetic field produced thereby is at right angles to the electric field. The relationship is reciprocal: a changing magnetic field creates an electric field at right angles to itself.

Without asking how such a peculiar combination of fields can be created in the first place, it is clear that the arrangement illustrated in Figure 12 is self-perpetuating. The changing electric field generates a magnetic field which, since it too is changing, regenerates the electric field. The process continues indefinitely. The wave moves in a direction perpendicular to both fields.

Maxwell calculated the speed at which such a wave would travel and found it agreed exactly with the speed of light. The coincidence was too striking to be ignored. Maxwell concluded that light itself must be an electromagnetic wave.

How such a wave could be produced was evident from the laws of electricity and magnetism. Suppose an electric charge is going through some sort of repeated, periodic motion. Motion in a circle would do, as would simple back-and-forth oscillation. In either case, both an electric field and a magnetic field are generated, for the charge is in motion. The field is also a changing one, because the position of the charge is changing, and field strength varies with distance. Thus, any object which is giving off light must contain electric charges oscillating very rapidly, since the frequencies of light waves are in the range of 10^{14} Hz, or 10 trillion oscillations per second!

Any object oscillating so fast would have to be very tiny, and so to directly observe its oscillations seemed a hopeless task.   But Maxwell reasoned that slower oscillations must also produce electromagnetic waves, whose strength would be sufficient to detect by electrical means.   At frequencies of a few thousand hertz, comparable to those of sound waves, it is possible to set large quantities of charge in motion on electric wires.   Twenty years after Maxwell published his theory, in 1887, the German physicist Heinrich Hertz was able to do the trick.

Hertz set up violent electrical oscillations in an electric circuit.   In another circuit several feet away in the laboratory, not connected to any source of power, electrical oscillations of the same frequency were produced.   The frequencies of the oscillations were easy to measure; from the interference properties of the waves, the wavelengths could be estimated.   Thus, the speed could be computed, and it agreed with the speed of light.   After these experiments, few could doubt that Maxwell had been

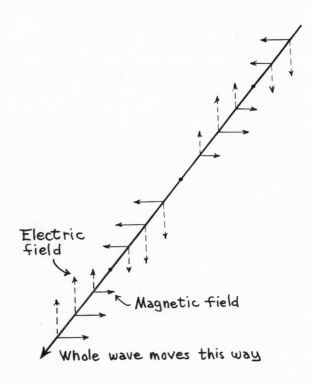

Electric field

Magnetic field

Whole wave moves this way

Figure 12

right.   Hertz's waves later became the basis of modern radio communications.

Shortly after the work of Hertz, x-rays were discovered. These proved to be electromagnetic waves, too, but of frequencies about a thousand times *greater* than those of visible light.   Later, the gamma rays emitted by radioactive substances proved to be electromagnetic waves with frequencies a thousand times greater still!

Today, we have a technology for handling electromagnetic waves of nearly any desired frequency.   Maxwell's theory of electromagnetism has proved probably the most striking example of a "pure" scientific theory leading to practical results that could never have been stumbled upon by accident.

9

Surpise:
The Earth Doesn't Move!

Struck as they were by the beautiful description of a light wave given by Maxwell, it was nonetheless hard for the physicists of his time to imagine a wave without also imagining some sort of medium for it to travel in. Sound waves have air, ocean waves propagate on water, and so on. Furthermore, in the case of these material waves, their behavior could be attributed to the mechanical properties of the medium. The implied invitation was irresistible: find the medium, and the behavior of light (and thus ultimately of electrical forces) might thereby be shown to result merely from Newton's laws, putting the final capstone on the unity of physics. To this hypothetical medium Maxwell gave the name Luminiferous (i.e., "light-bearing") Aether. Light would represent waves in the Aether, and electrical forces would be transmitted by "stretching" it.

It could easily be shown that this Aether would have to be a rather peculiar substance indeed. From the fact that light propagates at the same speed throughout the universe, it is clear that it would have to fill space uniformly. In particular, this made it unlikely that it was affected much by gravity. And since the motions of the planets had by then been studied to high precision and observed over millenia without any change, it was clear that the Aether must offer at most an infinitesimal resistance to the passage of ordinary matter. Indeed, the most likely possibility was that it could freely penetrate ordinary matter without exerting the least force. Only electrically charged objects could interact with the Aether. And from the fantastic velocity of light, 3×10^8 m/sec, it was clear that the Aether must be low in density, yet very "hard," for both of these properties contribute to a high speed for waves.

What a troublesome substance for the poor experimental physicist to get a handle on! Transparent, incompressible, and difficult to exert a force on—how could one hope to study it or even prove its existence, aside from the indirect evidence provided by light itself?

Nonetheless, a few opportunities presented themselves. The most promising was that any point on the earth must be moving through the Aether at a considerable speed. Our planet clips along in its orbit at the rather brisk pace of thirty kilometers per second; add to this a somewhat smaller speed resulting from the earth's rotation, and whatever comes from the little-known motion of the sun, and you expect a considerable "wind" of Aether "blowing" through the laboratory. It might be small compared to the 300,000 km/sec of the velocity of light, but the Aether wind should still be strong enough to have observable consequences in the behavior of light on earth.

The first experiment capable of detecting this Aether wind was performed by a young professor at the Case School of Applied Sciences in Cleveland, Ohio, Albert A. Michelson, with the aid of Edward W. Morley, a chemist from Western Reserve University.* The results were announced in 1887. That one of the most significant experiments in the history of physics could come from two relatively obscure schools in an industrial boom town on the shores of Lake Erie came as a bit of a surprise both in the United States and abroad. Though America had produced a few scientists of note by the end of the nineteenth century, it was still very much of a scientific backwater, especially in the more abstract areas of physics. The great centers of learning, the private universities of the East, were primarily concerned with educating America's governing elite; scientific studies rated low in their standard of values. Thus, American science was dominated by the technical schools and land-grant colleges, where it took on a very gadget-oriented, pragmatic bent that still survives to some extent today as an element of the American "style" in physics. Indeed, until the United States absorbed a major portion of the European scientific community as World War II refugees, a young man bent on becoming a first-class research physicist was well advised to go

* An early example of the collaboration between these neighboring schools which culminated in their merger in 1965.

abroad to finish his education, especially if he was interested in fundamental problems.

Michelson was no exception to either trend. Graduated from Annapolis in 1873, he was assigned to work at the Nautical Almanac Office. Because of the traditional interest of all navies in optical and astronomical measurements, he had a great deal of freedom to pursue experiments in these areas. Bitten by the experimental "bug," he followed a well-established route, taking leave from his naval duties in 1879 for several years of polishing in Berlin, Heidelberg, and Paris. In Europe he found the problem of detecting the Aether occupying the center of attention among those physicists who were experts on optical phenomena, and he made his first attempt at his celebrated experiment. Though he failed to find the Aether wind, his first instrument was too crude to be sure the failure was not purely an instrumental error.

The trademark of this man who was to become America's first Nobel laureate was his ability to conceive instruments of high precision on a grandiose scale that transcended the traditional idea of a laboratory device. Michelson chose the Aether wind experiment at least partly because of the opportunity it provided to show his imaginative virtuosity at instrument design. The European experience also settled his career plans: shortly after returning to the United States, he resigned his Navy commission to become the first physics professor at the newly founded Case Institute.

Swimming Across a Stream

Michelson's gadget was based on a remarkably simple idea. In ordinary language, it is that *it takes less time to swim across a stream and back than to swim the same distance upstream and back.* This fact is by no means self-evident, so we will establish it here. The required mathematics is rather straightforward and will be useful later in the treatment of relativity.

Suppose a swimmer swims with velocity c and heads across a stream of width w by the most direct (i.e., the perpendicular) route, as shown in Figure 1. If the stream moves with velocity v (which obviously had better be less than c, or the swimmer has had it!), the swimmer must point himself a bit upstream to compensate for the motion of the stream. As a result he must actually swim a greater distance in the water, as indicated in Figure 1. If s is the distance he actually moves through the *water*, it is greater than w by the factor

$$\frac{s}{w} = \frac{ct}{c't} = \frac{c}{c'}$$

But by the theorem of Pythagoras,

$$c' = \sqrt{c^2 - v^2}$$

Thus, we have,

$$\frac{s}{w} = \frac{c}{\sqrt{c^2 - v^2}} = \frac{1}{\sqrt{1 - v^2/c^2}} \qquad (1)$$

Equation (1) should be inspected very closely; it will reappear many times in the theory of relativity. The factor $1/\sqrt{1 - v^2/c^2}$ is designated in Einstein's theory by the lowercase Greek letter γ (gamma). Because of its importance, the way γ varies with velocity is shown in the graph in Figure 2. As a numerical example, suppose the swimmer can do 5 mph in a stream that moves at 3 mph. Then $v/c = 0.6$, $v^2/c^2 = 0.36$, and $1 - v^2/c^2 = 0.64$; since the square root of 0.64 is 0.8, we have

$$\frac{s}{w} = 1.25$$

i.e., the swimmer must swim 25 percent farther than if the stream is quiet. The reader may verify for himself that if $v = 0$, the results is $s = w$.

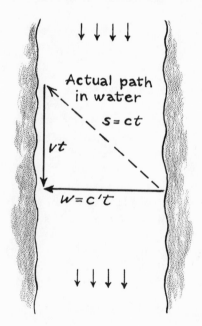

Figure 1

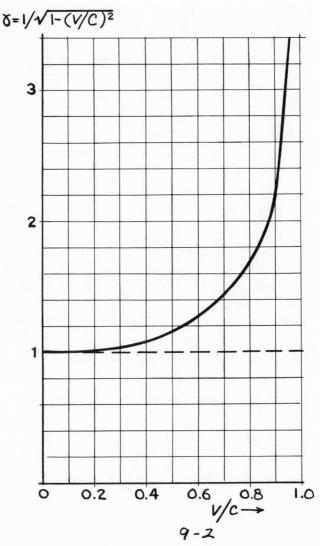

$$\gamma = 1/\sqrt{1-(v/c)^2}$$

9-2

Figure 2

To calculate the distance covered in the water for the upstream-downstream case is just as simple. Upstream, the swimmer's "ground speed" is $c-v$, and downstream it is $c+v$. Thus, the time he must spend in the water is

upstream   *downstream*

$$t_u = \frac{w}{c-v} \qquad t_d = \frac{w}{c+v}$$

119

The total time in the water is $t_u + t_d$. During this time he is swimming with velocity c. Thus, the distance covered *in the water is*

$$s = (t_u + t_d)c = \frac{cw}{c - v} + \frac{cw}{c + v}$$

giving the result:

$$\frac{s}{w} = \frac{c}{c - v} + \frac{c}{c + v} = \frac{1}{1 - v/c} + \frac{1}{1 + v/c} = \frac{2}{1 - (v/c)^2} = 2\gamma^2$$

Returning to our numerical example, going up and downstream we have:

$$\frac{s}{w} = 2\gamma^2 = 2 \times (1.25)^2 = 3.125$$

Thus, he swims 3.125 times as far as one stream-width in moving water. For the *across*-stream trip, he swims $1.25w$ each way (both trips are obviously identical), for a total of $2.5w$. Table 1 compares the formulas for the two cases.

TABLE 1

Actual distance covered in water

Across stream and back:	$\dfrac{2w}{\sqrt{1 - (v/c)^2}}$
Up and down stream:	$\dfrac{2w}{1 - (v/c)^2}$

A Racecourse for Light

Now we turn to the Michelson-Morley apparatus. The reader has probably anticipated the next step. Replace the stream with the Aether wind, the swimmer with a ray of light (which is why we chose the symbol c, the conventional symbol for the velocity of light). But in this case, v/c is not 0.6—it is about 0.0001! How can we measure such a tiny difference?

The answer is that light carries its own yardstick, and a remarkably fine one it is. The "inch" on this yardstick is the length of a single light wave—typically, about 0.00005 cm. What Michelson needed to do was build a device that sets up a race between two light rays, with a way to judge the winner to a fraction of a light wave.

Michelson's racecourse is depicted in Figure 3. A partially silvered mirror transmits half the light falling on it, reflecting the rest, thus setting up two light beams at right angles. Two ordinary mirrors send these back along their paths, returning to the half-silvered mirror, which "recombines" them. If the waves arrive crest-to-crest, the center of the pattern in the eyepiece will be bright. If they arrive trough-to-crest, it will be dark. But how equal are the two paths? Michelson avoided this question by *rotating the apparatus.* Thus, he need never know which light ray actually "won" the race—only that by switching around the upstream and cross-stream paths the margin of victory was changed by some fraction of a light wave.

One might reasonably ask how Michelson really knew which way the Aether wind was blowing. While the motion of the earth in its orbit is 30 km/sec, perhaps the whole solar system is moving through space in a manner that counteracts this. But if the sun's motion cancels that of the earth in January, it must add to it in July, when the earth is traveling the other way in its orbit.

Indeed, Michelson's measurement was nearly sensitive enough to detect an Aether wind from the earth's *rotation* alone, even were all other motions canceled. And later refinements of the experiment were more sensitive still.

Building a successful apparatus was no mean feat. The racecourse, now called a *Michelson interferometer,* must be capable of being rotated

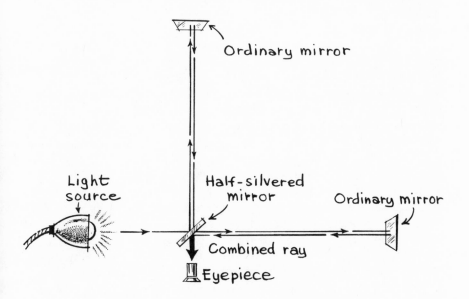

Figure 3 Michelson interferometer.

without changing its dimensions by even a small fraction of a wavelength of light. For his first attempt, in Berlin in 1880, he tried using a massive structure of precision-machined steel. Even so, it was so sensitive to vibrations that it could be used only at night, and when an assistant 100 yards outside the laboratory stamped on the ground the effect was visible. In the Cleveland version, the device was mounted on a huge sandstone slab floated on a pool of mercury, with multiple mirrors to lengthen the race-course to over 30 ft. All was set to go; Michelson had a gadget that could measure the speed of the earth to an accuracy of one km/sec.

The sandstone slab was set into slow rotation, taking over a minute to turn all the way around. Michelson looked through the eyepiece, seeing a pattern of concentric light and dark rings. Had there been any change in path length, he would have seen these rings shink and expand as the apparatus turned. The pattern stayed frozen, much to Michelson's surprise. The news was very upsetting to a world of physicists convinced they might be the last generation of their kind. Refining, rechecking, repeating, or just trying to explain away Michelson's result became a major activity for several decades.

Early Attempts to Explain the Result

The full story of attempts to explain away the Michelson-Morley experiment is interesting and at times amusing, for it still ranks as one of the biggest surprises in the history of physics. Only one such attempt is worth mentioning, however, for it was the one that was on the right track, at least mathematically.

Following a suggestion by C. F. FitzGerald, H. A. Lorentz, a remarkably able Dutch theoretical physicist, saw a clue to the mystery of the failure to detect the Aether wind in the discovery of the electrical structure of atoms, which came only a few years after the original Michelson result. Seeing that matter was held together by electrical forces, Lorentz speculated, and seeing that it is the Aether that transmits these forces, it is just possible that the Aether wind "flattens" matter in the direction along the wind as it passes through. It must flatten it by exactly the required amount, γ, to make the Michelson race come out in a dead heat. Of course, no material ruler could detect the effect, for it would conveniently shrink the same amount as whatever it was measuring.

But in the Lorentz theory there remained optical ways of measuring the shrinkage. While a trip across the Aether wind would always end in a dead heat with one up and down the wind, the total length of each path in light wavelengths would change as the Aether wind changed. Since the speed of the Aether wind changes at any point on the earth's surface as the earth rotates, an optical measurement of the length of an object would change with the time of day. Several of the most renowned physicists of the time tried such experiments, but failed to observe the contraction.

Meanwhile, Michelson was enjoying to the full the fruits of his success. Had he succeeded in finding the Aether wind, he would have gained no mean reputation as a gadgeteer and a careful experimenter. To *fail* to find it, in a convincing manner, and to have a spectacular array of scientific talent out looking for a way to account for the result, made him a real celebrity. Following the accepted academic success formula, he kept moving. First leaving Case Institute for Clark University, he was later lured away to found the physics department of the new University of Chicago, where boy-wonder President William Rainey Harper was using generous libations of Rockefeller money in an attempt to create an "instant Oxford." Sticking to his chosen specialty of large optical instruments, he had a number of celebrated successes. One of the most notable, for sheer physical size, was the mile-long vacuum pipe he set up on the California desert to make a precise determination of the velocity of light.

Despite its cosmopolitanization during World War II, American physics research has retained some of the Michelson flavor. The willingness to build research instruments on a stupendous scale has always been a distinguishing feature of the American style. Many a physicist in this country has carved an illustrious career out of his skill as a gadgeteer, without ever personally contributing to physical thought. The giant particle accelerators (popularly known as atom-smashers), which are currently the most expansive (and expensive) monuments ever erected to man's curiosity, would probably have tickled Michelson's fancy.

10

Origins of Relativity: How Long Is a Moving Train?

But in physics I soon learned to scent out the
paths that led to the depths, and to disregard everything
else, all the many things that clutter up the mind,
and divert it from the essential. The hitch in this
was, of course, the fact that one had to cram all this
stuff into one's mind for the examination, whether one
liked it or not.

—ALBERT EINSTEIN

Biographical sketches of famous physicists contain the phrase "his brilliance became obvious early in his schooling" with monotonous regularity. From this cliché it is necessary to exempt Albert Einstein, one of the handful of twentieth-century physicists whose name has become a household word. In contemporary journalese, Einstein in his late teens would have been described as an undisciplined, confused, middle-class high school dropout.

Einstein was born in 1879 to a family of minor industrialists in Bavaria. When in his mid-teens he withdrew from his Gymnasium (roughly the equivalent of a prep school), his strict schoolmasters breathed a sigh of relief, for the dreamy-eyed woolgatherer was clearly "uneducable." After a year of wandering in Northern Italy, Einstein resolved to take one more crack at obtaining an education in the somewhat less demanding Swiss school system. He finally managed after several tries and a year of makeup studies to restore some honor to his name by passing the *arbitureinten*. This examination, which exists in one form or another in all continental nations, is a state exam required for admission to any form of professional or university training. Given in the late teens, it remains to this day the crucial dividing line in the life of a youth from the educated middle classes. His somewhat tainted success gave Einstein the right to enter the Swiss Federal Polytechnic School in Zurich, which, like MIT in contemporary America, was a prestige engineering school.

His classmates in Zurich have described Einstein as charming and witty, but an indifferent student who attended cafés regularly and lectures sporadically. His voracious appetite for reading rarely extended to the books required for his courses. Though his friends were convinced that this charming fellow must possess some sort of brilliance, there were no indications that it was the kind required for success in as disciplined a field as physics, but they did their best to help him get through. Both his friends and the few sympathetic professors rejoiced when he actually managed to graduate in 1900 with an uneven record, showing obvious talent in some areas but nearly total ignorance of others.

For a year or so he earned an irregular income as a tutor, until the influence of one particularly close friend, Marcel Grossmann, landed him an undemanding sinecure as a patent examiner in the Swiss capital of Bern. In this unlikely bureaucratic niche he enjoyed eight of the most productive years in the history of physics. Not only did he develop the theory of relativity, perhaps the greatest single-handed contribution to physics since the time of Newton, but he took some of the most important first steps toward the quantum theory, as well as achieving some of the early insights into the nature of solid matter. He also gave the first exact treatment of the Brownian motion, the irregular movement of microscopic objects resulting from the bombardment of moving atoms, an important direct confirmation of the existence of atoms. It reflects to the credit of the European scientific community that despite his obscurity and questionable credentials, the value of his work was almost immediately recognized. From 1909 to 1914 he served in a succession of professorial chairs in Zurich and Prague, culminating in the creation of a special position, totally free of specified duties, for him at the University of Berlin. He looked upon this honor with mixed emotions, for his Patent Office days

Einstein during his Bern days.
(Photo by Lotte Jacobi.)

had been a welcome obscurity that gave him several precious years of freedom from the pressures that normally beset a young academic. The publish-or-perish policy had already become established at Central European universities, and in his later years Einstein was to comment:

> For an academic career puts a young man into a kind of embarrassing position by requiring him to produce scientific publications in impressive quantity—a seduction into superficiality which only strong characters are able to withstand. Most practical occupations, however, are of such a nature that a man of normal ability is able to accomplish what is expected of him. His day-to-day existence does not depend on any special illuminations. If he has deeper scientific interests he may plunge into his favorite problems in addition to doing his required work. He need not be oppressed by the fear that his efforts may lead to no results. I owed it to Marcel Grossman that I was in such a fortunate position.

The spectacular result of Grossmann's patronage was that in 1905, while he was only 25, Einstein promulgated the theory of relativity, which struck even its most enthusiastic early adherents as bizarre.

What Einstein did was to explain the result of the Michelson-Morley experiment by the audacious step of deliberately postulating what appeared to be a paradox, and then insisting that this paradox be resolved by a complete reexamination of the concepts of distance and time, notions which had been taken as self-evident and undefinable throughout the history of physics.

The Postulate of Relativity

The central postulate of relativity is deceptively simple:

> *The velocity of light is the same for all observers, in all directions, regardless of their state of rest or motion.*

Obviously, the postulate takes care of the Michelson-Morley result by *fiat*. The velocity of the light signal in both arms of the interferometer is assumed to be the same, regardless of the speed or direction of the earth's motion. Rotating the apparatus changes nothing. But the paradox, too, is inescapable. If one observer finds light moving at c with respect to him, how can another observer moving in the direction of the signal get the same answer? Clearly, if it moves at the velocity of light with respect to one, it cannot so move with respect to the other.

Put another way, the postulate seems to give two conflicting answers to the question: "Does light behave like a bullet or like the sound of the gunshot?" If a bullet is fired off the front of a moving train, it acquires the velocity of the train in addition to its normal speed. The sound does not, but travels through the air at its usual rate. Thus, a stationary observer would find the sound traveling normally, and the bullet traveling faster than usual. If an observer on the train were to perform the measurements, he would find the bullet traveling at its normal speed and the sound moving slower than normal forward, faster than normal backward. What Einstein's postulate suggests is that, to the man on the train, light behaves like a bullet, while to the man on the ground it behaves like the sound of the shot!

Though Einstein's step was a bold one, it was not totally out of harmony with the thinking of others. A few years previously, the French physicist-philosopher Henri Poincaré had placed a strikingly similar interpretation on the Michelson-Morley experiment. Poincaré noted that such concepts as "absolute" motion and rest had never really had a place in physics, ever since the formulation of the principle of inertia. Perhaps the Michelson-Morley result was just one specific manifestation of a general principle: *no experiment whatsoever can measure absolute motion.* One remains free to regard any body that moves in a straight line at constant speed as standing still. Though unaware of Poincaré's suggestion, Einstein was to carry through its realization, the reformulation of physics so that the propagation of light would not seem to violate this general principle. For it was in the hope that the earth's "absolute" motion could be detected that the experiment was undertaken.

Einstein's insight was to see that while the crucial problem was the propagation of light, the problems it raised were far more general. He examined the paradox in detail to see just what its consequences were, and whether physics could learn to live with them. Before entering into the presentation of his arguments, it is best to begin with a warning: the arguments back of relativity are simple and straightforward, but the consequences, though also reasonably simple, seem to fly in the face of common sense. The normal reaction to a first exposure to relativity is: "I think I understand it; I just don't believe it." Thus, the reader is likely to feel the same frustration as Alice talking to the Queen of Hearts. Normally it takes a physicist about five years of contact with the ideas of relativity before he feels comfortable with them—not because they are complex or obscure, but just terribly strange.

The rule of the game to be played in the next few chapters is to *accept* the consequences of the postulate no matter how weird. We must never ask *how* they can be so; we accept that they must be so, and see if any of the strange things they imply actually contradict our experience. So the reader is implored to *have faith,* in the hope that all will turn out self-consistent in the end.

Simultaneity Depends on Whom

Einstein's analysis turns on a single point: if his postulate is valid, *two observers relatively in motion cannot agree whether two events happening in different places occurred simultaneously.* This has further consequences, of which the two most significant are that the speed of light must be an upper limit for all velocities, and that observers relatively in motion cannot agree on measurements of length or time. The explanation of these points will occupy the remainder of this chapter and the next.

Relativity lends itself naturally and pleasantly to exposition by means of examples. Einstein himself referred to these as "thought experiments" *(gedanken experimenten)*. Choosing one of his own favorites, let us imagine a remarkable train traveling at an appreciable fraction of the speed of light. This pedagogical express is depicted in Figure 1. Let us imagine observers at either end of the train, another pair on the ground, and a light flashed in the middle of the train. Let the observers on the ground position themselves so that when the flash reaches the two ends of the train, each will be standing at one of the ends.

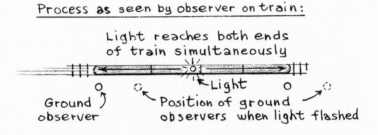

Process as seen by observer on train:

Light reaches both ends of train simultaneously

←Light

Ground observer

Position of ground observers when light flashed

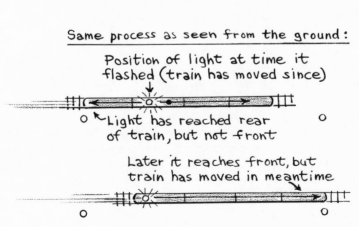

Same process as seen from the ground:

Position of light at time it flashed (train has moved since)

←Light has reached rear of train, but not front

Later it reaches front, but train has moved in meantime

Figure 1

The observers on the train feel that the light arrives at both ends of the train simultaneously, for, by applying Einstein's postulate, they say it travels the same speed with respect to the *train* in both directions. But those on the ground have a different point of view. The train has moved since the light flashed, and was not halfway between them when it flashed. To the stationary observers, light travels at the same speed in both directions with respect to the *ground*. Since the light flashed closer to the rear observer than the front one, he must have seen the flash first! Those on the train reply that while it was true the rear observer on the ground was closer to the flash when it came, he has moved in the meantime and was really at the same position as the rear observer on the train when it arrived. And so the argument goes back and forth. Each insists he is right, and according to the postulate they must both be right. How can this be?

Clearly, we must accept the notion that observers in different states of motion will have different definitions of simultaneity when applied to remote events. The observers standing side by side at the rear of the train both agree that they saw the light flash at the same time. The same goes for those at the front. What they disagree about is that the events at opposite ends of the train were simultaneous. Two observers at the same point can always agree what time it is *there*—they are close together and can easily compare notes. But their opinion as to what time it is *elsewhere* depends on their state of motion, because this affects their interpretation of how a light signal "gets the word" between the two points.

For example, the two observers in the train could use the flash of light from the middle of the train to set their watches. Then, while they would feel their watches were synchronized, those on the ground would insist that the watch at the rear of the train was set a bit ahead of that at the front. They would insist on using a light further forward, halfway between *them,* to set their watches by. But then the observers on the train would insist that the watch of the forward observer was fast. They could verify this by setting their watches with the same light signal used by the men on the ground. When they compared notes, they would find the watches out of time, just as their friends on the ground did when the light on the train was used.

That Figure 1 has three separate drawings shows an essential fact: What the observers on the train see as one single instant in which the light arrives at all four observers, those on the ground see as *two instants*— one when the two observers at the back (simultaneously) see the light signal there, and a later instant when the same thing happens at the front of the train.

It is important to emphasize that it is not necessary that the setting of watches actually be done by a light signal to get this peculiar result—whatever means is used, in order for the propagation of light to obey the Einstein postulate, each set of observers must feel that the other set is off on its timing. Any system of setting watches that made the ground observers and the observers on the train agree that the watches on the train were synchronized would lead the observers on the train to conclude that those on the ground were right—the light reached the rear of the train first. This would contradict the Einstein postulate, for if light travels with equal speed in all directions, the observers on the train *must* believe it arrived at both ends at the same time.

The obvious example is for them to meet at some point and check their watches on the spot. To avoid contradicting Einstein's postulate, we must then insist that, as viewed by the observers on the ground, the watches of the observers on the train must drift out of synchronization as they move to take up their positions. At this stage of the game, we cannot describe in detail or justify this process—this will become possible in the next chapter. But we must insist that something of the sort will happen, or abandon Einstein's postulate. And remember that the "game" we are playing is to accept the consequences of the postulate, no matter how strange, and to see if we can live with them.

It is clear, however, that this drifting out of time must not just apply to the ends of the train, but must be a continuous process. For example, if we made the train twice as long, the time required for light to traverse its length would be twice as great, and thus, the apparent lack of synchronization of watches at either end of the train would be twice as great to an observer on the ground, while a watch at the middle of the train would have the original time lag. That is to say that the stationary observers would see it as reading halfway between the ones at the end. If we then imagine watches spaced out at regular intervals along an endless train, they just continue to look farther and farther behind in their settings as we move along the train.

Can We Trust a Clock?

This leads to perhaps the most startling implication of relativity. If the watches are to appear farther and farther out of time as we move forward in the train, *then the watches on the train must appear to be running slower,* because as they move they get more and more out of time with respect to watches on the ground. In the next chapter we shall use a completely different argument to justify this assertion and to find quantitatively how much slower they appear to run.

By now the reader could hardly have overlooked the key role we have assigned to the velocity of light. The whole chain of reasoning falls apart if there exists a faster means of communication than light signals, such as, for example, an object moving faster than light. For if instantaneous signals were possible, or at least ones much faster than light, the moving and stationary observers could use these signals to eliminate or at least decrease their disagreements about how to set clocks. But the point of the example is that this disagreement is *necessary* in order for light to obey the Einstein postulate. The conclusion is absolutely inescapable. *The Einstein postulate can only work if nothing can move faster than light.**

Put another way, if there exists *anything* that is so queer as to obey Einstein's postulate, its velocity must be unique and the limit of all possible velocities. There cannot be two separate phenomena both of which obey the postulate, with different speeds of propagation.

This represents an enormous change in our attitude toward the velocity of light. No longer is it a property of light itself, or of the medium in which light travels (which we have obviously abandoned anyway). It is a fundamental property of the universe, applying to material objects as well as to light. We shall see in the next chapter that the true significance of the speed of light is not that it is an accidental property of electromagnetic waves, but that it is a fundamental scale factor in the universe between measurements of distance and time.

It is interesting that though Poincaré was not bold enough to himself create the "new dynamics" for which he foresaw the necessity, he was able to anticipate this feature of it—that "superlight" velocities would be impossible.

At the present point we are in no position to say how this speed limit is enforced. Why can't a material object be accelerated beyond the speed of light? In Chapter 12, when we come to grips with the changes in Newton's laws required by relativity, we shall find the speed limit is self-enforcing.

How Long Is the Train?

Let us now return to the train example, in order to show that the two observers must necessarily disagree as to the length of the train. For when the light signals arrive at the ends of the train, the observers on the train insist that both they and the men on the ground are standing exactly

---

* It has recently been proved that a special form of matter could exist that would travel faster than the speed of light without violating the Einstein postulate. But the prohibition still applies to ordinary matter, and this other hypothetical form has never actually been observed.

one train-length apart. But those on the ground reply with a resounding "no!" They feel the light arrived at the rear before the head—the train moved in the meantime. To both be at the opposite ends of the train *at the same time,* they would have had to stand closer together. Thus, they will get a lower figure for the length of the train. A glimpse at Figure 1 makes it obvious that the ground observers must believe the train to be shorter than the spacing between them.

Note the symmetric character of the disagreement. To the observers on the train it is the *moving* length, the spacing of observers on the ground, that appears shortened. To those on the ground, it is the train that appears shorter. To preserve the feature that each set of observers has the right to regard the other as in motion, we must conclude that whenever one observes an object to be moving, it appears shortened. However, the situation depicted in Figure 1 is *not* perfectly symmetric. It was chosen deliberately so that, *as seen from the train,* the observers on the ground are exactly a train's length apart. This was done to make the example cleaner, so that at least from the point of view of one set of observers (those on the train) there is an instant when both pairs of observers were in the same place. Were the train to stop, it would still be shorter than the distance between the two stationary observers, but not so much as it appears to them to be when the train is moving. Shortly we shall consider a symmetric example, two identical trains passing, where there is *no* instant at which either pair of observers feels the two trains are lined up exactly. If both groups of observers are provided with identical tape measures, the ones on the ground will see both the train and its tape measure as shrunken. And since those on the train have an equal right to consider themselves at rest and the ground as moving, it will be the tape measure on the *ground* that appears shrunken!

But in one sense both points of view are *not* equally valid. Clearly the right way to measure the length of anything is with a ruler that is at rest with respect to it. If the object is moving with respect to the ruler, you are in trouble. Then two observers disagree as to when the ruler and the train are exactly lined up, because they cannot agree as to the time at the two ends. A little thought should convince you that any measurement of the length of a moving object with a stationary instrument must be upset by the problem of ambiguous definition of simultaneity at opposite ends. The problems with length and with time are inseparable.

This was Einstein's analysis of the Lorentz contraction, and we shall see in the next chapter that it gives quantitatively the right result for the contraction. But where Lorentz viewed it as a real contraction, Einstein saw it as an apparent one resulting from the difficulty of deciding unambiguously when the two ends of a moving object are where. And the result is not peculiar to this somewhat abstract method of measuring the length of a moving train. A different method will be used in the next chapter. But unlike Lorentz's "real" contraction, there is no way for the contracted observer to see his own contraction. It is not really there for him, but only for the stationary observer.

Once again, though we are arguing on the basis of what may be particular examples, the rules of our "game" force us to accept that the result is quite general. If Einstein's postulate is to be compatible with the rest of physics, the method described for measuring the length of the moving train is a reasonable one, and any other method used by stationary observers will give the same result. It is for this reason that, in the first few decades after its promulgation, when relativity was still a controversial theory, much of the argument against it took the form of a search for one *gedanken* experiment that would contradict the others.

Two Identical Trains Pass

In order to clear up any confusion arising from the lack of symmetry in the preceding example, consider the case of two identical trains, each equipped with synchronized clocks at both ends and in the middle, with an observer stationed by each middle clock. At the instant the centers of the trains pass, depicted in Figure 2, each observer feels as follows:

1 The other train is shorter.
2 The clock at the head of the other train is set slow.
3 The clock at the rear of the other train is set fast.
4 All the clocks on the other train are running slow.

Analyzed in detail, the disagreement is not as irreconcilable as it seems. For example, both agree that, comparing the two clocks at the left end of the picture, *B*'s is reading ahead of *A*'s. They only disagree as to which of these two clocks agrees with the ones at the centers of the trains.

The disagreement is completely resolved if one considers what each observer *actually sees* at the instant depicted, which is *not what is shown in the figure*. This is because it takes time for the light signal to reach the center of the train. Each must correct for this time lapse to make a meaningful statement of where the end of each train is, and what each clock reads, at that instant. And the two observers disagree as to how long the time lapse was.

Let us concentrate on the clock at the left end of train *A* and assume that it can be seen by both observers. At the instant shown in the figure, since both are looking at the same clock at the same time, they must

Two identical trains passing

As seen from train A

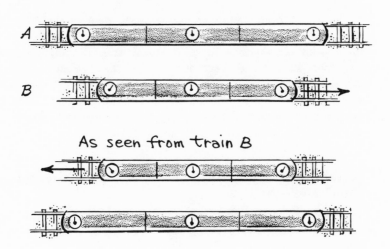

As seen from train B

Figure 2

agree as to what it used to read, not *now* but back when the light they are now seeing left it. How long ago was that? *A* feels the clock is stationary; he feels the time lapse is the time required for light to pass one-half the length of the train. *B*, on the other hand, says this clock is moving away from him. It was closer than one-half the length of the train when the light signal left it, so his correction factor is smaller than *A*'s. When *A* takes into account the larger correction factor, he concludes that the clock agrees with the ones at the centers of the trains. *B* adds a smaller correction, and concludes that the clock is slow compared to those at the centers.

What each saw as he looked toward the left end of the picture was the same: the end of train *B* protruded beyond the end of train *A*. The observer on train *A* feels that the time lapse in the meantime was sufficient to permit the rear of train *B* to pass the end of train *A*. The observer on train *B* feels that the time lapse was shorter, so his train still sticks out beyond the other. Thus, it is just because of the disagreement as to time lapse that it is possible for each observer to feel his train is longer than the other.

This example illustrates a crucial point about the disagreements implied by relativity. Two observers momentarily in the same place looking at the same thing do not disagree as to what they see. It is when they *interpret* their observations, taking into account that remote events happened some time in the past, that the disagreement arises.

The Garage Paradox

One final and rather amusing example will help to show that, while it is true that the contraction is only *apparent,* in the sense that an observer moving with the object will see it at its "true" length, it is nonetheless not quite correct to regard this peculiar effect as merely an *illusion.* Imagine, as in Figure 3, a garage with doors at both ends. Imagine also a car which at rest would be slightly longer than the garage. The car sails through the garage at a speed approaching that of light;

A car passes through a garage at six-tenths the velocity of light. The car is actually slightly longer than the garage

An observer in the garage feels there is an instant when the shrunken car is inside a closed garage...

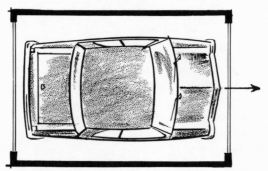

...while the driver of the car, who believes the garage has shrunk, feels quite differently

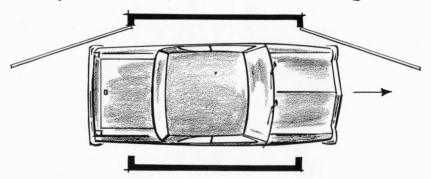

Figure 3

it is thus shortened, at least from the point of view of someone in the garage. He can open the rear door to admit the car, and then close it behind the shortened car before he opens the front door to permit its exit.

But from the point of view of the car's rather reckless driver, it is the garage that gets shortened. As he sees the process, the car must at some point stick out at both ends, and both doors must have been open at once! Common sense tells us one or the other must be wrong— either the car was at one point in a closed garage, or it wasn't!

Again, relativity insists that this is *not* a question with an unambiguous answer. The secret lies in the difference in the sequence of door openings and closings, as seen by the two observers. These are summarized below:

Man in garage	*Driver*
"In" door opened	"In" door opened
"In" door closed	"Out" door opened
"Out" door opened	"In" door closed

The man in the garage is sure he knows in what order he opened the doors; but the driver is equally sure both doors were open at the same time. Again, as in the case of the identical trains in the preceding section, *what they actually see at the instant they are directly opposite one another is the same.* Both actually see the door toward the front of the car closed and the other door open, but both maintain that this represents an earlier state of events, because of the time required for the light to reach the center of the garage. The man in the garage maintains the back door has closed in the meantime, while the driver maintains the front door has opened in the meantime. This disagreement is possible because the man in the garage feels that light reaches him from the two ends of the garage in the same amount of time, while the driver, who regards the garage as moving, feels that the light reaching him from the front of the garage left earlier than that from the rear.

Lest this analysis restore the feeling that the whole effect is an illusion, let us emphasize that *for all practical purposes the man in the garage can act as if the shrinkage of the car were real.* That is to say, he can set up the sequence of door openings and closings under the assumption that the car has shrunk, and he will not be contradicted by the splintering sound of a car crashing through a garage door.

The example illustrates how the disagreement as to time sequence leads to a different interpretation of the spatial relations of objects. This is the source of the intimate connection of space and time which is the most striking feature of relativity.

Measuring the Speed of Light

The shrinkage and other effects cited in this chapter also give a simple resolution of the paradox of Einstein's postulate: How can the same light signal move the same speed with respect to two different observers? The answer is that neither feels this is actually the case; each feels the light goes at the correct speed c with respect to *him,* and *not* with respect to the other. He explains the fact that the other observer gets the same result as he does for c from the fact that he is measuring its speed over a shrunken path, with slow clocks that aren't synchronized, and somehow all these mistakes conspire to give him the right answer.

11

The Wedding
of Space and Time

Alice laughed: "There's no use trying," she said;
"one can't believe in impossible things."
   "I daresay you haven't had much practice,"
said the Queen. "When I was younger, I always did
it for half an hour a day. Why, sometimes I've
believed in as many as six impossible things before
breakfast."

—LEWIS CARROLL, THROUGH THE LOOKING GLASS

This chapter will serve to put relativity on a quantitative basis by answering the question, "Just how much does a moving clock slow down and a moving object shrink along its line of motion?" The arguments themselves will be child's play, but once again the implications of the simple formulas may prove bewildering. The problem is complicated by the fact that three separate but related effects are occurring at once:

1   Moving clocks appear to run slow.
2   Moving objects appear shrunken along their line of motion.
3   The setting of clocks in two different places depends on the motion of the observer.

To cope with these effects, we must find a *gedanken* experiment that allows us to handle the clock slowdown without worrying about the other two effects.   Next we use the result obtained to deal with the shrinkage without worrying about clock settings.   Then the third problem can be solved using the solutions of the first two.   Finally, with all three problems separately solved, we can reunite our view of the universe in the concept of "space-time," the most "psychedelic" of all of Einstein's ideas.   This is the task of this chapter.

How Slow Does the Clock Run?

To handle the clock slowdown, we choose for an example a measurement of the speed of light *across* a train, rather than along the direction of motion.   This is because a stationary observer and one on the train have no disagreement as to its width; the position of the sides of the train with regard to its center does not vary as it moves.   Both will agree, for example, that a light ray from the center of the train reaches both sides simultaneously.   This eliminates the problem of having to deal at the same time with the contraction along the line of motion.   To eliminate the third problem, let us use a measurement the *moving* observer can perform with a single clock: let him measure the time it takes for a beam of light to cross the train, bounce off a mirror, and return to its source.   Meanwhile, a stationary observer times the same light beam with his own clocks, and each observer reports his results to the other.

It is clear from Figure 1 that the two observers disagree as to the distance traveled by the same light ray.   Since the man on the train believes it has crossed the train directly, the man on the ground believes it has traveled forward a bit and thus has gone farther.   If the train has width w, the man on the train believes it has gone exactly $2w$.   How far the man on the ground believes it to have gone was derived in Chapter 9 in the analysis of the Michelson-Morley experiment.   It is $2\gamma w$, to be exact, for the path of the light ray as seen from the ground is exactly the sort of diagonal that goes with a cross-stream swim.

Now the Einstein postulate requires that when each observer measures the speed of light, both get the same value.   That is, when each divides what he believes to be the length of the light path by the elapsed time read from his clock, the result must be the same number.   Since the moving

Path of light ray across train

As seen by observer on train

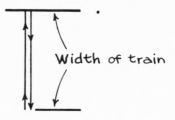

Width of train

As seen by observer on ground

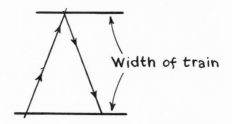

Width of train

Figure 1

observer uses a smaller figure for the length of the light path, his clock must also have recorded a shorter time than the stationary one. Thus, it must be running *slower,* by exactly the factor of $\gamma = 1/\sqrt{1 - (v/c)^2}$ required to make up the discrepancy.

We can reverse this argument and ask what the observer on the train thinks is happening to the watch of the observer on the ground; that is, let us regard the observer on the *ground* as moving. Then let us use a ray the observer on the ground regards as going directly across the train. In this case it is our groundling who feels the light has traveled $2w$, while the observer on the train feels it has gone farther. By the same reasoning as in the preceding case, he must believe it is the watch on the *ground* that runs slow.

If the reader is incredulous (which he should be!) and has the debater's instinct, it is legitimate to ask whether it was fair to switch light rays between the two situations. Thus must be done because it is important to use a light ray that *returns to the same place with respect to the observer we regard as moving;* otherwise he would have to use clocks in two different places to measure the elapsed time, and we would have to take into account the difference in clock settings at these two points.   The only way to avoid this problem is to insist that whichever observer we regard as moving use only one clock.

Now we can see why the two observers on the train cannot resolve the problem of synchronizing their watches by meeting for a direct comparison.   Suppose the observer from the front of the train were to walk to the rear and set his watch to that of the observer there.   As he walks forward to his post, his motion would be added to that of the train, with the result that he would be moving faster than the train itself.   Thus, his watch would run even slower than that of the observer at the rear.   By the time he got to the front, his watch would once again be behind that of his companion, from the point of view of a stationary observer.   It can be shown that, provided he walks much slower than the train is moving, the disagreement would be the same as if they set their watches with a light signal.

Now that we have the quantitative measure of the apparent slowdown of a moving clock, it is easy to use the result to derive the apparent shrinkage of a moving object along its direction of motion.   Again we roll out our familiar train.   How are we to measure its length?

The FitzGerald Shrinkage

The easiest way to measure the length of a train is to measure its speed and then measure how long it takes to pass by a fixed point, such as a telegraph pole.   On the pole is an observer with a stopwatch.   The observer on the train, looking at his own clock, then says, "Wait a minute— you performed that measurement with a slow clock.   Thus, your result must be wrong.   My clock says it took longer, and your result is too short."

Now it is the observer *on the train* who must use two clocks to perform the measurement: one at the front and one at the rear of the train.   Thus, it is *he* we must regard as the "stationary" observer.   Furthermore, since he is the one at rest with respect to the train, it is he who is going to be right in any measurement of its length.   The observer up the pole must be getting a value shorter than its real length.   The ratio must be the same as the clock slowdown—that famous factor γ.

Remember also that to the observer on the train the telegraph pole is just an abstract point that moves at a known speed from the front of the train to the rear.   There is no reason to suppose that this is an invalid way to measure the length of the train.   The fact that there is a man on the pole with a stopwatch that looks slow, and who therefore finds a shorter length for the train, is of no consequence to the observer on the train. It cannot affect *his* measurement in any way.

This is of course only one way to measure the length of a train, but for the others the mathematics are more complicated. Again, the point is that, if relativity is correct, this way is as good as any other and will yield the same result.

If the reader is now thoroughly dazed (a common feeling at this stage in the study of relativity) by a world in which moving objects shrink and moving clocks lose time, a numerical reminder may prove reassuring. The most rapid large man-made objects (interplanetary rockets) move at speeds less than one ten-thousandth of the velocity of light. Thus, γ differs from 1 by about one part in 100 million. For more leisurely vehicles, such as supersonic jets, the effect is more like one part in 100 billion.

Now we are prepared to cope with the problem of the difference in clock settings at the two ends of the train. As the endless train example shows, this can be regarded as a consequence of the clock slowdown. A stationary observer regards a clock at the front of the train as out of time because it has been running slow. Though it agreed with his when it passed him, it is now behind. To see *how much* behind, we must compare the time elapsed on the moving clock while the train is passing a stationary observer, as seen by that observer, and as seen by one on the train.

The stationary observer sees two effects. First, the train is contracted, and thus it takes a reduced time to pass him. Second, the clock on the train appears to be running slow. If L_c is the contracted length of the train, it takes L_c/v sec for the train to pass. Since the moving clock appears to him to go slower, it only shows a time of

$$t_s = \frac{1}{\gamma} \times \frac{L_c}{v} \tag{1}$$

To reexpress this result in terms of the true length L of the train, its length as known to its passengers, we note that L_c is simply the true length divided by γ. Thus:

$$t_s = \frac{1}{\gamma} \times \frac{L/\gamma}{v} = \frac{L}{\gamma^2 v} \tag{2}$$

This should be compared with the time taken for the same trip as seen by the train passenger, the far simpler expression

$$t = \frac{L}{v} \tag{3}$$

Since the clock-setting difference seen by the man on the ground is the difference between t and t_s, we have

$$\Delta t = t - t_s = \frac{L}{v} - \frac{L}{\gamma^2 v} = \frac{L}{v}\left(1 - \frac{1}{\gamma^2}\right) = \frac{L}{v}\left[1 - \left(1 - \frac{v^2}{c^2}\right)\right] = \frac{Lv}{c^2} \quad (4)$$

This is the amount by which clocks at the two ends of the train appear to differ, when viewed by an observer on the ground.

Space-Time: A Four-dimensional World

One of Einstein's more profound observations on the significance of relativity was that it removes the separateness of the age-old concepts of time and distance. This view is reflected in the term "space-time" or the more ominous-sounding "fourth dimension" that occasionally filters down into popular speech.

This is illustrated already by our imaginary train. To its passengers, it has a perfectly reasonable length, and time is the same throughout its length. To an observer on the ground, it has shortened but, as if in compensation, has been spread out in time. Time is different at one end of the train than at the other. What to its riders is an object that extends purely in space becomes to others an object with an "extent in time."

The next two steps in this discussion may appear quite arbitrary, but when the conclusion is reached they will be justified. We wish to somehow compare this time interval with the length of the train. Thus, we must connect it to a length. The most convenient way to do so is to multiply it by c. This is by no means silly—as long as we are going to speak of space and time as unified, we might as well measure them in the same units—that is to say, denote a time interval by saying how far a light signal would get in that time. Astronomers have long done the opposite—measured distances with a time-based unit, the light-year. Thus, they state how far a remote star is by stating the time required for light to get here from it.

Our contracted train now has a space extent:

$$L_c = \frac{L}{\gamma}$$

and a "spacified time" extent:

$$c\Delta t = \frac{v}{c}L$$

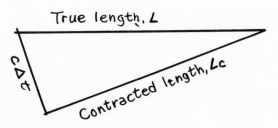

Figure 2

Now, again at the risk of seeming arbitrary, let us treat these two quantities as if they were two sides of a right triangle. Then we could use the pythagorean theorem to obtain the length of the hypotenuse:

$$\left(\frac{v}{c}L\right)^2 + \left(1 - \frac{v^2}{c^2}\right)L^2 = L^2 \qquad ! \tag{5}$$

That is, the two combined this way give us back the original length of the train.

The significance of this startling result is illustrated in Figure 2. If we regard time as a *dimension* on a par with the three spatial ones of, for example, north, east, and up, *the combined length of an object in space and time will be the same for all observers.** For an observer at rest with respect to the object, it will be purely spatial in extent; for anyone else, its full extent will be part in space and part in time, but if we measure the disagreement of clocks at the two ends of the object in length units and treat this as a "fourth dimension" to space, the total space-time length of an object remains the same.

Put another way, what one observer calls a pure *length* another sees

---

* To avoid confusing readers familiar with conventional treatments of relativity (others will be totally mystified by this footnote), it must be emphasized that Equation (5) is not a "relativistic invariant" in the usual sense, being composed of a time interval in one frame and a length in another. Its constancy, however, follows from the invariance of the space-time interval involved in measuring the length of a moving object, i.e., the interval between simultaneous position measurements in the stationary frame:

$$L_c{}^2 = L_0{}^2 - c^2\Delta t^2$$

The device employed in the argument above avoids the necessity for introducing the negative time metric, which in the intuitive context of the treatment in this chapter may be viewed as a consequence of the relative motion of the two coordinate systems during the time interval in one of them. The author defends this rather unconventional concept as appropriate to the description of a rigid body, rather than the more abstract concept of a space-time interval, which is the more natural and conventional language of relativity.

as a *combination* of a length and a time interval. Space and time thus lose their separateness, becoming a unified concept.

The point is that the *existence* of an object, those properties of it that are independent of the observer's frame of reference, can only be described in the four-dimensional realm called space-time. To quote a simple but very close analogy, suppose you hold a piece of paper up to a bright light and observe its shadow on the wall. Edge on, it produces a thin shadow. Held with its broad face toward the light, it produces a shadow in the form of a broad rectangle. The two-dimensional world of shadows on a wall cannot represent the full solid reality of the paper all at once; it exists in its own natural three-dimensional world. Thus, the shrunken "shadows" of moving four-dimensional objects are all we see in our three-dimensional world. The different positions of the paper correspond to the different vantage points of moving observers.

By an interesting coincidence the exactly contemporaneous artistic movement of cubist painting sought a very similar vision of reality. By their own description, the cubists sought to escape the prison of a three-dimensional world of movement and change represented on a static two-dimensional canvas by presenting the multiple views of an active, moving observer. Much of their language describing their art to laymen takes on the same tone as Einstein's similar efforts.

To complete this section, the author offers what can only be termed a speculation. One possible interpretation of the significance of the relativistic unity of space and time is to regard the distinction between the two as purely man-made, a peculiarity having something to do with the nature of life and man's consciousness. Then the "velocity of light" becomes no more than a conversion factor between two sets of units, one for space and one for time, set up by man before he realized that they were one and the same thing. This role for the velocity of light will arise again in the next chapter, in connection with the mass-energy relationship. But it is not necessary to leap to such flights of fancy in order to comprehend and make use of the laws of relativity; the equations speak for themselves, and their predictions have been amply confirmed by experiment, as will be seen in the next chapter.

The Twin Paradox

One of the most startling predictions of relativity is illustrated by the following science fiction story.

A young astronaut takes a trip to a star 25 light-years away, in a spaceship that can travel at 99.98 percent the speed of light. The astronaut has a twin brother, who remains home on earth. Fifty years pass, and the earth-bound twin, a grandfather bent with age, goes to the spaceport to welcome his adventurous brother.   The astronaut bounds down the gangplank, because for him only one year has elapsed, and he is still young and vigorous!

From the point of view of the twin on earth, this is because time slowed down on the ship.   Clocks, and biological aging processes, are slowed to one-fiftieth their normal speed on this fast spaceship.   To the astronaut, the round trip only took a year, because the distance shrank to one-half light year.   But both agree that the astronaut is now 49 years younger than his twin!

Early in the history of relativity, this story was offered as a refutation of the theory.   Why isn't the twin *on earth* the younger?   After all, from the point of view of the astronaut, it is the *earthbound* clock that ran slower!   There appears to be a contradiction.

The answer is that one *can* make a distinction between the astronaut and his brother.   The astronaut had to leave the earth, accelerate to a stupendous speed, and turn around (another period of acceleration) at the star.   Thus, he is not in uniform motion at constant speed, and the symmetry of relativity, by which he feels the earthbound clock runs slow, does not apply.   Analyzed in detail, the problem reveals that from the point of view of the astronaut, most of the 50 years passed on earth during the short time he was turning around at the star.

That this is the resolution of the paradox can easily be seen if we imagine that, at the star, there is a clock set to "earth time."   Since the astronaut regards this clock and one on the earth as moving clocks, they are indeed running very slow.   But since the one near the star is far back along the line of apparent motion, it is also set ahead of the earth clock. In fact, it reads nearly 25 years ahead.

When the astronaut reaches the star and fires his rocket to stop and then turn around, he reverses the situation.   The two "earth time" clocks are now headed in the opposite direction, with the one on earth trailing. Thus, it is now 25 years *ahead of,* rather than behind, the clock at the star.   But the astronaut is close to that other earth-time clock.   In the short time he spends turning around, very little time elapses on it, and it certainly doesn't run backward.   If the remote clock on earth switched from being almost 25 years behind to almost 25 years ahead, nearly 50 years must have passed on earth in the brief time he spent turning around. Thus, the astronaut agrees with his twin brother: more time has passed on earth than on the spaceship, and he is now some 49 years the younger of the two!

If you find this argument unconvincing, perhaps it will reassure you to know that the twin paradox *has been experimentally confirmed!*   In 1967, at a laboratory in Geneva, Switzerland, subatomic particles known as "mu-mesons" were sent around a circular track, at a speed roughly equal to that of the hypothetical spaceship in our example. The mu-meson is an unstable particle that normally breaks up spontaneously in about a millionth of a second. Yet making repeated round trips around the racecourse, the particles kept returning to their starting point again and again, long after their stationary cousins had died.

If nothing else, the twin paradox should be the final convincer that relativity concerns more than illusion, for there is nothing more concrete than returning from a trip to find yourself younger than your twin—or even than your own children!

The literary possibilities of this phenomenon have been fully exploited by science fiction writers. One series of such stories visualized an age when man has spread to habitable planets scattered throughout the galaxy, a civilization spanning thousands of light-years. In their powerful, speedy spaceships, a breed of astronauts maintains the skimpy "commerce" of this vast civilization, condemned to a strange existence in which they return to a familiar port only after centuries or millennia have elapsed, thus enjoying a peculiar sort of alienated immortality within man's normal three-score-and-ten.

12

$E=mc^2$
and All That

We are about to reach a turning point in the discussion of relativity. So far, the problem has been, "What do we have to pay for believing in Einstein's postulate?" The arguments have carried the force of necessity: if we want to keep the postulate, we must learn to put up with a lot of outrage to our common sense. We have no way out of radically revamping our notions of space and time.

Since these concepts are the whole basis for the description of motion, the reader should by now have the uncomfortable suspicion that the whole science of mechanics may now be on mighty shaky ground. Must we discard three centuries of thought, sweep away Newton's laws, energy and momentum conservation, and the like? It turns out that the answer is no. Surprisingly, most of the edifice of classical mechanics emerges from Einstein's revolution intact.

Intact, yes, but by no means unchanged. And the major changes center on the concept of mass. Newton's first and third laws are obviously untouchable; unless we insist that mechanics concern itself with the problem of change of state of motion, and that such changes come about through mutual interactions of bodies, nothing recognizably newtonian would survive. We will find that momentum conservation and the second law survive, merely by allowing mass to depend on velocity in a way that is unimportant except at speeds approaching that of light. Moving on to energy conservation, we will find that this result leads to the duality between mass and energy expressed in the most widely publicized formula of twentieth-century physics, $E = mc^2$.

But the arguments in this chapter should be far less of a strain on the imagination than those in the preceding. Though they will still appear arbitrary, their consequences will not seem so outrageous.

The Mass Increase

The first task is to establish the dependence of mass on velocity. The example of choice is a "grazing" collision between two identical bodies, familiar to all billiard players. The moving body is hardly deflected and loses little speed, while the struck body comes out at a slow speed nearly at a right angle to the original motion. How this looks to two observers, each of which was at rest with respect to one of the bodies before collision, is shown in Figure 1. In subsequent arguments we shall concern ourselves

Collision as seen by observer at
rest with respect to body *a* before
the collision   (observer *A*)

Same collision from point of view of observer
at rest with respect to *b* (observer *B*)

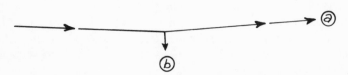

Figure 1

only with that portion of the motion of each body which is at right angles to the original line of motion.

There are two reasons for choosing this example. The first is that it is possible by this device to have two observers in relative motion at a high velocity, yet the part of the motion of the bodies we are studying is at a low velocity. The second is that this motion is perpendicular to the high-velocity motion. As pointed out early in the preceding chapter, in this direction there are no disagreements in measurements of length.

We now ask what happens if we assume momentum is conserved in the perpendicular direction. This means that the product of the mass and the perpendicular component of the velocity must have the same value for both bodies. It does not matter that for the initially stationary body this is essentially the whole momentum, while the' other body has a much larger component along the original line of motion. Ever since Galileo we have had the right to separately study components of motion in perpendicular directions.

Not only must both bodies have the same perpendicular momentum for each of the observers, but the actual *value* of these momenta must be the same for both observers. Since the bodies are identical, the situation shown in Figure 1 is completely symmetric. Thus, for example, the perpendicular momentum of body *a* is the same whether observer *A* or observer *B* actually performs the measurement.

Now to measure momentum we must measure velocity. Let both observer *A* and observer *B* measure body *a's* perpendicular velocity. From *B*'s point of view, *A* is using a slow clock. Since they agree on the distance part of the measurement, using a slow clock must give a higher value for the velocity: *A* feels the body goes the same distance in less time.

But then if the *momentum* is to be the same, *A* must be using a smaller *mass*. And since it is *A* who is nearly at rest with respect to body *a*, it is he who must be more nearly right.

The conclusion is that *momentum conservation can only hold if a fast-moving body appears to have more mass than a slow-moving one.* Since it is the same old clock-slowing factor that is involved, the mathematical statement of this fact takes the form

$$m = \gamma m_0 \tag{1}$$

where m_0 is the *rest mass*, the mass of a body as measured by an observer at rest with respect to that body.

The preceding argument shows it is *necessary* to consider mass to depend on velocity, but not that this is enough to save momentum conservation. It takes much more difficult analysis to show that the same formula saves momentum conservation along the line of relative motion, but it does prove to be the case.

Newton's Laws and the Relativistic Speed Limit

Now what of Newton's second law? In Chapter 3 we showed that, once one agrees on a method of defining mass, the second law is merely the quantitative definition of force. Though the definition of mass is now somewhat complicated by the necessity for specifying the velocity at which it is measured, it still gives us a unique value for mass. But since now the mass of a body changes as it accelerates, we can no longer write the second law as

$$F = ma \qquad (2)$$

because both mass and velocity change. We must return to Newton's original statement:

$$F = \frac{dp}{dt} \qquad (3)$$

that is, force is the rate of change of momentum. At low speeds, $F = ma$ is nearly correct, for the mass changes very little, so all the increase in momentum comes about through changing the velocity. At speeds approaching that of light, the body becomes more and more massive. Then the increase in momentum involves a large change in mass and a small change in velocity.

This property of mass also assures us that Einstein's requirement that nothing move faster than light will never be violated by a material object. As a body approaches the speed of light, the application of a force in the direction of motion will only make it more massive and not change its speed appreciably.

For example, consider a body moving at one one-hundredth of the velocity of light, already a fantastic speed by terrestrial standards. If we let a force act on it until its momentum is doubled, its mass only changes by 0.015 percent, while its velocity very nearly doubles. If, on the other hand, we double the momentum of a body already moving at $0.99c$, we then will nearly double its mass, while its velocity will increase only to $0.997c$.

It seems striking that Newton insisted on Equation (3) rather than (2) as his statement of the second law, but it is perhaps pressing the point a bit to speculate that he may have clairvoyantly anticipated relativity.

Energy and Mass

The next logical step is to ask what happens to the conservation of energy. Clearly, energy needs to be redefined. For example, a falling body that is given an initial downward thrust at nearly the velocity of light will have its mass increased, but very little change in velocity, under the influence of gravity.   The logical starting point for the discussion is to consider the *work* done by a force.   In the preceding example, the change in momentum was the same whether the result was a large change in velocity and a small change in mass, as for a slow object, or a large change in mass accompanied by a small change in velocity, as for a fast one.   But in the latter case much more distance is covered in the process, because the body is moving much faster.   Since work is force times distance, *much more work is required when the change in mass is large.*

Though the computation is difficult, it can be shown that the change in mass is just exactly proportional to the work done; thus, the energy of a body is merely proportional to its mass, and kinetic energy would not depend on velocity were it not for the fact that mass depends on velocity.   But energy conservation, as has been emphasized, is not merely a mechanical law.   Therefore, let us establish the relation between mass and energy by the simpler and more universal device of insisting that light itself obey momentum and energy conservation.

As we saw in Chapter 7, electromagnetic forces can only conserve momentum if we ascribe momentum to the field (and hence to light) itself.   If an object emits light in one direction, in order to conserve momentum it must itself "recoil" in the opposite direction.   Maxwell established a formula giving the momentum carried by light in terms of its energy:

$$p = \frac{E}{c} \tag{4}$$

If we stick to the definition of momentum as $p = mv$, we can associate a "mass" with a flash of light:

$$m = \frac{p}{v} = \frac{p}{c} = \frac{E}{c^2}$$

which leads to the famous formula $E = mc^2$.

Is this mass merely a mathematical fiction?   Consider the situation depicted in Figure 2.   Inside a closed box that is free to move, a flash of light is emitted at the left end.   If we insist that this process conserve momentum, the box must recoil ever so slightly to the left.   Then let the light flash be absorbed at the right end.   The momentum of the light is also transmitted to the box, and it is brought to a halt.   Without any external force acting, an initially stationary box has been moved to the left.   Since momentum conservation insists that the center of mass of the box can't move as the result of internal forces, as was shown in Chapter 2, the result is exactly as if some real object had moved to the right inside the box.

Closed box at rest...

```
┌─┬──────────────────────┐
│ Ⓠ                      │
└─┴──────────────────────┘
```

begins to move to left when light flashed
at left end

(Momentum of box equals momentum of light)

Stops when light absorbed at right end...

```
┌─┬─────────────────┬────┐
│ Ⓠ                ))) │
└─┴─────────────────┴────┘
```

Thus light has transferred mass from one
end of the box to the other

Figure 2

One might reply that this merely proves that light can be used to transfer mass, not that there is any general relation between mass and energy. But consider the state of the box after it stops. The light no longer exists. None of the actual material of the box has been removed from the left and transferred to the right, yet mass has been transferred between the two ends! What other change in the state of the box must have taken place? What evidence remains of the transfer of the light?

The answer is that absorbing the light has heated up the right end of the box. Conversely, if energy was conserved when the light was produced at the left end, the law of conservation of energy tells us some energy has been removed. For example, the source of energy for the flash might have been the chemical energy in a battery.

What is the net result of the process? Some chemical energy at the left end of the box has been transformed into heat at the right end, and mass has been transferred from the left to the right! Thus chemical energy and heat must also obey a mass-energy relationship. A discharged battery must be lighter than a charged one, a hot object heavier than the same object cold.   But since heat is nothing but the energy of motion of molecules, this too must obey a mass-energy relationship.   And through the law of the conservation of energy, the mass-energy equivalence can be extended to any form of energy whatsoever.

It must be emphasized that $E = mc^2$ is the *one and only* formula for energy in relativity.   What then has become of our old definition of kinetic energy, $\frac{1}{2}mv^2$, which still ought to work at low speeds?   The answer is that the kinetic energy merely represents the tiny increase in mass of a slow-moving body.   For readers familiar with the calculus, this can easily be verified from Equation (1).*   At very small velocities, the additional mass is $v^2/2c^2$ of the rest mass.   Thus, by the formula $E = mc^2$, we obtain $\frac{1}{2}m_0v^2$ for the added energy.   This formula only works if the speed is quite small compared to light; it is no longer the *definition* of kinetic energy, but merely an approximate formula valid at very small velocities.

The Meaning of $E = mc^2$

Since Hiroshima, in the popular media, the formula $E = mc^2$ has become associated with nuclear energy.   At the risk of repetition, it must be stated emphatically that it applies equally well to all forms of energy; it is a quite universal and unique formula, as valid for a bonfire as for a nuclear weapon.   The only distinction of nuclear energy is that it is the one energy source powerful enough for the changes in mass to be really sub-stantial.   Heating water from its freezing point to its boiling point only increases its mass by about one part in 10^{11}.   In an ordinary chemical reaction, such as a fire, the combustion products are lighter than the fuel and oxygen used in the fire by about one part in 10^9.   Such small changes are just beyond the range of measurement.   But in the more violent nuclear reactions, mass changes of about one part in 1,000 can take place.   This is easily within the range of accuracy of mass measurements.   From a table of nuclear masses, a physicist can use Einstein's formula to predict the energy release of a previously unstudied reaction.

The crucial factor for the development of nuclear energy and nuclear weapons was the discovery of the nuclear fission chain reaction, one where each disintegrating nucleus triggers several neighbors.   The formula $E = mc^2$ by no means predicts the existence of such a reaction, nor is it essential to the understanding of the fission process.   Einstein himself played no role in the discovery of fission, nor in the development of the atomic bomb, aside from the initial one of providing a letter of introduction for the scientists who approached President Franklin D. Roosevelt with

---

* Do a Taylor's expansion of the formula at $v = 0$.   The term $v^2/2c^2$ is the second term.   See the section of the Appendix on this chapter.

the proposal for the project. Had relativity not yet been discovered, it would probably have hampered the efforts of the Manhattan Project very little.

The formula is sometimes mistakenly referred to as a formula for the conversion of energy into mass. It is more than that; *it is a statement that, for all practical purposes, the two are identical.* If you want to know how much energy is in a system, measure its mass.

For example, if a bonfire occurs in a sealed box, insulated so that the heat cannot escape, no change in its weight can occur. Despite the transformation of chemical energy to heat, which represents kinetic energy of the molecules, no change in mass has taken place. If we allow the heat to escape, however, the box will become slightly lighter.

As a last example to illustrate the generality of the mass-energy equivalence, it should be pointed out that it applies equally well to potential energy. A compressed spring weighs more than the same spring relaxed. Whenever a force binds two objects together so that it would take the addition of energy to separate them, their combined mass is less than the sum of their separate masses. The negative potential energy appears as a defect in mass. This is the real source of nuclear energy: the potential energy of the powerful forces that bind the component particles of the nucleus together. A rearrangement of a large, loosely bound nucleus into smaller, more tightly bound ones increases the strength of the binding, lowering the mass of the nuclei. Since this mass is associated with the *field* of force, it can be thought of as distributed in space; indeed, the very presence of a field in a region of space implies energy "stored" there, and therefore mass. Thus, as the concept of field matures in physics, it tends to seem more and more real.

The leftover mass is the equivalent of the change in potential energy. A typical nucleus weighs about 1 percent less than the combined mass of its component particles. The atomic bomb works on the fact that the heaviest nuclei weigh about 0.1 percent more per constituent particle than nuclei near the middle of the table of elements, and on the existence of a process (fission) that makes it possible to trigger certain heavy nuclei into splitting into two smaller parts.

The energy-mass equivalence once again illustrates the role of the velocity of light as a conversion factor between quantities man originally regarded as distinct. Had the equivalence of mass and energy been understood from the outset, there might not have been separate units for the two. Today, physicists working with subatomic particles, where grams are horrendously large and awkward units, use energy units for mass as a matter of course. Viewed in this context, the formula $E = mc^2$ has no more profound significance than the conversion formula 1 km = 0.62 miles. This interpretation of the role of the velocity of light in the mass-energy relationship is by no means as speculative as the interpretation of its role in the space-time relationship offered at the end of Chapter 11.   Both are motivated by the same spirit, a pervading one in modern physics: the desire to eliminate arbitrariness as far as possible.   The idea is essentially metaphysical in nature; it expresses a faith that there are very few or perhaps ultimately no arbitrary fundamental constants in nature, such as the velocity of light.   Many attempts have been made in recent years, most a bit premature, to eliminate all such constants or to interpret their meaning on purely mathematical grounds.

The dependence of mass on velocity was one of the first predictions of relativity to be experimentally confirmed.   Electrons are so light that it is rather easy to accelerate them to considerable velocities.   Those in a typical TV picture tube travel at nearly one-fourth the velocity of light and have a mass nearly 3 percent greater than when standing still.   And even higher velocities are easy to obtain.   Measurements of the mass of fast-moving electrons were performed as early as 1908 and bore out Equation (1) exactly.   The energy-mass relation in nuclear reactions was confirmed to high precision in 1932 in the first artificial disintegration of a nucleus.

The other well-verified aspect of relativity is that of the time dilation.   The American physicist Herbert Ives confirmed it in 1938 by measuring the frequency of light emitted by fast-moving atoms.   Interestingly, Ives was himself one of the last prominent opponents of relativity.

Today, experimental confirmations of all aspects of relativity are commonplace.   Physicists studying subatomic particles work daily with objects traveling close to the speed of light.   In observing particle collisions, they bear out all details of Einstein's predictions.   For example, some of these particles are highly unstable and break up spontaneously in the time it takes for a light signal to travel several meters.   Yet, at close to the velocity of light, they can be transported hundreds or even thousands of meters with no difficulty, because of the slowdown in their internal "clocks."   From the point of view of the particle, it is not the slowing of time but the contraction of the laboratory that is responsible for the effect.   Yet the end result is the same: it reaches the detector.   And when a particle that would be very light when standing still is brought up to a high speed, it acts like a heavy particle in collisions.   Finally, the extra mass obtained by accelerating a particle close to the speed of light can be used to produce new particles not previously present.

The final triumph of relativity was to complete the work of Faraday and Maxwell in uniting electricity and magnetism.   Einstein was able to show that a magnetic field appears when a purely electric field is seen by a moving observer, and an electric field appears when a purely magnetic one is seen from a moving vantage point.

Though Einstein's genius was quickly recognized and rewarded, relativity took a long time to gain truly general acceptance. This was particularly true in English-speaking nations, which have had a pragmatic style in physics that sometimes leads to a distrust of theoretical physics in general. Many textbooks used in the United States as late as the 1940s treated relativity as a purely speculative and decidedly suspect idea.

Einstein and Newton

The parallels between the work of Einstein and that of Newton are striking, despite the contrast in personalities. Both did their greatest work in isolation, during their early twenties. Each was a great work of synthesis, in which a few key insights were used to combine the incomplete and poorly connected ideas of others into a complete system. Einstein always acknowledged his debt to Lorentz, just as Newton had acknowledged his to Descartes. Einstein's particular genius was the ability to work through all the details of a problem without losing sight of general principles. In this way he was able to combine the general insights of a Poincaré with the skill at handling details of a Lorentz. In this respect his style is strikingly similar to that of Newton, who combined the breadth of scope of Descartes with the deeply penetrating analytic skills of Galileo.

Though revolutionary in conception, the end result of Einstein's relativity was to save classical physics by reformulating it in a manner consistent with the known properties of light. But this only holds for that part of the theory that has been outlined here, which Einstein called *special relativity*. Like many a revolutionary dissatisfied after his triumph by the incompleteness of his revolution, Einstein moved on in 1916 to a bolder step, called *general relativity*. In this theory he attempted to analyze the problem of light as observed not by uniformly moving observers but by accelerated ones. At the same time he attempted to bring gravitation within the scope of his theory.

The end result was a complete reformulation of mechanics in which the concept of force, for all intents and purposes, disappears altogether. Instead, the action of fields is to distort the very fabric of space itself, until a straight line is no longer the shortest path between two points. The mathematics of general relativity presents formidable difficulties, and even very few physicists outside of a handful of specialists know much about it; it is far too difficult to develop to an interesting level in a popular text.

The principal reason for the obscurity of general relativity, however, is that the only predictions in which it differs from special relativity concern phenomena on a cosmic scale, that of immense distances and huge

masses.   There have been a few somewhat shaky astronomical confirmations
of some of these predictions, notably that of the bending of the path of
starlight as it passes near the sun (a phenomenon observable only during
solar eclipses and requiring fantastically precise measurement), and Einstein's explanation of some long-known irregularities in the orbit of the
planet Mercury.   But in both cases the measurements are not sufficiently
precise to really provide a severe test of the theory, and there are those
who maintain that even these comparatively crude measurements disagree
with Einstein's theory.

Moreover, general relativity does not develop out of the same logical
necessity as special relativity.   There are many conceivable answers to the
questions Einstein raised in formulating it.   The attitude of even the more
enlightened enthusiasts for the theory is that something like it is probably
right, and only when experiments become possible (which should be soon,
as man moves out into space) will it become clear what the correct theory
is.

Relativity in the General Culture

Perhaps no idea in the whole history of physics can match the record
of relativity for creating a widespread public stir while being understood
by practically nobody.   A number of moral and political thinkers quickly
became aware that some physicist named Einstein was challenging age-old
beliefs with a theory that maintained that seemingly contradictory points
of view can be equally valid.   Their appetites were whetted in part by
a semantic accident, for one of the points of view then attaining popularity
with the disintegration of the "old order" in Europe was called "moral
relativism," which maintained that human acts could only be judged in
their social context, rather than by absolute moral standards.   To many
intellectuals it seemed that Einstein's work was merely the physicist's equivalent of the political views of England's Fabian Socialists or the sexual
mores championed by Havelock Ellis.   Meeting the man Einstein himself,
with the merry twinkle in the eye and the flowing mane, the lively but
modest wit and the deep humanitarian convictions, only reinforced their
sympathy.   It is perhaps characteristic of the disjointed spirit of our century
that this sympathy did not lead to even greater efforts to disseminate
his ideas more widely, though relativity is the most avidly popularized
aspect of twentieth century physical thought.   For since the day of Einstein
there has been a growing gulf between the world of science and the world
of letters.   Almost by accident, Einstein the man and his works were one
of the few bridges spanning the gulf.

13

The Atom Returns

One might have thought that the birth of relativity was quite enough excitement for one decade. But the opening decade of our century also saw physicists begin to look inside the atom, and what they were to find there proved to be a shock far more unsettling than Einstein's union of space with time. As background to this development, let us begin with the story of how the atom reentered respectable scientific thought during the nineteenth century.

The Ancient Origins of Atomism

It is mandatory to preface any discussion of atoms by paying homage to Democritus, an Ionian philosopher of the fifth century B.C., the earliest known proponent of an atomic theory. Though Democritus' ideas were in many ways strikingly modern and were promulgated by his more celebrated successor Epicurus, his theory never gained wide acceptance in Greek thought. It had largely been forgotten by the time of the late Renaissance rebirth of science. While the dramatic rise of the atomic theory over the last century and a half seems to have vindicated Democritus, only the Greek name *atom* ("indivisible") remains to establish his claim as the father of the theory.

Nonetheless, Democritus' thinking contained the seed of the idea that has dominated twentieth-century physical thought. He was one of the first to perceive that nature on a sufficiently small scale might be qualitatively different in a striking way from the world of our ordinary experience. And he was the first to voice the hope, today almost an obsession, that underlying all the complex richness, texture, and variety of our everyday life might be a level of reality of stark simplicity, with the turmoil we perceive representing only the nearly infinite variety of arrangements of a small number of simple constituents.

Democritus' theory was motivated in large measure by the difficulties all his contemporaries had with the notion of continuity. The thought of anything being infinitely divisible was apparently very disturbing to the ancient Greeks, perhaps (as some scholars have speculated) for reasons having to do with the structure of their language. Atoms failed to gain broad adherence for equally abstract reasons: to account for the differing properties of atoms of different substances, Democritus and Epicurus were forced to assign them different shapes. To have *shapes* meant to have *parts*, and the notion of parts contradicted the indivisibility implied by the name *atom*. On just such a semantic difficulty did a promising theory founder, two millennia before the establishment of the more pragmatic experimental approach that was to revive it. Today, the notion that greater simplicity is to be found by searching nature on a smaller level is embedded in physical thought to the point where few physicists can imagine any other approach.

Despite its failure to gain acceptance, Democritus' theory was able to explain in a qualitatively satisfying way many obvious and simple properties of matter. Its most notable success was the way in which it accounted for the properties of the three *phases* of matter—gas, liquid, and solid. Democritus saw the rigidity of a solid as an indication that its atoms were hooked solidly together. In a liquid they were still close together but free to move around; this accounted for the ability of fluids to settle into the shape of their containers and yet remain as difficult to compress as solids; for the atoms already being essentially in contact, it is hard to press them closer together. It also explained why there is little change in volume when a solid melts into a liquid. A gas, finally, owes its apparently unlimited ability to expand rapidly to fill any container to being composed of widely separated atoms in rapid motion. This picture survives intact to this day, except for a few details that have been filled in.

Democritus' ideas were popular among the philosophically sophisticated founders of modern physics. Galileo, Newton, and most of their contemporaries were atomists, but their beliefs were based more on intuition than on concrete evidence. Moreover, the invention of the calculus had eliminated the difficulties with continuity that had in part motivated the Greek atomists, so the theory received little attention in the century following Newton's work. Still, the atomic theory remained a popular speculation among physicists, because it offered the hope that all the properties of matter might ultimately be explained in terms of the motion of the atoms themselves.

It remained for the chemists of the early nineteenth century to find the first solid empirical support for atomism. Without stretching the point too far, it is fair to say that in 1800 the atomic theory was something physicists believed but couldn't prove, while the chemists were proving it but didn't believe it. Thus, at this point a brief digression into chemistry is in order.

The Birth of Modern Chemistry

The latter half of the eighteenth century had been to chemistry what Galileo's time had been for physics. The outstanding achievement had been to put chemistry on a sound, precise quantitative basis. The symbol of the modern chemist of the late 1700s was the balance, which enabled him to substitute precise weights for the crude recipes of the medieval alchemist.

This refined approach helped lead to a number of important discoveries. One of the most significant was clarifying the distinction between a true chemical reaction and a mere process of mixing. This distinction had been dimly perceived before; mixtures displayed properties that were a blend of those of their components, in a manner which depended on their relative proportions. A chemical reaction, however, might produce a substance totally unlike the materials that went into its formation. For example, common water arises from the union of two gases, oxygen and hydrogen. Similarly, the putty-like metal sodium reacts with the green gas chlorine to form ordinary table salt. But at times the basis for the distinction seemed hazy, until the analytic balance revealed the key. By careful weighing one found that mixtures could be formed in any desired proportions, but chemical reactions had an exact recipe. The constituents had to be present in some exact proportion of weights. If too much of one of them was present, some would be left over after the reaction.

Finally, the founders of modern chemistry had clarified yet another distinction between types of substances. They classified some as *elements,* which could not be broken down into other substances, and others as *compounds,* which could.

The whole picture was terribly inviting to an atomist. All one need do is identify the elements as representing the different kinds of atoms, chemical compounds as substances formed by attaching atoms of different elements together, and mixtures as a free mingling of independent atoms without any ties between them. But atomism, and indeed the whole intellectual style of imaginary model-building that lay behind it, was mainly the province of physicists. One such, the Italian Amedeo Avogadro, pushed the atomic idea in chemistry very forcefully well before the end of the eighteenth century. But while his arguments satisfied many of his own colleagues, the vast majority of chemists remained skeptical of such wild talk. Throughout its history chemistry has tended to be a far more conservative science than physics, sticking close to its empirical roots and disdaining abstractions and speculations. The chemists paid little attention to atomism until one of their own number, the English chemist Thomas Dalton, brought it forcefully to their attention by showing that an atomic structure to matter could explain the peculiar regularities that kept popping up in the recipes uncovered by the analytic balance.

This regularity was expressed in the *law of constant proportions*. Stated crudely, it indicated that the amounts of an element that entered into forming all of its compounds were related. Hydrogen, for example, was always vastly outweighed by its partner when entering into combination, while lead always dominated its compounds.

In more exact terms, it was found that each element seemed to have a characteristic "equivalent weight." Hydrogen was the lightest and could be taken as the starting point on the scale. Oxygen was 8 times heavier, sodium 23 times, chlorine 35, and so on. All recipes for compounds could be formed from these equivalent weights.

In the first decade of the nineteenth century, Dalton pointed out that the whole scheme could be simply understood by taking the equivalent weights to represent the relative weights of the atoms of the elements. Then the recipe for common salt, 23 parts sodium to 35 parts chlorine, merely represented the fact that chlorine atoms were 35/23 as heavy as sodium atoms, and salt was formed by joining each sodium atom to one chlorine atom. Such a combination Dalton christened a *molecule*. The molecule is the smallest constituent of a chemical compound, just as an atom represents the smallest unit of an element.

Still, a lot of facts remained unexplained. Some elements seemed to have more than one characteristic weight. It gradually became clear that the simple pairing off of elements into two-atom molecules proposed by Dalton was too simple; some molecules must contain three or more atoms. For example, oxygen atoms prove to be 16, not 8 times as heavy as hydrogen. The proportion 8:1 of oxygen to hydrogen in the recipe for water reflects the fact that two hydrogen atoms join each oxygen atom when a molecule of water is formed.

The whole situation was very confusing. As is usual in such situations, there was of course a certain amount of bad data in circulation to confuse the issue further. It took 50 years to untangle the mass of chemical data, but in 1858 the patient Italian chemist Cannizzaro published a book that finally established the correct relative weights of the atoms of the better known elements and gave the atomic composition of their known compounds. The atomic theory has been the foundation stone of chemistry ever since.

The Physicists Pick Up the Ball

The success of atomism in chemistry was bound to encourage the physicists in their natural predilection for the theory. Old ideas were resurrected, cloaked in a new mantle of respectability. One important idea dated from Newton's celebrated contemporary (and rival) Robert Hooke, whose independent discovery of the inverse-square character of gravitation had touched off one of the first priority fights in the history of physics. A confirmed atomist, Hooke speculated that the outward pressure exerted by a gas on the walls of its container might originate in a hail of tiny atoms. Each atom exerts a force on the wall when it hits, and there are so many such impacts that the result seems a constant outward push.

Hooke found support for his view in the careful pneumatic experiments of Robert Boyle, performed a generation before Newton and Hooke. Boyle found empirically that if a gas is compressed in a closed container, as shown in Figure 1, the pressure on the walls varied inversely with the volume available to a gas. For example, if the piston is pushed in far enough to reduce the volume to half its original value, the pressure of the gas is thereby doubled.

This effect is quite easy to understand in atomic terms. With half the volume to roam in, the atoms are packed in closer, so there are twice as many of them in any region of the cylinder. Since their motion presumably is unaffected by this crowding, they strike the walls with the same impact, but there are twice as many impacts taking place, thereby doubling the pressure. This alone was a rather weak boost for Hooke's atomic theory, but later experiments on the effects of heat on gases gave it firmer support.

Even before the days of Galileo the notion that heat might represent some form of microscopic motion enjoyed some vogue. Francis Bacon, the fifteenth-century English philosopher, subscribed to the theory. After the discovery of the mechanical energy equivalent of heat, as a consequence of the work of Count Rumford and others, the idea became even more appealing. But far more compelling evidence could be found in the very regular behavior of gases when heated or cooled. Heating a gas in a sealed container always causes a rise in pressure. If heat were somehow related to atomic motion, this seemed natural, but again the speculation lacked the sort of quantitative handle required for a convincing test. The issue was further clouded by the arbitrary character of temperature measurement. Zero on a thermometer, whether Fahrenheit or Celsius (centigrade), doesn't represent zero *of* anything: it is merely an arbitrarily chosen point, a convenient cold temperature. Gabriel Fahrenheit had chosen the lowest temperature he could produce in his laboratory, the freezing point of very salty water, as the "zero" for the scale in common use in English-speaking countries. Celsius, whose scale is in wider use, chose the freezing point of fresh water.

Studies on the behavior of gases heated in closed containers showed that the pressure seemed to rise linearly with temperature, as shown in Figure 2, but zero on whatever thermometer used seemed to have no special significance. There was still some pressure from the gas at zero degrees, and if one cooled below zero, the pressure continued to drop linearly, as long as one stayed well above the boiling point.

Yet by Dalton's time, careful work on the temperature-pressure relation in gases revealed a significant clue. No matter *what* gas was used, or what might be its original pressure or the shape of the container, the pressure always behaved as if it would reach zero at the same temperature: —273° on the Celsius scale. This is also illustrated in Figure 2. If gases

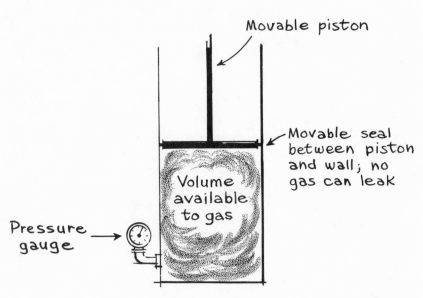

Movable piston

Movable seal
between piston
and wall; no
gas can leak

Volume
available
to gas

Pressure
gauge

Figure 1

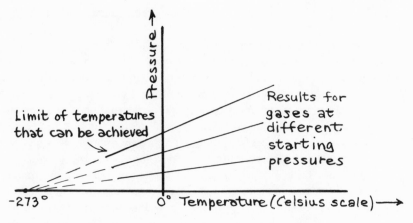

Figure 2   Pressure changes due to heating and cooling gases.

under different conditions were studied, for example, by starting with compressed gas like the air in an ordinary tire, the pressure would be higher but would also rise and fall faster with changes in temperature. The graphs always crossed zero pressure at −273°C. Gleeful atomists christened this temperature "absolute zero" and hypothesized that it represented the cessation of all atomic motion, for that would bring an end to the pressure by ending the hail of molecules on the walls.

Though the atomic case was building, its empirical props remained weak. Absolute zero itself was rather hypothetical. No means of cooling was available to let one get anywhere near it; even as refrigerators improved, most gases annoyingly dropped out of the game by going liquid, somewhere above absolute zero.

But in 1847, Rudolf Clausius showed that one could account completely for the behavior of gases by one simple hypothesis: *the "absolute" temperature of a gas is merely a measure of the kinetic energy of its molecules.*

To demonstrate this required little in the way of mathematical sophistication. If pressure is due, as Hooke guessed, to a hail of molecules, speeding them up raises the pressure in two ways. First, the rate of collisions with the walls of the container increases. This effect would of course be proportional to the speed of the molecules; if a molecule moves twice as fast, it will strike the walls twice as often. Second, the force due to each molecular impact is increased. The *force* exerted by a molecule on impact is, by Newton's second law, proportional to the change in its *momentum.* The two effects taken together indicate that speeding up molecules will cause the pressure to increase proportionally to the product of the momentum and the speed:

$$\text{Pressure} \propto (mv)v = mv^2$$

and thus in proportion to the kinetic energy. Thus, equating absolute temperature with kinetic energy of the molecules would account for the pressure-temperature law, as well as Boyle's law.

Clausius' theory also gave a natural explanation of the role of heat in the law of energy conservation (see Chapter 6). If temperature is merely a measure of the kinetic energy of molecules, the conversion of mechanical energy to heat merely represents the conversion of the motion of a large object to the random motion of its individual atoms. No real conversion has taken place—kinetic energy resulting from a combined motion of a large number of atoms in the same direction has merely been changed to kinetic energy of motion in different directions, and since energy is a nondirectional measure of motion, this does not matter.

Note that we have said *average* kinetic energy. It readily became apparent to the atomists that it was unreasonable to assume that all molecules in a gas were moving at the same speed. Even if at some instant they were, the collisions between molecules would quickly disrupt this order. For example, a "sideswipe" collision between two molecules moving at right angles to one another could stop one dead, by transmitting its forward motion to the other, as shown in Figure 3. But this presented no difficulties for the theory; the pressure being generated by a fantastic multitude of impacts, the slow ones make up for the fast ones.

The details of the picture were filled in over the next few decades

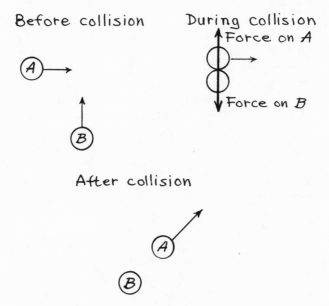

Figure 3   How collisions change speeds of atoms.

after Clausius by a number of gifted contributors, most notable among them the same James Clerk Maxwell who unified electromagnetism. This complete picture of gases as composed of widely separated, rapidly moving molecules is known as the *kinetic theory of gases*, the success of which turned most physicists and chemists into convinced partisans of the atomic theory. By the end of the nineteenth century the picture was complete.

How Big Is an Atom?

One vexing problem remained to cloud the success of the atomic theory; neither physicists with their gas laws nor chemists with their reaction recipes had any clue as to how big their atoms were or any way to tell how many there were in a given substance. The same pressure could be obtained in a gas by having more molecules each individually lighter. Put another way, the chemists could establish that an oxygen atom was sixteen times heavier than one of hydrogen, but no one knew how much either actually weighed.

Interestingly enough, the long-sought direct evidence for the atomic theory and a means of estimating the size of atoms had been at hand, yet overlooked, since 1827, in the form of an accidental discovery by the botanist Robert Brown. Observing through a microscope pollen grains suspended in water, he was disturbed by a phenomenon that had plagued microscopists looking at exceptionally small objects for over a century: the pollen grains refused to sit still, but instead insisted on hopping about in a jerky erratic fashion. Convinced in advance that pollen was an inert spore possessed of no means of locomotion, Brown proved his point by showing that the motion was most rapid for the smallest grains, hardly the sort of behavior expected out of a living microorganism. But how natural for the atomists! Finally they had found an object small enough to be disturbed by the unevenness of the hail of molecules, one on which a few particularly swift molecular impacts that happened to come on the same side could pile up to produce a noticeable effect. But the nineteenth century was nearly over and the controversy over the existence of atoms in full swing before the physicists rediscovered Brown's work. And not until 1905 did Einstein, in his fabulously productive year, work out the quantitative details to permit an estimate of absolute atomic weights from measurements of Brownian motion.

From the fact that in liquid and solid elements the density is more or less proportional to the atomic weight, it was clear that atoms were all pretty much the same *size,* despite the disparity in weights. Using a variety of evidence, by the turn of the century it began to appear plausible that typical atoms were about 10^{-8} cm in diameter, and that there were about 6×10^{23} atomic weight units in a gram. Thus, as physics entered the twentieth century, the atom was no longer regarded as a hypothetical and probably unobservable object, but a fit object of study in itself, if only the right probes could be found to look into this tiny world beyond the range of the finest microscopes.

What's "Inside" an Atom?

The natural next step was for a few bold souls to speculate on what an atom might really look like. Though atomism in its naïve infancy presumed atoms to be simple and nearly structureless, by 1900 there was plenty of evidence to the contrary. First and foremost, some means had to be found for hooking atoms together into molecules. Secondly, the existence of trends and similarities in chemical properties indicated by the periodic table of the elements was strongly suggestive of underlying structure. Still, the word "atom" meant *indivisible,* and it was not respectable to speculate much about dividing the indivisible until two sensational discoveries just before the turn of the century made it obvious that atoms were by no means structureless, and furthermore that there were experimental means to take them apart. These were the discovery of radioactivity by Becquerel (1889) and that of the electron by J. J. Thomson 7 years later.

Becquerel's discovery had the more sensational popular impact. One of the marvels of the eighties had been the x-ray. The practical implications of a form of "light" that could penetrate opaque objects titillated the late Victorian public and led to sensationalized and amusing newspaper articles. Following a hunch, Becquerel tried to find a substance that would give off x-rays when placed in ordinary light. Instead, he found that minerals containing the element uranium did indeed give off penetrating radiation, but it was not identical to x-rays and seemed to arise spontaneously, not only in the absence of light, but in fact oblivious to all outside influences. No amount of heating, treating, or cajoling could change the inborn rate at which a radioactive substance gave off rays. What was even more sensational, within a few years Ernest Rutherford (of whom we shall hear a great deal more in the next chapter) established that the emission of radiation was accompanied by a chemical change—one that transformed one element into another!

It is hard to imagine any discovery that could have been more shocking. The proudest boast of nineteenth-century chemistry was that it had proved the futility of the medieval alchemist's search for a means of turning base metals into gold. The atoms were immutable, and there was no way to *produce* an element; one simply had to go out and find it. Despite the existence of radioactive disintegration, a spontaneous process, there still remained no means of transmuting the elements by means of a chemical reaction, and thus the basic ideas of chemistry were not threatened. If an atom occasionally decided to change its identity, and there was no way to persuade or dissuade it from this step, chemistry was little affected. But to physicists, the impact of the discovery of radioactivity was to suddenly make probing within the atom not only respectable but imperative. Anything that could up and change in this fashion must have internal workings of quite a complex order.

The leading clue to the structure of the atom was the discovery of the electron, found in studies of electric currents in gases, a phenomenon familiar to anyone who has seen a neon sign.

Ions and Cathode Rays

Back in the 1830s Michael Faraday had done studies of the conduction of electricity in liquids. There the flow of electricity is usually accompanied by an actual movement of material to the points where the current entered or left the liquid. For example, the passage of electric current through water results in the liberation of hydrogen at one electrode and oxygen at the other, a phenomenon known as "electrolysis." Faraday found that the amount of an element that arrived at a point of electrical contact was *proportional to the total electric charge flow and to the chemical "equivalent weight" of the element,* the same equivalent weight discovered from the law of constant proportions. To anyone who believed in an atomic picture of matter, the interpretation of this law was obvious: all one needed was that electricity be transported in the form of an electric charge on the atoms. If for some unknown reason all atoms regardless of type carried the same electric charge, the total material flow corresponding to a given electric flow would depend only on the atomic weight, explaining Faraday's law. The charged atoms were christened *ions,* a Greek word meaning "wanderer" and thus a fit companion for the term *atom* itself.

In later Victorian England, J. J. Thomson was the most celebrated experimenter in a proud imperial nation boastful of her scientific achievements, and in his study of electrical conduction in gases, important to the mushrooming electrical industry, he was working on a fashionable problem. In the spirit of Faraday's work with liquids, many experimenters sought to identify the carriers of electricity in gases. They reasoned that if the gas were sufficiently rarified, its atoms could travel great distances without colliding with one another. In unimpeded flight, ions in the gas could be studied by applying electric and magnetic forces from outside the tube and observing the deflection.

Though still no one knew the absolute mass of an atom, the amount of charge carried per unit mass of ions had been established by Faraday. This would be sufficient to predict their response to electric and magnetic forces, for these forces are proportional to the electric charge. Thus, a larger mass would be offset by a proportionally larger force because of the larger charge; the acceleration produced by an electromagnetic force is thus determined solely by the ratio of charge to mass.

The negative charge carriers were the first ones found. If a hole is pierced through the positive electrode in a gas tube, the negative carriers fly through and leave a telltale glowing spot where they touched the glass. Such an experimental setup is shown schematically in Figure 4.

But the behavior of these *cathode rays,* as they came to be called, seemed at odds with the notion that they were like Faraday's ions. For one thing, they had identical properties regardless of the gas used to fill the tube. Secondly, they easily penetrated very thin sheets of matter placed in their path. If they resembled atoms, they should rebound from the densely packed atoms of a solid material. Thus, they might represent a new form of matter, possibly one smaller than atoms and therefore more able to penetrate.

Finally, while moderate magnetic fields easily deflected the beam of cathode rays, it took enormous electric fields to budge them from their paths. To Thomson, this was the key to the mystery. It suggested that they were moving very fast. For the magnetic force on a charged particle is proportional not only to its electric charge but also to its speed, while electric force depends on the charge alone. Thus, magnetic fields are far more effective in deflecting fast-moving particles than electrical fields, which do not benefit from the increased velocity.

In fact, since all other factors are equal, comparing the relative strengths of the electrical and magnetic fields required to produce equal

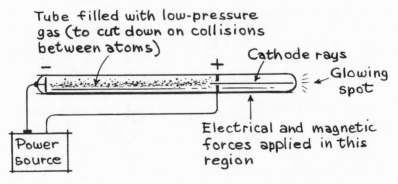

Figure 4   Apparatus for the discovery of the electron.

deflections of the cathode ray particles enabled Thomson to compute their velocity. They proved to be fast, indeed—more than one-tenth the speed of light, an unprecedented speed for material objects!

Once the speed was known, Thomson could use the deflection to calculate the acceleration, using the formula in Chapter 3 for acceleration in curved motion. From the acceleration he got the ratio of charge to mass. The result was surprising: nearly 2,000 times higher than the charge/mass ratio of hydrogen, the lightest known ion. Since the ratio proved independent of the gas in the tube, Thomson in 1897 announced the discovery of a new form of matter, which was christened the *electron*.

Either Thomson's electrons carried an enormous charge compared to ions, or they were far lighter. All the evidence as to their speed and penetrating power pointed to the latter conclusion: electrons, if they carried the same charge as ions, were 2,000 times lighter than a hydrogen ion.

Shortly afterward, studies of the positive carriers moving opposite to the electrons in the tube confirmed that they were ordinary ions. Since the electrons apparently arose from the atoms of the gas, it seemed reasonable to presume that they carried the same charge as the positive ions, to make the electrical charges balance when the electrons were recombined with the positive ions.

The Electron and the Atom

Thomson's electron was immediately hailed by some as the "atom of electricity," the solution to the mystery of the nature of electricity. Of course, its positive counterpart eluded discovery, and why it alone should be subject to such powerful forces remained a mystery, but the existence of this unsuspected light object seemed to explain the great mobility of electricity. But the true significance of his discovery was by no means lost on Thomson; since it had been produced from the dissociation of gas atoms, his electron must be a component of the atom itself. Where lesser minds saw the solution to an old mystery, Thomson saw the opening of a new adventure. A potential building block of the atom had been uncovered, and the rush was on; led by Thomson himself, the more imaginative citizens of the world of physics began inventing hypothetical models of the atom, not as a mere pastime or for purposes of illustration, as a few years earlier, but in dead earnest. A few clever experiments might tell physicists what really went on in an atom!

In their bold optimism, these early speculators on atomic structure little realized that they had opened a Pandora's box and that the demons resident therein had the power to bring down the edifice of classical physics patiently erected over three centuries.

14

Rutherford
Picks Apart the Atom

Imagine a group of proud and inventive men quarreling over the contents of a locked box and you have a pretty good picture of the mood of the early thinking on atomic structure. It only took a few years for most of the protagonists to sift out into one of two camps: the "planetary" and the "plum pudding" schools.

Given the similarity between Coulomb's law of electrical force and Newton's law of gravitation, an atom that resembled the solar system with an electrically positive sun and negative electrons for planets was too pretty an analogy to pass up. Furthermore, it placed at the disposal of its supporters the powerful computational tools developed over two centuries of study of the motion of the planets.

But the opposing camp had at *its* disposal the formidable authority of its founder, none other than the illustrious J. J. Thomson himself, soon to become one of the first Nobel laureates in physics for his discovery of the electron. He proposed a sphere of positive charge in which the electrons were embedded, as shown in Figure 1; the descriptive albeit pejorative term "plum pudding" was his own choice.

With two
electrons

With four electrons
(they are at the
corners of a
regular pyramid)

Figure 1   Plum-pudding atoms.

Light Emission Is the Arbiter

The debate would have been abandoned as sterile had there not been a body of data crying for explanation by an electrical model of the atom.   This was the data on the emission of light by atoms.

Light from a source containing a single element in a gaseous state, such as a neon sign or the mercury lamps now widely used for street lights, always has a characteristic color.   When this light is broken up into its component colors by a prism, a striking result is obtained.   Instead of a continuous spectrum (rainbow), which occurs when a solid or liquid is heated to glowing, one finds the light is composed of a few very pure, sharply defined colors.   The best way to observe this is to have the light originate from a thin slit, as illustrated in Figure 2.   If it then falls on a viewing screen or photographic plate, the result is a series of thin lines, each of a different color.   For this reason, this type of light pattern is referred to as a *line spectrum*.   For most elements, only a few lines are bright enough to be seen with the naked eye.   But if a long photographic exposure is made, many fainter lines appear; for some elements, hundreds have been catalogued.

Ever since Maxwell uncovered the electromagnetic nature of light, it had been clear that there was only one way to produce light: somewhere, an electrical charge must be going through a regular, periodic motion.   The frequency of this motion determines the frequency of the light; and since light regardless of color travels at the same speed, the frequency determines the wavelength.   This was one reason why Thomson's insistence that his electrons must be part of ordinary matter was so readily accepted; Maxwell's theory implied that anything that emitted light had to be electrical in nature.

It was also clear that in a gas the light must be emitted by individual atoms.   Not only are the atoms separated by many times their own size, but the oscillations of light waves have enormous frequencies, around 10^{14} Hz.   There are many oscillations in the time between encounters with

another atom, and thus it is hard to imagine how many atoms could coop-
erate to produce such a rapid oscillation.   Furthermore, the striking differences between the continuous spectrum of light emitted by densely packed
solids or liquids and the line spectrum from rarified gases gave support
to the notion that line spectra represent light from individual atoms.

Thomson's model gave a quite natural explanation for this light emission.   He imagined his electron plums were able to move freely in their
positively charged pudding, held in place by a delicate balance between
their attraction to the center of the positive charge and their mutual repulsion.   He and his supporters devoted a great deal of energy to finding
the patterns the electrons would assume.   If disturbed from this pattern
by a collision between atoms, they would oscillate around their normal
positions, just as a pendulum oscillates when disturbed from its equilibrium
point of hanging straight down.   Whenever a charge is accelerated, as
indicated in Chapter 6, its electromagnetic field changes.   This change
radiates out in the form of light, which carries away the energy of motion,
so that the vibration would gradually die out like the motion of a pendulum
dying as it yields up its energy to air resistance.   It took no great skill
to calculate the natural frequency of these oscillations, which would set
the frequency of the waves emitted; for atoms around the known atomic
diameter of 10^{-8} cm, they were appropriate frequencies for visible light.
This was a very encouraging result: that the electron had just the right
amount of charge and mass to connect the 10^{-8} cm of atomic size to the
10^{14} Hz of light frequencies had to be more than a coincidence.   The
plum-pudding atomists were sure they must be on the right track.

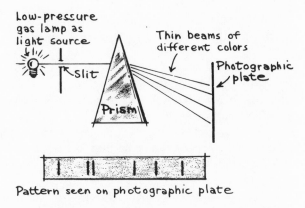

Figure 2   Apparatus for producing line spectra.

The same numerical coincidence also encouraged the planetary enthusiasts. Orbits around 10^{-8} cm in diameter gave the right frequency of rotation to produce visible light. But this also proved the undoing of the model. Unlike Thomson's atom, there was no natural way to stop the light emission or to give it a definite natural frequency. An orbit could have any size and thus could radiate light at any frequency. As the electron lost energy, its orbit would gradually shrink. Spiraling in to its doom, the electron would gradually change its frequency of rotation, unlike Thomson's electron oscillations, which kept the same frequency as their amplitude decreased. Even worse, simple calculations using Maxwell's laws showed that an electron took no longer than a millionth of a second to complete the spiral into the nucleus. Thus, the planetary atom was unstable and gave no natural explanation of the line spectrum. Despite heroic and ingenious efforts to eliminate these faults, the model fell into disfavor.

Still, until the Thomson model could be shown to explain the observed spectrum lines in all their quantitative detail, the field was open to all comers. And the quantitative detail was immense. The wavelengths of spectral lines are among the easiest physical quantities to measure to high precision; one part in 100,000 is child's play. Furthermore, precise data had been piling up for decades, motivated in part by their practical value. The set of spectrographic lines produced by an element is its fingerprint, and spectrographic analysis was a marvelous tool for chemistry. One bright line could reveal a small trace of one element in the presence of another that had only faint lines near the same wavelength.

While the chemists were content to amass their fingerprint file, physicists were doing much of the actual experimental work, because the techniques involved fell in the realm of optics. And the physicists could not resist the temptation to search for regularities in their data.

Order in the Confusion of Spectral Lines

With the added spur of the debate on the structure of the atom, the search for order in the confusing mass of data on spectra hit a peak around the turn of the century. By the first decade of the new century, two striking features had emerged.

The simplest of the two, but the more difficult to establish because of the immense amount of data that had to be examined, was the *combination principle* enunciated by W. Ritz. He observed that, far too often to be explained by coincidence, adding the frequencies of two lines in the spectrum of some element gave the frequency of a third. In the case of elements where the fainter lines had been carefully mapped out, nearly

all the lines fit into such a relationship. Allowing that to cover the exceptions there might be a few lines too faint to have yet been discovered, Ritz formulated a general principle: *all spectral lines have frequencies that are either the sum or the difference of the frequencies of two others.* There was no simple way to account for this principle in Thomson's atomic model.

The second important regularity applied only to the spectrum of the element hydrogen. As early as the 1880s, it had been recognized that hydrogen, the lightest of the elements, also had a far more orderly spectrum than the others. A Swiss schoolteacher by the name of Balmer found that the frequency of every line in the hydrogen spectrum could be obtained from a single formula:

$$\nu = \text{const} \times \left(\frac{1}{n^2} - \frac{1}{m^2} \right)$$

where n and m are integers (whole numbers). Later, the Swedish spectroscopist Rydberg showed that the same formula very nearly held true for the elements that most resemble hydrogen chemically, the alkalis that share with hydrogen the first column of the periodic table. Once again, the Thomson model offered no simple explanation of this formula.

But while the model-builders were struggling with the problem of how to impose these regularities on light emitted by a plum-pudding atom, a surprise experimental result from the Manchester laboratory of Ernest Rutherford indicated they were betting on the wrong horse. Rutherford was such a towering figure in the physics of his time that it is fitting to pause here and introduce the man.

Ernest Rutherford

In the 1920s, when he was at the zenith of his fame and recently elevated to the peerage as Lord Rutherford of Nelson, Ernest Rutherford was told by an envious colleague that he was "lucky to be riding the crest of a wave." Rutherford retorted, "Lucky, nothing!—I *made* the wave." While this rebuke is hardly indicative of excessive modesty, it was perfectly justified. Practically everything known about radioactivity and the atomic nucleus, and by then a great deal indeed was known, was the work of Rutherford, his students, or his coworkers. His fierce pride never allowed him to forget the few important discoveries in his chosen field that did not bear his name. Not since Faraday had one man so dominated an experimental discipline. There was no way to beat Rutherford—you just had to join him. Young physicists flocked to his laboratory, and in an environment where several startling discoveries per year were regarded as commonplace, they stretched and developed their talents to the full. It wasn't even safe to stay out of his field; if an exciting problem arose in any area of physics, Rutherford might very well pounce on it. And the more important it was, the more likely that he would beat the specialists in that field at their own game.

Rutherford's fame began almost the moment he stepped off the boat in England in 1895, a raw colonial from New Zealand. Some clever studies on the effect of radio waves on magnetic iron, conducted under unbelievably primitive conditions in a converted coat closet at Canterbury College in

Rutherford (right) with Geiger in their Manchester laboratory.

Christchurch had earned the ambitious 24-year-old a scholarship to Cambridge as a research student at J. J. Thomson's Cavendish Laboratory. The Cavendish was the most outstanding example of a new genre of university research laboratory that had developed with the secularization of universities in the nineteenth century.

The dominant activity at universities since their creation in the Middle Ages had been the training of the clergy, with as secondary duties the training of practitioners of such learned secular callings as medicine and law. Within this framework, experimental work in the sciences was almost an outside activity, a private activity of the professor in which the university as an institution could hardly be expected to take much interest. But with the growth of the natural sciences, a pattern emerged in which the university itself, with the aid of funds from both private donors and public sources, provided the professor with a laboratory. Working under his direction in this laboratory would be a number of more junior researchers who had not yet reached the olympian level of professor, a title still reserved to a small elite even today at most European institutions. Normally there was only one professorial chair in each field. At the top of the scale, the professor's assistants included established scientists awaiting his retirement or demise, that of a professor at another institution, or creation of a new chair at a new or growing school. Below this came various positions of varying degrees of permanency, down to the lowly research student, usually but not necessarily a candidate for the doctoral degree.

This system did much to encourage the internationalization of science and the free flow of ideas. Under it, a young scientist with high ambitions was more or less forced to move every few years. Any one nation of course had a limited number of laboratories in his field. By the time he settled down, he was likely to have had some degree of personal contact with most of the people working in his area, at home and abroad.

J. J. Thomson was among the few professors who permitted a great deal of independence to the junior staff, and in this free environment Rutherford quickly made his mark. In only three years he had attracted enough attention to be offered a chair at McGill University in Montreal, Canada. Though a native-born Englishman might have regarded this as an exile with a dubious future, as a colonial Rutherford had few qualms about taking his chances at a fast-rising institution that was already possibly the best in the Empire outside the mother country. And despite Rutherford's youth, his own reputation and the praise of Thomson were sufficient to attract a stream of first-class assistants from Britain, the United States, and the Continent. The productivity of his laboratory over his nine years in Montreal was phenomenal, and in 1907 he returned to England to assume a chair at the University of Manchester. Later he was to cap his career by succeeding Thomson himself as the director of the Cavendish Laboratory, but it is in his Manchester days that we find the most of interest for our current topic, for it was there that he administered the *coup de grâce* to the plum-pudding atom.

The Cannonball in the Hailstorm

Observing what happened to the radiation emanating from radioactive substances when it passed through matter had been just part of Rutherford's bag of tricks at McGill, where his primary task had been to identify the composition of the radiation. This problem solved (and the 1908 Nobel Prize earned thereby), Rutherford had the insight to guess that the technique might be turned around, that the now well-understood radioactive emanations could be used as a probe to see what might be inside matter. Nagging his thoughts was the observation that alpha radiation, which he had shown to consist of helium atoms with two electrons stripped away, was deflected somewhat when passing through thin sheets of mica. It was a small effect which most experimenters might well have overlooked. But Rutherford quickly realized that his alpha particles were too heavy and too fast-moving to budge from their paths except by means of a strong electrical force. Careful measurements of the deflection could be used to reason back to the size of the force, which might in turn give a clue as to how electrons were arranged in an atom.

But like most of his contemporaries, Rutherford had little doubt that Thomson had found the right picture of the atom. A mere corroborative experiment, and one that might prove difficult to interpret, was hardly worth his personal attention. However, there was a young research assistant named Marsden available for the task. A check as to whether there might be anything interesting in alpha scattering would make an ideal assignment for Marsden to cut his teeth on.

The prospects for anything interesting coming out of the experiment were not very bright. An alpha particle approaching one of Thomson's plum puddings, as shown in Figure 3, would experience no force until it got very close to or inside the atom, for the negative electrons would balance the positive charge on the pudding. Once inside, the forces would be considerable, but they would be exerted mainly by the electrons. Since these were many times lighter than the alpha particle, the electrons rather than the heavy, swift projectile would be the most disrupted by the encounter. It would be like a cannonball fired into a hailstorm. After traversing many atoms, the cumulative effect of many small encounters with electrons might have deflected the alpha particle a bit, but no large deflections could be expected. If the deflections resulted from many small scat-

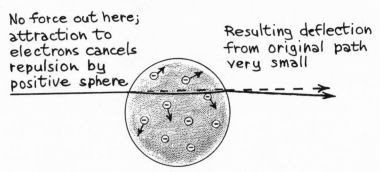

Inside, those electrons
close to path disrupted;
heavier alpha particle
little affected

No force out here;
attraction to
electrons cancels
repulsion by
positive sphere

Resulting deflection
from original path
very small

Figure 3 Passage of an alpha particle through a plum-pudding atom.

ters, it seemed unlikely that much detailed information about the structure of the atom would be retained.

So Marsden seemingly had little to look forward to, even considering that he was a novice research student inured to routine laboratory jobs.   The task he faced is depicted in Figure 4.   Inside a vacuum chamber (to prevent atoms in the air from interfering), he had to place a thin tube containing a source of alpha radiation.   This produced a narrow beam of alphas emerging from the tube.   The beam had to be narrow in order to permit observation of tiny deflections as the alphas traversed the target, a thin sheet of gold leaf.   Gold had been chosen because since medieval times craftsmen had mastered the art of hammering this soft metal to an incredible thinness; good gold foil is translucent.   This was essential, because even a sheet of cardboard is sufficient to stop a beam of alphas (it is the more penetrating beta and gamma particles that are primarily responsible for the fearsome reputation of radiation).

To detect the alphas, Marsden had to patiently count the tiny flashes produced when they struck a fluorescent screen; to see these flashes reliably required long hours of adaptation to a dark room.

On the whole, the results were not terribly surprising.   On the average, the alphas were deflected by only a few degrees.   But a very few of them, perhaps one in a thousand, were deflected through substantial angles.   Some even came off backwards!

Again, many physicists might have been content that the average scattering was reasonable, but Rutherford was nagged by those few scatterings through large angles.   If they resulted from a cumulative effect of many small scatters, we would expect the average scatter to be

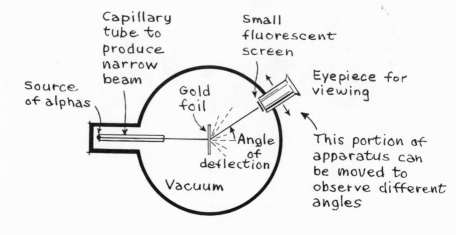

Figure 4 Geiger-Marsden apparatus.

larger. Marsden's immediate research supervisor, Hans Geiger (inventor of the Geiger counter), got directly involved in the work, and a systematic quantitative study was undertaken.

By 1911, though the data were still crude, Rutherford was sure the results ruled out the plum-pudding atom. Instead, he suggested that the positive charge on the atom might be confined to a tiny region; the large-angle scatters came from single close encounters with this "nucleus," as he called it.

With this picture of the atom, shown in Figure 5, it is easy to explain both the small average scattering angle and the occasional large one. With the atom mostly empty space, the alphas rarely came near a nucleus. Those that did would experience tremendous forces, since Coulomb's law gives a force that varies inversely as the square of the distance. Since the nucleus contains most of the mass of the atom, the cannonball is meeting a *bigger* cannonball off which it can recoil backwards. So the small average deflection comes from the fact that most of the alphas traverse the gold foil without ever getting near a nucleus. Yet the few large deflections can be explained as examples of the rare near misses.

More importantly, it was possible to exactly calculate the pattern of this type of scattering. In the Thomson model, the scattering resulted from many tiny deflections from encounters with individual electrons. The result would thus be a pattern that followed the familiar bell-shaped curve of random processes. But in Rutherford's picture the paths of the alphas could be calculated exactly from Newton's and Coulomb's laws, for there is nothing simpler than the motion of a body repelled from a single center of force. The result could be expressed in a simple mathematical statement: the number of alphas per minute hitting the fluorescent screen at some particular angle was inversely proportional to the sine of one-half of the angle, raised to the fourth power.

Geiger and Marsden pushed on with ever more careful measurements, in order to check this quantitative prediction in detail. In 1913 their final results were published. The data fit an "inverse-sine-to-the-fourth" curve beautifully. Table 1 gives the actual data as it appeared in their article in *Philosophical Magazine* (vol. 25, p. 604), a physics journal whose name betrays its ancient origins, when physics was still "natural philosophy." It is the third column of this table that spelled the death knell of the Thomson atom. Though 4,000 times as many flashes are seen on the screen at 15° as when it is placed at 150°, dividing the measured numbers of the second column by the computed ones in the first column, which give the value of $1/(\sin \frac{1}{2}\theta)^4$, results in a number that is nearly the same for all measurements. The differences between values in the third column merely reflect the fact that the data are only accurate to about 15 percent. The values of the numbers themselves are of no consequence, for they depend on the size of the screen and the time spent observing it, which was several hours for the data reported here. But the approximate constancy was significant. It indicated that the enormously varying counting rates were merely multiples of the factor $1/(\sin \frac{1}{2}\theta)^4$.

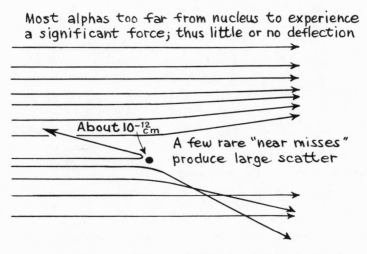

Figure 5 Scattering of alphas by a nucleus.

The errors were of no importance. Had Thomson's atom been correct, using the number of flashes at 15° to predict the number of larger angle ones, one would have expected only 16 instead of 1,435 at 45°, and one could have waited all day without seeing a flash beyond 75°. The fractional numbers given for some of the high angles reflect the fact that a longer period of observation was required for these measurements, because of the rarity of large-angle scatters; the results are averages of several measurements.

TABLE 1

(1) Angle of deflection θ, °	(2) Theoretical scattering rate $\dfrac{1}{(\sin \theta/2)^4}$	(3) Number of flashes observed	(4) Col. 3 ÷ Col. 2
150	1.15	33.1	28.8
135	1.38	43.0	31.2
120	1.79	51.9	29.0
105	2.53	69.5	27.5
75	7.25	211	29.1
60	16.0	477	29.8
45	46.6	1,435	30.8
37.5	93.7	3,300	35.3
30	223	7,800	35.0
22.5	690	27,300	39.6
15	3,445	132,000	38.4

The Geiger-Marsden data serve to illustrate that while physics is often described as a "precise" science, most experiments are no more precise than they need be. The discrepancy between the predictions of the plum-pudding and nuclear atoms was so enormous that a 15 percent measurement was enough to settle the issue. To strive for greater precision would have been a waste of time, especially for one with such a broad range of interests as Rutherford. Further refinements of the experiment were left to less original minds, and no one remembers their names.

The data are graphed in Figure 6 to more vividly show the agreement between theory and experiment. In order to graph such a wide range of values of number of counts, a *logarithmic scale* is used: that is, the vertical height of each point on the graph represents the logarithm of the number of counts. This has the effect of compressing the larger numbers, so that the region 100 to 1,000 occupies no more space on the graph than the region 10 to 100, rather than taking up ten times as much space.   It is a frequent device of scientists to represent graphically numbers which vary over an enormous range.

Rutherford was able to draw even further conclusions from this data.   Coulomb's law and the known velocity of the alphas enabled him to calculate just how close the alphas had come to the nucleus; the alphas that come off in the backward direction have made the closest approaches, as indicated in Figure 5.   Had they struck the nucleus, one would expect to find a deviation from the predicted scattering of backward particles, since new forces would have come into play.   Rutherford concluded the nucleus must be smaller than 10^{-12} cm, or one ten-thousandth the diameter of the whole atom!   As it turns out, the alphas had made a near miss—a gold nucleus is about 10^{-12} cm in diameter.

This is the first time in this book we have presented the full details of an experiment.   It was done in part because of the importance of the experiment for all of atomic physics, and also because it came in the era when reporting the data and experimental details, rather than merely the

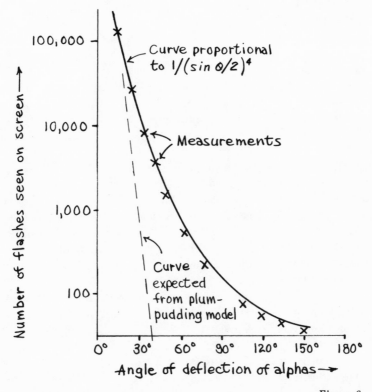

Figure 6

conclusions, became standard practice in physics journals. But this particular experiment has further historical significance. It was the first demonstration of the power of the study of particle scattering as a tool for uncovering the nature of forces that operate in the subatomic world. Most of the experiments conducted today with nuclei and subnuclear particles are in a sense variations on a theme by Rutherford, Geiger, and Marsden. Shooting things at atoms and nuclei and studying where they go after the collision is one of the few probes physicists have to get at the workings of matter on the submicroscopic level.

Of course, Rutherford's work raised more questions than it answered. If the positive charge and most of the mass were concentrated in a tiny core of the atom, where were the electrons? Rutherford himself had no idea how to proceed. If the theorists said it couldn't work, let *them* figure out why it worked nonetheless. Rutherford dealt in experimental fact.

But there was at least one young theorist who greeted Rutherford's results with enthusiasm. This enthusiasm would eventually make Niels Bohr the guiding spirit in the development of the new physics, the man who dared to make the final break with three centuries of physical thought.

Bohr had come in the autumn of 1911 to J. J. Thomson's Cavendish Laboratory, to cap his rigorous continental training in theory with an exposure to the British style of experimental physics. Though he arrived highly recommended and bubbling with enthusiasm, this 26-year-old Dane found the Cavendish no bed of roses. First there was the petty arrogance of the Cambridge tradition. His easy-going, boyish character rebelled against the formality of a medieval university town. In a letter home, he complained that his tutor had presented him with "a whole book" on the do's and don't's of academic protocol.

In the laboratory itself Bohr fared little better. The Cavendish had grown in response to Thomson's reputation, and was by then far too large for one man to handle. Bohr described the atmosphere of the laboratory as "a state of molecular chaos." Finally, Thomson had shown little interest in Bohr's doctoral thesis, which was based in large measure on Thomson's own work on electrons. Bohr had translated it into English, hoping that his host could help find a publisher that would guarantee a wider audience than was available in Denmark. But it remained on the busy professor's desk, unread.

When Rutherford visited Cambridge for a reunion of Thomson's "old boys," he and Bohr took an immediate liking to one another. This led to a short visit to Manchester, from which Bohr returned preaching the gospel of Rutherford's nuclear atom.

To Thomson this was the last straw. It was bad enough that his most illustrious student was challenging his model of the room. That Rutherford should seduce a guest at the Cavendish into his heresies was too much. By mutual agreement of all parties, Bohr left in April, 1912, to finish out his English sojourn at Manchester.

The industrial Midlands were a far cry from the formality of Cambridge. The laboratory was young, the University was young, and above all Bohr was in day-to-day contact with physicists as young and enthusiastic as himself. This was not a place where one had to apologize for one's crazier ideas; Bohr was in his element.

The unique skill that Bohr brought to Manchester was a thorough knowledge of a hodge-podge of radical new ideas called the quantum theory, which was still practically unknown in Britain. Bohr was convinced that in these ideas lay the key that would make the nuclear atom work. To see how right he was, we must now begin the story of the quantum itself. This is the task of the next chapter.

15

The Atom
and the Quantum

The universe is not only queerer than we imagine,
but it is queerer than we can imagine.

—J. B. S. HALDANE

Any physicist writing on the early steps in the development of quantum mechanics is faced with an embarrassment similar to that of a Victorian author writing an uplifting biography of a statesman of illegitimate origins. The problem is to get over the birth and early years as quickly and discreetly as possible, without sowing the seeds of confusion and thereby placing in jeopardy the inspirational message.

For the origins of the quantum theory are obscure and embarrassing indeed. It was bad enough that the idea of discontinuity on the atomic scale should have entered physics through the study of a phenomenon that is neither atomic nor discontinuous. But on top of this, the phenomenon is so difficult and obscure both mathematically and physically that few physicists are at all familiar with it.

Planck's Stab in the Dark

The phenomenon that led to the birth of the quantum theory is that of the continuous spectrum of light emitted by densely packed matter heated to incandescence, as in the filament of a light bulb or a bar of red-hot steel.   The phenomenon is not atomic, because the atoms are closely packed and in continuous interaction with one another, completely disrupting their natural way of producing light.   And it is certainly continuous: light is emitted at all wavelengths, the relative brightness of the different colors depending solely on the temperature of the material.   Extensive experimental studies were conducted in the last two decades of the nineteenth century, finding the brightness (energy radiated) at various frequencies.   A typical result is shown in Figure 1.

Understanding this spectrum was viewed as a problem in thermodynamics, the theory of the conversion of heat into other forms of energy, which was then perhaps the most sophisticated and highly developed branch of physics.   The theory had successfully explained the conversion of heat to mechanical energy in engines, to chemical energy in chemical reactions, and a host of other phenomena.   And it had shown that the detailed properties of the materials involved in these transformations were of little

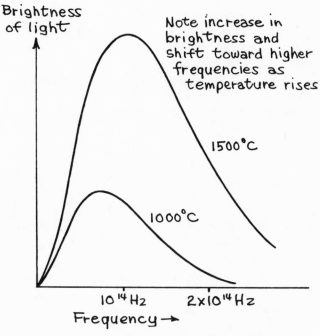

Figure 1   Incandescent light spectrum.

importance, which also seemed to be the case with incandescent light emission. A bar of any red-hot metal looks much the same as any other. Surely thermodynamics was the right theory to cope with the conversion of heat into light.

The first attempts showed encouraging results. It proved simple to account for the fact that the total energy radiated increased as the fourth power of the absolute temperature; the theory also satisfactorily explained why when an object is heated, the color of light emitted changes from a dull red through orange to white and on to blue, as the temperature rises. But the exact spectrum shown in Figure 1 eluded mathematical description.

Just before the turn of the century, Max Planck, a young German theorist, undertook the study of the problem. With the common sense that was typical of his approach, Planck realized that most mathematically difficult problems are solved only when the correct answer has already been guessed. Accordingly, he set out, by a process of trial and error guided by the successes and failures of previous attempts at the problem, to find a formula that would fit the experimental curve in Figure 1.

His search was rewarded early in the first year of the new century. But, as Planck fully realized, finding an empirical formula, one that fits the data but is not based on a physical picture of the process being described, can never be an end in itself in physics. Without an explanation of its underlying significance, the formula would remain an obscure curiosity.

By the end of the year, Planck had found a supporting argument for his lucky guess, but it involved a peculiar assumption. He found he was forced to assume that the conversion of heat into light could not occur in any amount whatsoever, but came in the form of chunks whose size depended on the frequency of the light produced. The smallest amount of heat energy that could be converted to light of frequency ν was given by the formula:

$$E = h\nu \tag{1}$$

and only whole number multiples of this amount could be produced. The constant h appeared in Planck's empirical formula. It is known to this day as "Planck's constant" and ranks with the velocity of light as one of the two basic constants of nature, though its significance is perhaps somewhat more mysterious than that of c. The introduction of this constant and Equation (1) before a meeting of the German Physical Society on December 14, 1900, is usually taken as the birthdate of the quantum theory.

Nothing could have been more unnatural in the physical thought of the time than to arbitrarily restrict energy changes to granular *quanta*, as Planck called them. Not even the author of the assumption could take it very seriously. Perhaps there was some way to explain or eliminate this granularity.   For example, the empirical formula might not be correct; after all, experimental data are never perfect.   A slightly different formula, derived without the assumption, might fit the data just as well.   Or perhaps a different route to the same formula could be found, one that did not involve such an arbitrary and unreasonable assumption.   The theory of heat was so mathematically involved that no one could be sure.   At the worst, if the assumption held up, it might represent some obscure property of the electron, which after all had to do the job of energy transformation, since light can only be produced by a moving electric charge, and the lightweight mobile electron was the ideal candidate.   Not even Planck really believed the assumption would remain a significant or even a permanent feature of the theory.   The idea of the quantum was regarded as no more than a way station on the route to a deeper understanding, and physicists working on the problem assumed it would eventually disappear.

Einstein and 1905 Again

There are always a few bold thinkers who, confronted with a puzzling new idea, will look not for ways around it, but for new ways to extend and test it, to see if it crops up somewhere else in nature.   Hardly anyone was bolder than Einstein in 1905, the same year in which he announced the theory of relativity.   The problem Einstein dealt with was not, like Planck's, a heavily studied phenomenon right at center stage in the attention of physicists, but a relatively obscure one called the *photoelectric effect*.

A series of accidental discoveries late in the nineteenth century had led to the conclusion that light was capable of knocking electrons out of metals.   This surprised no one, for light being an oscillatory electromagnetic field, it was bound to give an electron a good shaking and might actually shake it loose from its moorings.   Few experiments had been undertaken on this relatively obscure effect, but some qualitative facts were known about it, and these had no obvious explanation:

1   The effect was easy to produce with blue or ultraviolet light, but not with red light.
2   The rate at which electrons were given off was proportional to the brightness of the light.
3   If one measured the energies of the electrons given off, however, they proved to be independent of the brightness of the light, but there were indications that the energy did depend on the wavelength.

The apparatus for observing the photoelectric effect is depicted in Figure 2.   Light shining on the photocathode liberates electrons, which

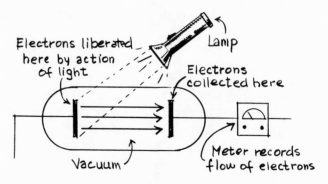

Figure 2   Photoelectric effect.

are collected at the anode, producing a measurable electric current. By charging the anode negatively, so that it repels electrons, the current can be stopped. From the size of the force required to repel the electrons, their energies can be calculated.

The third fact above was the key clue and was in part another contribution of Ernest Rutherford, from his last paper as a research student at Cambridge before departing for Montreal. It was certainly the most peculiar fact of all. By simple reasoning, brighter light meant stronger electric fields, which in turn meant greater forces on the electrons. Surely they must come out faster. Yet the experiments were still crude, and it seemed premature to get unduly alarmed about a few peculiarities.

Einstein had been worrying about what seemed to him an awkward point in Planck's theory. How he even found time to think about it, in view of his other preoccupations, is somewhat of a mystery. Planck had assumed the emission of light in quanta was due to limitations on the motion of the oscillating electrons that produced the light; yet otherwise he used the laws of classical physics to deal with the process. Since there were no other examples of limits on motion outside the requirements of Newton's laws, to Einstein it seemed more logically consistent to ascribe this peculiar behavior to the light itself. Once he came to this point of view, he began to return to a particle picture of light to explain Planck's quanta. It occurred to him that the few known experimental facts about the photoelectric effect seemed to lend themselves naturally to a particle theory, in which light would be a hail of quanta, which Einstein christened *photons*. The most puzzling feature, point 3 above, was then naturally explainable. An electron could at most absorb a single photon—it would be removed from the metal so fast that in light beams of normal strength it would never get a chance to trap another. Thus, the energy of the electron would depend solely on the energy of the photon, and therefore on the frequency (color) of the light. It would not depend on the brightness, which was merely a measure of how many photons were available.

More photons meant more electrons, but not faster ones, which explained point 2 on page 191.

Point 1 also seemed reasonable in a quantum picture. A certain amount of energy is required to pull an electron free of the forces of attraction that hold it in the metal. If one photon didn't provide enough energy, the electron was stuck. It would quickly lose its added energy before another photon came by. And red light, being lower in frequency than blue, had less energetic photons.

Like any good theory, Einstein's picture of the photoelectric effect permitted a conclusive experimental test. The maximum possible energy of the electrons should be $h\nu$, minus the energy lost in pulling an electron loose. But h was a constant obtained from an empirical formula for incandescent light! If it turned up again in the photoelectric effect, the coincidence would be too much to swallow; Einstein must be right. If the same granularity appeared when light was created and when it was absorbed, it seemed more natural to ascribe the granularity to the light itself than to the two unrelated processes that produced and absorbed it. But the experiment was a difficult one, and 11 years were to pass before the American physicist Robert Millikan confirmed the prediction.

The prediction confirmed by Millikan is depicted graphically in Figure 3. Until the frequency gets sufficiently high that a single quantum can free an electron from the forces that bind it to the metal, no electrons are liberated. From then on, the electron energy is equal to the quantum energy, diminished by the amount lost in overcoming the binding

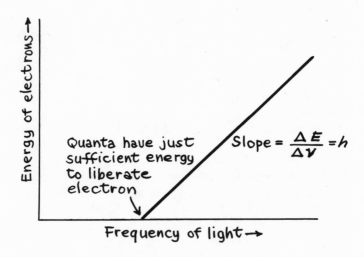

Figure 3   Einstein's prediction of the relationship of electron energy to light frequency in the photoelectric effect.

force. The crucial quantitative point is that the slope of the graph, which is the ratio of the increase in electron energy to the increase in frequency, is Planck's constant h, even if the process that produced the light has nothing to do with the process described by Planck. Thus, the relationship $E = h\nu$ must pertain to light itself.

Until the experimental confirmation was forthcoming, the theory of the photoelectric effect remained the least respectable of Einstein's many achievements. How could it be reconciled with the overwhelming evidence for the wave theory of light? His quanta of light must obviously be more like particles than waves, so how could they produce all the wave effects that had been observed in the century since the work of Young? How could light be *both* a particle and a wave at the same time? Einstein's attempts to struggle with this "dual" character of light, today a central concept in the quantum theory, reassured nobody. When he was put up for membership in the Prussian Academy of Sciences in 1913, Einstein's sponsors felt compelled to excuse this peculiar lapse of an otherwise obviously brilliant man. But only three years later Millikan's work was to show that Einstein was devastatingly right in this, his least solid contribution. The photoelectric effect, rather than the theory of relativity, was the basis for awarding Einstein the 1921 Nobel Prize in physics, for relativity was still a bit controversial at that time.

But the spirit of the time was receptive to new ideas. With young men seeking new directions in the world of art, music, and literature, Einstein and his café companions had learned to question established ideas in politics, morals, the arts. Why not try it in physics? To a new generation of physicists, Einstein's photoelectric theory was a hope rather than a problem; clearly, there was more to Planck's quantum than some obscure feature of the theory of heat.

Bohr Asks the Right Question

It was as a representative of the new breed of theorist that Niels Bohr arrived at Rutherford's Manchester laboratory in the spring of 1912. Rutherford was bound to be flattered that such a well-recommended young man viewed his nuclear atom with enthusiasm rather than the dismay expressed by most of his own contemporaries. But an intuitive thinker like Rutherford, who liked to visualize the unseen objects he worked with, was bound to view Bohr's interest in quanta with some skepticism. Rutherford had once answered a colleague's dinner-table query as to whether he actually thought electrons and alpha particles really existed with the reproof: "Not exist—not exist—why, I can see the little beggars there in front of me as plainly as I can see that spoon!" Quanta were an

Bohr's engagement photo, taken shortly before his departure for England.

(*American Institute of Physics.*)

entirely different matter, a bit too abstract for Rutherford's liking. Yet he took a personal liking to the eager young Dane, explaining this deviation from a proper British disdain for theorists (and especially continentals) with the remark, "Bohr's different. He's a football player!"

Others before had applied Einstein's and Planck's quantum concept to the atom, usually in the context of the more popular Thomson model. Most of these studies had been efforts to explain away Planck's constant by showing it to be a consequence of the size of the atom and the charge and mass of the electron. Bohr immediately saw that in dealing with a nuclear atom, the correct approach must be precisely in the opposite direction. Since in the classical theory electron orbits could be any size whatsoever, some new principle must be found to explain atomic size, and perhaps this principle could get rid of the "death spiral." It was not the duty of the atom to explain Planck's constant, but for the constant to explain the size and stability of the atom.

This insight was a fortuitous bonus of the research institute structure mentioned in the preceding chapter, in which the best young physicists traveled a great deal. Bohr's continental education had given him the required familiarity with the quantum theory; but only at Manchester could he find people who really believed in the nuclear atom and would encourage his efforts. Despite the existence of scientific journals, the emotional impact of scientific ideas is always greatest at their source. Elsewhere in the world, Rutherford's nuclear atom seemed a possibility. At Manchester, Bohr was in the midst of a group of talented young physicists who took it as established fact. While at the Cavendish or in Copenhagen Bohr might have toyed with the idea that the quantum theory might permit a stable planetary atom. At Manchester, day-to-day results from the darkened laboratory down the hall, and the enthusiasm with which his coworkers received them, changed the whole picture. The planetary atom *had* to be made to work, and all the signs were that the quantum theory held the key.

The work of Planck and Einstein inseparably ties the frequency of light to its energy. Bohr reasoned that this implied that an atom can only exist in a limited set of *states* of internal motion, each with a definite energy. Light is emitted when an atom changes it state, with the frequency determined by the difference in energy between the initial and final states.

In a planetary atom, the energy of internal motion depends solely on the size of the orbit. Bohr realized he must find a new quantum rule that restricted the motion of electrons to a limited set of orbits. The Einstein-Planck rule $E = h\nu$ was not enough; if the electrons were free to move in any way they chose, all energies would be possible, and thus all frequencies of light would be emitted. Only by restricting the orbits could a line spectrum be obtained.

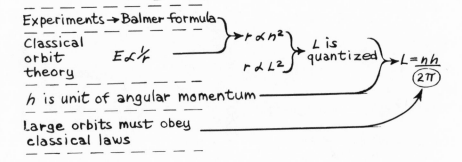

Figure 4   Logical steps leading to Bohr's orbit rule.

This restriction could also account for the stability of atoms; once in the smallest orbit, the electron would have no place to go.   A collision between atoms could knock it into a higher energy orbit, and it would emit light once or several times in the process of returning to the smallest orbit, or "ground state," in which it normally existed.

Bohr was forced to assume that the electrons would ignore the classical laws of electromagnetism while in the legal orbits and radiate no light. Otherwise there would be a gradual loss of energy, inconsistent with both the quantum picture of light and the rule restricting orbits.   Only while shifting orbits could the electron produce light.

He also guessed that the orbit rule would somehow involve Planck's constant.   Some sort of constant was needed to set the scale of the orbits, and he hoped he could use Planck's and not have to introduce a new one.

Once the problem had been thus formulated, the task was clear: find the orbit rule.   But his scholarship to England had run out.   He was married upon his return to Copenhagen, and a honeymoon in Norway took care of the rest of the summer of 1912.   Starting his first teaching job in the fall, he had little time to concentrate on the problem.   He played with orbit calculations, but with no experimental data to guide him, he bogged down.   It was only his ignorance of atomic spectra that hampered him.   He had asked the right question; he was soon to find that nature had already given the answer.

Balmer's Formula—the End of the Search

At the end of January 1913, H. M. Hansen, an old classmate of Bohr's and a spectroscopist, paid a visit to Copenhagen.   When he asked Bohr if the theory on which he was working might explain the Balmer formula, the reply was, "What formula?"   He advised Bohr to look it up.   The moment Bohr set eyes on the formula, he knew his search was over.   The

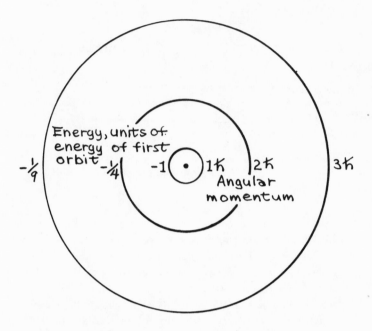

Figure 5   First three Bohr orbits.

allowed orbits were circles for which *the angular momentum is a whole multiple of h/2π.*

To anyone familiar as Bohr was with orbit theory, the reasoning that led to this rule was simple.   The chain of logic is outlined in Figure 4.

The Balmer formula gave the lines in the hydrogen spectrum in terms of differences of inverse squares of whole numbers.   Bohr knew the frequencies of spectrum lines must depend on differences in energies of orbits, so the formula immediately suggested that the allowed orbits had energies that followed the same proportionality, that is, they went in the series $1, \frac{1}{4}, \frac{1}{9}, \frac{1}{16}, \ldots$.   From playing around with circular orbits, Bohr knew well of two mathematical properties they obeyed: (1) the energy is inversely proportional to the radius, and (2) the angular momentum is proportional to the square root of the radius.   The first property, taken with Balmer's formula, indicated that the radii of successive orbits were 4, 9, 16, . . . times the radius of the inner orbit, as shown in Figure 5.*   Then the second told him the angular momenta of these orbits went as the whole numbers 1, 2, 3, 4, ...   Why should this be significant?   Because *Planck's constant is a unit of angular momentum!*   The last piece in

* If it appears that the energy is *highest* for the small orbits, remember that all these energies are *negative*.   That is, the (negative) potential energy exceeds the kinetic, and the orbits are bound, as explained in Chapter 6.

the jigsaw puzzle was in place (except for the factor 2π, which will be explained shortly).

Of course, the rule was completely ad hoc. Nothing in the work of Planck or Einstein even hinted that Planck's h could be used for such an outrageous purpose. And Bohr couldn't pretend to describe how an electron jumped from orbit to orbit, or why it didn't radiate light when it stayed in an orbit. As he himself explained it, the orbit rule was probably not the *real* rule. It was just an expression *in the language of the old physics* for a rule whose meaning would become clear when the true language of quantum mechanics was discovered. The next chapter will show just how right this impression was.

Bohr fully realized he was treading on thin ice. The old physics had three centuries of work to back it up; all he had was Rutherford's experiments and the Balmer formula. Somehow he had to work out a way for his fledgling theory to coexist with the old physics. This he provided for by means of his *correspondence principle.* The quantum theory would reign supreme on the atomic scale, classical physics on the gross scale of daily experience. Where they overlap, both theories should give the same answers.

For example, consider some of the very largest orbits of the hydrogen atom. Orbit number two is four times as large as number one. But orbits numbers 10 billion and 10 billion one would be very close in size. The jumps between such outer orbits would be almost unnoticeable; the process might well closely resemble the continuous spiraling-in of the classical theory. To complete the overlap between the quantum and classical picture, Bohr insisted, the frequency of light emitted must equal the frequency of rotation in the orbit, as the classical theory insists. It was from this requirement that he obtained the factor 2π; it was needed to make the frequencies match. In view of the fact that he was dealing with a circular motion, the presence of such a factor hardly came as a surprise. In fact, $h/2\pi$ is now regarded as a more fundamental quantity than Planck's constant. It has a symbol of its own, $\hbar$, pronounced "h-bar."

Numbers Are Powerful Convincers

Outrageous as it might be, nobody could quarrel with the fact that Bohr's theory came up with those marvelous little convincers, experimental numbers. Frequencies of spectrum lines can be measured to fantastic accuracy, and Bohr hit them right on the head. Let us summarize his quantitative results. To avoid interrupting the flow of the narrative, we relegate the simple algebra on which they are based to the section of the Appendix for this chapter.

The radius of the first orbit is given by the expression

$$r = \frac{\hbar^2}{me^2} = 0.53 \times 10^{-8} \text{ cm}$$

where m and e are the mass and electric charge of the electron. The energy of this orbit is

$$E_1 = \frac{me^4}{2\hbar^2}$$

The point of displaying these curious expressions is that they are, in fact, peculiar looking combinations of tiny quantities. That they turn out to give the right answer could hardly be a coincidence. The radius jibes with the known size of the hydrogen atom; the energy, divided by h, gives the constant in Balmer's formula, which was known to high precision.

The theory also explained the Ritz principle in a satisfying fashion, as illustrated in Figure 6. If the frequency of a spectral line turns out to be the sum of two others, it merely means that the line comes from

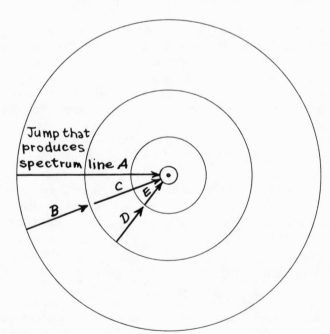

Figure 6 *Bohr's explanation of the Ritz principle.*

a big jump that skips one or more orbits; the other two lines complete the same transition in two steps. Bohr's work suggested the Ritz rule might apply to sums of three or more frequencies, and examples were quickly found.

The Bohr theory also explained one curious fact about atomic spectra: atoms cannot absorb light at all of the frequencies they emit. In the Thomson atom, light whose frequency matched the natural frequency for one of the electrons to oscillate would set the electron in motion, soaking up the energy of the light, a natural reversal of the process of light emission. In the Bohr theory, since undisturbed electrons are always in the lowest orbit, only light of the frequencies produced by jumps from higher orbits to the lowest could be absorbed. In Bohr's scheme, light absorption is also the reverse of light emission; a photon is "sucked in," and the electron jumps to a higher orbit. But if any photon came by whose frequency corresponded to a jump between two higher orbits, it would be ignored, because in undisturbed atoms these orbits are empty.

A more direct confirmation of Bohr's outrageous ideas was soon to come. The experimenters Franck and Hertz, in 1914, studied collisions between free electrons and gas atoms. They found that the energy losses suffered by the electrons exactly matched the energies of light quanta produced in the spectrum of the gas by the formula $E = h\nu$. If electrons were used that had too little energy to cause the first quantum jump, all collisions were elastic: no energy was lost. Once they were raised above this energy, in some of their collisions they would lose exactly enough energy to produce one quantum of light. What was happening, of course, was that the kinetic energy of the free-flying electron was being used to raise an orbiting electron in the atom to a higher orbit. This was finally a direct *mechanical* confirmation that the basic Bohr idea was right. The internal motion of electrons in atoms only permitted a limited set of energies. Even when light was not involved at all, Planck's constant came into play.

Like the Ritz principle, the Franck-Hertz result held for gases other than hydrogen, though there was no formula for the energies of these orbits—they had to be inferred from the observed line spectra. Thus, there was reason to believe Bohr's ideas could be extended to more complex atoms, with many electrons.

The Battle Is Joined

Bohr's theory was greeted with considerable skepticism. Some sort of fixed-energy-level picture of the atom was obviously called for, but was Bohr's absurd picture the right one? As Bohr himself realized, his theory was

only a step on the route to the truth. Rutherford, for all his dedication
to the nuclear atom, was afraid to give it much credence. Bohr was "onto
something big," but clearly more work had to be done.

And suddenly it was August 1914, and there was nobody left to
do the work. With the assassination of an Austrian archduke in the obscure
Bosnian city of Sarajevo, young scientists who had been working side by
side suddenly found themselves conscripted into rival armies, to face one
another across fields of barbed wire.

Rutherford's Manchester laboratory was quickly denuded of his
"boys," the young men who had made it hum. Rutherford patriotically
resigned himself to research on submarine detection, while his friends and
former coworkers in the German laboratories worked to frustrate his
efforts. Rutherford had good personal reasons to reflect bitterly on the
futility of the slaughter. His own most brilliant student and *protegé*, Os-
wald Moseley, died in the senseless and disastrous British attack on the
Dardanelles. Moseley's greatest achievement, just before he left for the
army, had been to show by experiment that the Bohr theory explained the
production of x-rays. But this did not exempt him from the horror that
cut down a major share of European youth of his age.

Physics in the Twenties

When the surviving young physicists returned from the trenches at the
end of 1918, the intellectual world was in no mood for caution. The
old political order had fallen in the defeated Central Powers and had
been discredited in the eyes of many intellectuals among the victorious
allies. The Bolshevik revolution in Russia had aroused the passions of
the whole world.

Physics often seems the most insulated of intellectual endeavors. Few
historians of science ever concern themselves with anything but its internal
history. Perhaps it was a mere coincidence that classical physics seemed
on the verge of ultimate triumph, in the complacent 1880s, only to be
replaced by a new physics born in the turbulent 1920s; in purely scientific terms, the time was ripe. Not all sciences experienced a similar flower-
ing. And great physics is usually done by men who, for the time being
at least, are thinking of little else.

Yet one can imagine the mood of a young man whose diversions
might include the plays of Brecht, the music of Hindemith, the novels
of Thomas Mann, and Dada art exhibits. His neighbors might be surrealist
painters, radical poets, Bauhaus architects, or devotees of the daring psycho-
logical theories of Jung or Adler. The mood of the cafés quickened the
pulse. Was this the time to dwell contentedly on the ancient traditions

of physics, to add one's little bit to the great edifice built on the foundations of Newton? The young Fellow or *Privatdozent* could hardly face his friends if he engaged in a pursuit that seemed so sterile by their values.

The revolutionary young physicists of the prewar era became the cautious moderates of the 1920s. Planck and Einstein, while sympathetic, remained cautious. Well into their forties, they were past their days of innovation, and they feared the quantum theorists were going a bit too far. The game belonged to a new generation—that of Heisenberg, Pauli, Schrödinger, and Born, and above all that of Niels Bohr.

The German references are no accident: the center of the stage was the great German universities. Principal among these was the Georgia Augusta University at Göttingen, a provincial university city reminiscent of American college towns. Göttingen had been a center of intellectual ferment and political rebellion since its foundation by George II, Prince of Hanover and later King of Britain. The cogent fact in the twenties was the presence of the mathematician David Hilbert, who created an atmosphere of intense scholarly debate that cut across traditional disciplinary boundaries. Hilbert's efforts had been aided by historical accident—a prize left to the university for a proof of one of the famous unsolved problems of mathematics, Fermat's theorem.* With no claimants for the prize, Hilbert used the income from the legacy to import distinguished lecturers to the otherwise isolated Hanoverian town. Hilbert chose his speakers judiciously, to maximize the atmosphere of controversy. The roster includes quite a list of Nobel laureates—who were usually invited *before* the award of the coveted prize. A speaker approaching a Göttingen lecture knew he faced an audience that would accept nothing less than his most original ideas, and that he must be prepared to defend his work against sharp attack. There were debates, long into the night, on the shape of the new physics. The young men who flocked to Göttingen were in no mood to be polite to their elders.

But the mecca of this new religion was unquestionably Copenhagen, and its unchallenged prophet was Niels Bohr. Barely into his thirties, Bohr headed a new institute supported in part by the profits of the venerable and world-renowned Carlsberg and Tuborg breweries. Bohr was to make Copenhagen nearly as famous for physics as for beer and pretty girls. Rumors of an important new development anywhere in Europe

---

* The mathematician Pierre de Fermat (1601–1665) stated in a marginal note found after his death that the equation

$$x^n + y^n = z^n$$

has no whole number solutions for n greater than 2 and that the proof of this was "obvious." It couldn't have been *terribly* obvious, for mathematicians have been looking for the proof to no avail in the three centuries since.

brought an automatic reaction to the young guard of physics—catch the next train to the charming and fun-loving city on the Øresund. Only in "The Presence" could the true significance of a new idea be evaluated, and the debates became legendary.

The settings were familiar. The Institutes of the German and French universities, the Cavendish Laboratory, a bit less stuffy after Rutherford succeeded J. J. Thomson in 1919, the gentle Scandinavian frivolity of Copenhagen. But the mood was new, and every bit as romantic as Hemingway's Paris or Brecht's Berlin. In Munich, in the same era that witnessed Hitler's beer hall *putsch,* the waiters at one café near theorist Arnold Sommerfeld's *Institut* had peculiar instructions. When the young physicists who passed their evenings there left the marble-topped tables covered with equations, they were under no circumstances to be cleaned; a number of the key ideas of the new physics went straight from those tables to the pages of *the* journal of the quantum-mechanical revolution, *Zeitschrift für Physik.*

But the spirit of the era is epitomized in the unforgettable image of Fritz Houtermans, who first untangled the chain of nuclear reactions that provides the sun with its energy. Few scientists have ever succeeded in fully articulating the terror and beauty of the feeling that comes with the realization that one has solved an age-old mystery. In the height of this mood, the day the last piece of the puzzle fell into place, Houtermans had a date. As they walked the quiet, dark streets of Göttingen, his frau- lein, sensing the exaltation of her escort's mood, remarked on the beauty of the night sky. "Yes," the young theorist replied, "and would you have guessed that you were arm-in-arm with the only man alive who knows why they shine?"

16

When Is a Particle a Wave?

Popular accounts of scientific discoveries often describe a research scientist as a hunter stalking his prey. The young men who built quantum mechanics in the early 1920s more nearly resembled a rowdy band of schoolboys chasing a rabbit across a rocky meadow. The order of the day was "anything goes," and the approach was scandalously empirical. Invent a quantum rule, like Bohr did, derive a formula, fit the data, and go on to the next problem. An understanding of what sort of physical reality might underlie a successful computation would come in its own good time. The hope was that after enough lucky guesses a pattern might emerge to guide physicists to a deeper level. In the meantime, the new game was just plain fun.

This period gave the first prominence to a new breed of physicist, the theory specialist. Physics was traditionally experimental, and the training followed this line. True, there had always been a few thinkers who built theories on the work of others, but many of them were basically mathematicians, and they were far inferior in number to experimenters. But the growth of scientific journals and societies facilitated this sort of labor. By the turn of the century, many continental schools were offering special curricula in theoretical physics, with only rudimentary laboratory training.

It took several decades before this model was copied in Britain and especially the United States, but it suited the needs of the universities. Theorists could teach either mathematics or physics, and they came cheap, since they needed no laboratory space.

The Bohr Atom Is Not Enough

The starting point for postwar quantum physics was tinkering with Bohr's model of the atom to make it work for heavier elements. This was no mean task; no longer could one work with a simple attractive force directed toward the nucleus. The mutual repulsion of the electrons had to be taken into account. How this might modify the orbits or affect the quantum rule that led to them was impossible to say on the basis of Bohr's ad hoc and patently incomplete rules. The scheme became more complex. A new quantum rule was concocted by Arnold Sommerfeld that gave each circular orbit a few elliptical companions, each as long as the diameter of the circle. Such an orbit had the same energy as the circular one. But the scheme remained as arbitrary as and more complex than Bohr's original model. Then it became necessary to arbitrarily limit the population of the orbits: two electrons could fit in an orbit, and no more. Where would all this arbitrary rule-making end? It seemed that every new problem brought into being a new rule. It was great fun, but was it physics?

Still, the scheme had some appealing features. Most notable was the fact that it seemed to explain, at least in a loose qualitative fashion, the chemists' periodic table of the elements. Every atom's "ambassadors" to the other world would be its outermost electrons. Its ability to form chemical compounds would depend on their behavior. The theory seemed to suggest that elements in the same column of the periodic table were similar in their outer orbital patterns, and thus the atoms should be chemically similar. There must be some truth in a picture that could shed light on this old mystery. What lay behind all these strange, arbitrary rules?

As is often the case when a group of scientists are caught up in trial-and-error speculation, the key to the muddle came from outside, from a more isolated thinker with the leisure to contemplate the problem in a detached manner. And it came not from Germany, but from France, where a less frenzied and more abstract type of speculation had long been the dominant style in physics. The protagonist, Prince Louis Victor de Broglie, was one of the most improbable characters in a drama full of improbable people.

A Prince Has a Crazy Idea

Few families in Europe outrank the de Broglies in the *Almanach de Gotha,* the quasi-official register of nobility. The eminence of his lineage is attested to by the fact that Louis bore the august title of *Prince* as a mere cadet honor; today, following the death of his older brother, he has assumed the higher title of *Duc.* The de Broglies have provided France with diplomats, cabinet ministers, and generals for centuries. One of Louis de Broglie's ancestors even fought on the American side in our War of Independence. Accordingly, de Broglie received the standard humanist education that is the traditional preparation for a role in the French ruling elite.

But the family also had a modest scientific tradition. Louis' elder brother Maurice was an experimental physicist of no mean reputation. Through his brother's influence, the young prince, newly matriculated in 1910 at the University of Paris, took an interest in the work of Einstein. He was particularly intrigued by the possibility of finding a connection between Einstein's two most celebrated works. He speculated that relativity itself might shed some light on the problem of the dual wave-particle character of light in Einstein's work on the photoelectric effect. Work in this field naturally went slowly for this rank amateur, who had in effect to start his education all over again to get into it. The war interrupted his studies before he had made much progress.

Returning from his military service determined to see his interest in physics through to the doctorate, de Broglie retained his preoccupation with the wave-particle problem. But in the meantime, the success of the Bohr model had changed the whole picture in the quantum theory. No longer could quantum effects be regarded as a mere peculiarity of light. The strange limits on the motion of electrons in atomic orbits were an even more disturbing mystery. Having been convinced that the wave-particle duality was the key to the earlier quantum theory, perhaps it was also the source of Bohr's rules. If light could be a particle, why could not an electron be a wave?

The idea had many inviting aspects. While it was difficult to imagine a mechanical law that would rule out all but a few orbits, similar restrictions on wave motion were quite normal. After all, musical instruments work precisely because the types of wave motion possible on a taut string or in an enclosed column of air are severely restricted. If the electron could in some sense be regarded as a wave, perhaps the Bohr orbits would prove to be standing waves and the atom not so much restricted as *tuned.*

But describing an electron as a wave was quite a bit more difficult than describing light as a particle. Light always travels at the same velocity; thus, its frequency and wavelength are closely related. Once one is known, the other is known from the relation given in Equation (1)

De Broglie.

of Chapter 8. For an electron, capable of moving at any velocity whatsoever, there would of necessity be separate rules for the wavelength and the frequency.

Again, it was to his knowledge of relativity that de Broglie turned. In his prewar speculations on the dual wave-particle character of light, he had succeeded in proving that the only way light could be a particle and still move always at the same velocity was for the photon to have zero "rest mass." In this way, *all* the mass would rise from its motion, and the motion would always be at the velocity of light.

If you find the concept of a particle with zero rest mass disturbing, imagine the photon to be a particle with a very tiny rest mass. Then giving it even a very small amount of energy, as long as it was much greater than the rest-mass energy of the photon, would bring it up to a speed very close to that of light. Most of its mass would be from the added energy; the small rest mass would be unnoticeable, and the small difference in speed of light of different energies (frequencies) would be impossible to measure.

Since the speed of radio waves, which are much lower in frequency than visible light, proves to be the same as that of light, we know that the photon could at most have a tiny rest mass indeed: about 10^{-20} as large as that of the electron.

But a material particle does *not* travel at the speed of light. Knowing the frequency of the electron wave thus did not automatically tell you its wavelength. And to test his surmise that Bohr orbits were standing waves, de Broglie must know the wavelength of the wave associated with the electron. A new rule had to be obtained; $E = h\nu$ may be enough for the photon, but a separate rule giving the wavelength was essential if the electron were to be described as a wave.

Here his familiarity with relativity proved de Broglie's foremost asset. He noticed that the *inverse of the wavelength* bears the same relation to the *frequency* of a wave that the momentum bears to the energy in the relativistic description of a particle. Both obey "triangle relationships" of space and time, as illustrated in Figure 1 of this chapter. Here was the key to the problem: if the frequency of a wave is related to the energy of a particle, as in Einstein's description of the photon, perhaps the inverse of the wavelength is related to the momentum. Of course, this could only be a surmise; the argument was an analogy rather than a rigorous derivation.

Accordingly, de Broglie set forth, in his celebrated 1924 doctoral thesis, the following formula:

$$p = \frac{h}{\lambda} \tag{1}$$

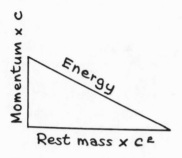

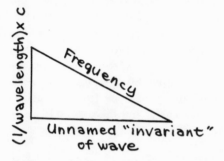

Figure 1   Relativistic analogy that suggested de Broglie's hypothesis.

relating the mometum p of an electron to the wavelength λ of a wave associated in some mysterious way with the electron.

Now de Broglie could test his surmise about Bohr's orbits. If they were really standing electron waves, the Bohr orbits must be the ones in which a whole number of wavelengths fit, as shown in Figure 2. In this way, the electron wave could travel around the orbit reinforcing itself constructively at each turn, just as the wave on a music string is constructively reinforced by its successive reflections. The waves must fit evenly into the circumference of the orbits. Stated mathematically:

$$\frac{\text{Circumference}}{\text{Wavelength}} = \frac{2\pi r}{\lambda} = n \qquad (2)$$

where n is a whole number. If de Broglie's surmise were to work, this formula must be shown to be equivalent to the Bohr orbit rule, when wavelength is replaced by momentum in accord with Equation (1). Since Equation (1) tells us that $\lambda = h/p$, we can substitute in Equation (2), giving:

$$\frac{2\pi r p}{h} = n$$

which leads to the formula

$$rp = n\frac{h}{2\pi} = n\hbar$$

Since rp is the definition of angular momentum, this formula is identical with Bohr's condition for allowed orbits! To summarize the conclusion: If an electron is described as a wave, with its wavelength determined by the momentum, then the standing waves produced by an electron circling a nucleus have the same momentum values as those for Bohr's orbits. As a final topper, de Broglie was able to show that the elliptical orbits later added to Bohr's theory were also standing waves.

De Broglie's thesis was an awfully hot potato for the Faculty of Sciences of the University of Paris. A thesis, while expected to be original, isn't often *that* original. A solid contribution to an established topic is more common, even for the most brilliant student. And here was a convert from the humanities, writing on a theory not yet well known in France, promulgating an outrageous idea. De Broglie couldn't explain how the electron, which so far had behaved like a particle, could at the same time be a wave. In his own words, de Broglie characterized his theory as "a formal scheme whose physical content is not yet determined." And aside from the curious coincidence of explaining the Bohr formula, itself still a suspect achievement, no experimental confirmation was offered.

But there were de Broglie's family connections to consider. His pro-

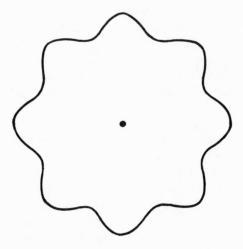

Figure 2 De Broglie's picture of a Bohr orbit.

fessors could hardly dare to insult a man who was at one and the same time a prince and the brother of an eminent colleague. Yet imagine the laughter if they were to allow their deference to family to lead them to award the doctorate for a crackpot thesis! The problem was resolved by de Broglie's leading sponsor, the eminent theorist Paul Langevin. He brought the young prince's work before the eyes of Einstein. The response was encouraging: "It may look crazy, but it really is sound!" Now matters were working to de Broglie's advantage. In Germany, home of the quantum theory, none other than the great Einstein was promoting his ideas. The story has an appropriately fairy-tale ending: the bold prince became the first (and remains the only) physicist ever to receive a Nobel Prize for his doctoral thesis.

Help from America

If the direct experimental proof that would have made his Parisian teachers breathe easier was lacking, it was not long in coming. Indeed, it had been there all along, though its significance had been overlooked. The scattering of electrons by matter had been studied for some time, and there were many features suggestive of a wave rather than a particle.

The best data had been taken by an American, Clinton Davisson. Like most United States physicists of his day, Davisson was a practical-minded man. His studies of the reflection of electrons off metals, conducted at the Bell Telephone Laboratory, were motivated by a desire to better understand the operation of vacuum tubes. When he found that electrons were reflected well at some angles and poorly at others, he regarded the result as a curiosity. He had barely heard of the quantum theory and did not have the benefit of an Einstein close at hand, filling his ear with wondrous tales of de Broglie's wild idea. When he learned that two German physicists, James Franck and Walter Elsasser, were touting his results as a proof of the wave nature of the electron, he was decidedly skeptical.

The Franck-Elsasser interpretation of Davisson's result is illustrated in Figure 3. If the electron were a wave, only at certain angles would the portions of the wave scattered from different atoms interfere constructively. The most suggestive feature of the data was that the angles for strong reflection depended on the velocity of the electrons. This was easy to account for if de Broglie were right; it merely resulted from the changing wavelength of the electron. Calculating the wavelengths of the electrons from the angles reported by Davisson, they found agreement with de Broglie's formula.

Once again, the value of publishing raw experimental data had been

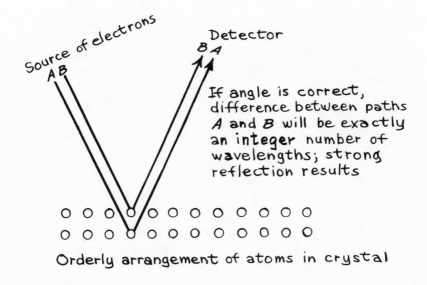

Figure 3 *Wave effects in the scattering of electrons off metals.*

demonstrated. Davisson, by reasons of education, motivation, and geographical isolation, could hardly have been expected to understand the full significance of his results. The availability of the raw data to the more cosmopolitan German physicists carried the day for de Broglie's crazy idea.

For two years Davisson continued his work, more bewildered than pleased by the furor it was creating in Europe. Finally, a trip to a scientific meeting in England helped Davisson to see the light. An able worker, he returned to the United States to attack the problem with enthusiasm. His final data were so thorough and precise as to leave no doubt. Davisson followed de Broglie into the august ranks of Nobel laureates.

A Wave Equation

At this point, the reader is probably terribly perplexed by the question of what all this wave business has to do with reality. How can a particle be a wave? What does the peculiar pattern in Figure 2 have to do with an electron traveling in an orbit? This consternation is historically appropriate: de Broglie and his contemporaries were every bit as puzzled by this problem. But one thing was clear to them: no great light could be shed on the subject until they obtained a better picture of what the wave looked like and how it behaved. Perhaps then the connection between the wave and the particle would become clearer. The problem of the connection between the wave and the particle was the crucial issue in the development of the quantum theory and will be the underlying theme of the remainder of this book.

One thing was obvious to all concerned: the simple picture in Figure 2 was a bit *too* simple. True, some of the outer orbits, many wavelengths long, might look very much like that. The wave would be confined to a narrow ring. But the inner orbits must be very different. Because of the proximity of the nucleus, the force on the electron would vary rapidly with distance, and so would its speed. The corresponding wave would have a wavelength that varied from place to place; distorted in this way, its standing wave pattern would look very different from that shown in Figure 2. A more fully developed theory was called for, one that would take into account the effect of a force on an object that was part particle and part wave.

The answer came in a matter of months from Erwin Schrödinger, a professor at Zurich. A true product of his time, Schrödinger had supplemented his Viennese education with short tours at Jena, Breslau, and Stuttgart. His thorough knowledge of mathematics convinced him that what was needed was a single, definitive equation whose solutions would describe the de Broglie wave in all circumstances. He quickly found it. It is reproduced below simply for the historical record; its mysterious symbols will make little sense to anyone with less than two years' training in the calculus. It is known technically as a *partial differential equation* and packs a remarkable amount of thought into a few symbols. The reader is advised to give it short attention and pass on to its "English translation," which follows.

$$\left[-\frac{h^2}{2m} \nabla^2 + V \right] \psi = i\hbar \frac{\partial \psi}{\partial t}$$

The symbol ψ is a mathematical function giving the strength of the de Broglie wave at various positions in space. In order to satisfy the Schrödinger equation, the wave must have the following properties:

1 The wave must satisfy the de Broglie rule $p = h/\lambda$.
2 Any force present is taken into account by means of the potential energy V it produces.
3 The wave obeys conservation of energy, in its classical (nonrelativistic) form.

The mathematical prescription for finding the wave is thus very straightforward. At any given position in space, one subtracts from the total energy the potential energy at this spot, obtaining the kinetic energy. From the kinetic energy one can calculate the velocity and therefore the momentum, leading finally to the wavelength. Knowing the wavelength everywhere, one knows exactly what the wave looks like.

An example of this is provided for a very simple case in Figure 4.

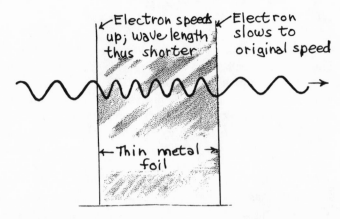

Figure 4 Wave picture of an electron passing through thin metal foil.

This is the case of an electron passing through a thin sheet of metal. Here the force is quite simple. When the electron reaches the surface of the metal, it is attracted to the atoms on the surface. Hence, it speeds up. Its kinetic energy is increased and thus its momentum as well. Therefore, its wavelength becomes shorter. Once inside the metal, the electron experiences no further force; it is equally attracted in all directions, since it is surrounded by atoms. At its exit, it once again is attracted by surface atoms; the effect is to slow it down to its original speed. Viewed in terms of the conservation of energy, potential energy is converted to kinetic energy as the electron enters the metal sheet, and kinetic back to potential as it leaves.

The hydrogen atom was a far tougher nut to crack. Here the force is present everywhere and varies with distance from the nucleus. Fortunately, the problem had already been solved, at least in part, by nineteenth-century mathematicians as a purely abstract mathematical exercise. Drawing upon these solutions, which bore such esoteric names as *confluent hypergeometric functions* and *spherical harmonics* (the latter term has always struck the author as a bit poetic), Schrödinger was able to give an exact picture of the standing electron waves that replace Bohr's orbits. Several of these, corresponding to some of the smaller Bohr orbits, are depicted in Figure 5. Where the pattern is brighest, the wave has greatest amplitude. Aside from being about the same size and corresponding to the same energy, they little resemble Bohr's circles.

Here at last was a complete theory, free from the ad hoc postulates of Bohr. The Schrödinger equation was the first quantum law that could pretend to the sort of generality possessed by Newton's laws. Any force, any situation whatsoever was covered by it, without any need for additional assumptions or arbitrary rules. Atoms turn out to have definite electron energies as a result of a phenomenon similar to that which makes musical instruments sound definite tones. It also eliminated the "dual role" of Planck's constant in the Bohr theory, for the orbit rule became itself a wave phenomenon, and thus both $E = h\nu$ and the orbit rule used Planck's constant to connect a wave phenomenon and a mechanical one.

The Schrödinger picture of the hydrogen atom did more than remove the arbitrariness of the Bohr orbits. It also eliminated from the quantum theory the even more vexing quantum "jump" from one orbit to another. The transition from one state (the word "orbit" hardly seems appropriate) to another, as described by Schrödinger, was a quite orderly process. Viewed in terms of the patterns shown in Figure 5, it represents a kind of motion picture "dissolve" from one pattern to another. One wave pattern gradually fades out, while the new state fades in. During this time, light is being continuously emitted. The word "gradually" must, however, be interpreted in the context of the strange time scale of the atomic physicist: the whole process takes, typically, somewhere around 10^{-8} sec. Hence it remains appropriate to consider the emitted light a quantum.

The development of the Schrödinger–de Broglie wave theory did throw some light on the significance of Planck's celebrated constant h. Clearly, on the submicroscopic level of the atom, the concepts of "wave" and "particle," carried over from the macroscopic world of our daily experience, begin to break down. At the same time, it becomes as meaningful to speak of *wavelength* and *frequency* as somehow related to *momentum* and *energy*. The constant h merely takes care of the quantitative aspects of going over from the wave language to the particle language. In this sense, it occupies a role similar to that of the velocity of light in the formula $E = mc^2$: it is no more than a conversion factor.

Where Is the Electron?

To Einstein and Planck, disturbed as they were by the peculiarities in the theory they had jointly fathered, Schrödinger appeared as a saviour. At last the accursed "quantum jump" had been replaced by a beautiful shifting wave pattern. But at Copenhagen and Göttingen, things were seen in a very different light. Here the young physicists learned to live with, and even glory in, the discontinuities of the new physics. They were quick to point out that Schrödinger's theory left open the question of the connection between his waves and the obvious particle characteristics of an electron. Was one to believe that an electron actually smeared out into the sort of patterns shown in Figure 5? There was a wealth of evidence that the electron was a perfectly good particle, probably about the same size as an atomic nucleus. They were confident that the connection between

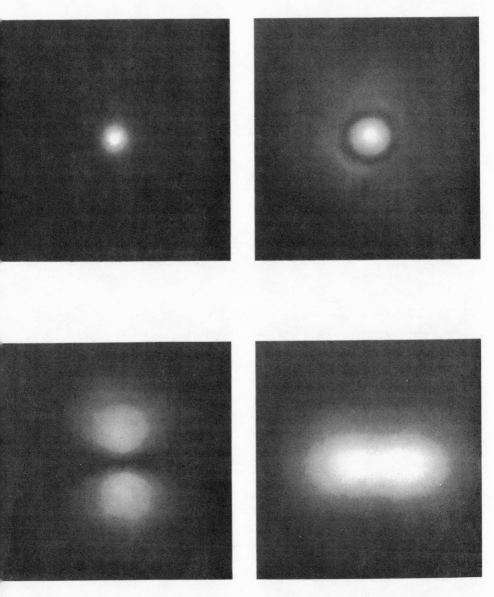

Figure 5 Examples of Schrödinger wave solutions for the electron in the hydrogen atom. The upper left picture corresponds to Bohr's original ground state; the others correspond to higher orbits.

(Reproduced by permission from Orear, Fundamental Physics, 2d ed., John Wiley & Sons, Inc., 1967.)

217

Wave "packet" representing free electron

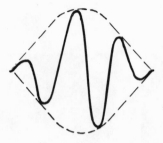

Same packet a very short time later

Figure 6

Schrödinger's wave and the particle must in itself have some of the discontinuous features of the earlier quantum theory.

From their point of view, the real tip-off lay in Schrödinger's description of the very simplest situation in mechanics, the behavior of a free particle, one moving at constant velocity free from the influence of any force. In this situation, Schrödinger's equation gave a most embarrassing result: a free particle is described as a wave packet, as in Figure 6, a bundle of waves confined to a small region in space. But a wave is not a particle, and this packet refused to stay small. Like the wake of a boat, which spreads out from being a single sharp bow wave to a whole train of waves, the wave packet would spread out and spread fast. If initially confined to a space the size of an atomic nucleus, it would spread in less than a millionth of a second to fill a space the size of the Pentagon!

While Schrödinger's imagination might accept an electron the size of a Bohr orbit, he could hardly reconcile himself to an electron as big as the Pentagon. The problem clearly had to be resolved. And its resolution touched off the greatest controversy in physics since Galileo liberated the science from theological disputes.

17

Does God Play Dice?

At the final stage you tell me that this multi-colored universe can be reduced to the atom and that the atom itself can be reduced to the electron. All this is good and I wait for you to continue. But you tell me of an invisible planetary system where electrons gravitate around a nucleus. You explain this to me with an image. I realize then that you have been reduced to poetry: I shall never know. Have I the time to become indignant? You have changed theories. So that science that was to teach me everything ends up in a hypothesis, that lucidity founders in metaphor, that uncertainty is resolved in a work of art.

—ALBERT CAMUS, THE MYTH OF SISYPHUS

If the Bohr theory was the final break with classical physics, the interpretation of Schrödinger's wave was the break with the whole picture of what a physical law should be like. As with relativity, the "new" quantum

Schrödinger.

(*Photo by Ullstein, courtesy American Institute of Physics.*)

220

theory based on waves is not so much obscure as strange; the statements seem simple enough, but their implications are unacceptable to our common sense. And this time what must be swallowed is even worse than a readjustment of such basic concepts as space and time. What the quantum theory seems to challenge is nothing less than the whole concept of continuity in nature. Words like "cause" and "effect" appear to lose their meaning. One speaks of motion, but no longer dares to imagine a continuous path. The very functioning of reality on its ultimate level seems reduced to a cosmic dice game, everything subject to the whims of chance.

The formulation of this viewpoint took little more than a year after the publication of Schrödinger's theory and consisted of three main steps. First, Max Born gave a statistical meaning to Schrödinger's wave, connecting it to reality by pure chance. Then Werner Heisenberg showed that Born's interpretation could be regarded as the consequence of an irreducible interference of the observer with the system being observed. Finally, Niels Bohr interpreted this unprecedented situation as the denial that the quantum description of the microworld corresponded to "reality" in the traditional sense of the word. This chapter will outline and explain the first two developments.

Max Born's Dice Game

The problem facing the quantum theorists in 1926 was without parallel in the history of physics. For over a century, physicists had speculated with increasing confidence about the connection between unseen atoms and the readings on their laboratory instruments. Building invisible models became a fine art, and they could with ease form mental images of what the atoms were doing, use reasoning based on these images to arrive at a formula for the things they could measure, and compare the predictions with the results. The example of Rutherford's experiment is an ideal one. The abstract mental picture of a nuclear atom led to a formula for the angular variation of alpha particle scattering, and the formula fit the measurements. One had no need to actually see the nucleus; the inference was certain enough.

But now the physicists had in Schrödinger's equation a formula that worked beautifully, yet one which gave no hint as to how to visualize the reality that lay behind it. It would have been so simple if one could merely, as Schrödinger did at first, accept that the electron was a wave. Still, many experiments had shown the electron to be a particle: its mass and charge were confined to a small region, smaller than an atomic nucleus. One could even follow the path of a single electron in a photograph of a Wilson cloud chamber, and it certainly did not seem to expand like Schrödinger's wave packet. Yet the quantitative details of the behavior of electrons, both inside and outside atoms, were obtained by treating them as waves. And the connection between the wave and the particle, now that Schrödinger had painted the wave picture in full detail, was if anything less clear than it had been when de Broglie first proposed the duality. How could such an unruly wave, one that refused to remain confined to a small region, have anything to do with a particle? What mental picture was the physicist to keep in mind when visualizing subatomic phenomena?

In a sense, the scientific part of the job had already been done: The things one could measure, spectral lines and such, were predicted to the satisfaction of all concerned. Many physicists were reluctant to press farther, for since the turn of the century a naïve empiricism had been the dominant philosophical view among natural scientists. The creed was, "Stick to your equations and instruments." The task of science was solely to find connections between measurements. To inquire into the reality that lay behind these connections, to ponder such hazy concepts as cause and effect, was regarded as both futile and unscientific, possibly no more than an exercise in language. Metaphysics was unfashionable, and the question of what an atom was really like seemed patently metaphysical.

Nonetheless, Schrödinger's wave seemed a permanent and ineradicable feature of the theory, and few physicists would be comfortable until they

Figure 1   Result of repeated measurements of the position of an electron in the first Bohr orbit.

had some way to reconcile it with their intuition. What were the observable consequences, if any, of the fact that the wave was strong in one place and weak in another? There had to be some sort of answer.

Once again the answer came from Göttingen, from Max Born, director of the theoretical institute. In retrospect, Born described his motivations: "My Institute and that of James Franck were housed in the same building. . . . Every experiment by Franck and his assistants on electron collisions . . . appeared to me as a new proof of the corpuscular nature of the electron." Thus, he felt Schrödinger's electron "cloud" had to go. In the spring of 1926, a few short months after Schrödinger's celebrated papers, he proposed that Schrödinger's wave must be a *probability* wave; to be exact, *the square of the wave amplitude at any point in space gives the probability of finding the electron at that point.*

Under this interpretation, Schrödinger's cloud-like patterns take on a peculiar significance. They don't tell the physicist where the electron *is* at any given moment, but merely where it is *likely to be.* An individual measurement of the position of the electron in, for example, the first Bohr state, can be as precise as the method used to measure it will allow. If one repeats the measurement many hundreds of times and plots the results in the form of dots on a picture, as in Figure 1, the resulting pattern of dots will come to resemble the wave patterns shown in the preceding chapter. But no *individual* measurement can be predicted with any greater precision than to say it will fall somewhere in the cloud. Schrödinger's cloud becomes, in a sense, a cloud *in the human mind;* it reflects our lack of precise knowledge of where to find the electron. One way to say this is to describe it as an "information wave"; the exact significance of this remark will become apparent after we discuss Heisenberg's uncertainty relations, the next step in the interpretation of quantum mechanics.

Here was the quantum theorists' most daring innovation: determinism itself had been abandoned. No longer could a physicist measure the position of an electron and use these measurements to predict with precision its future position. The wave itself remains perfectly continuous and determinate, but this is of no consequence, for the wave has only a random connection with observable reality: one can predict the average of a large number of repeated measurements, but the result of an individual measurement must forever remain a surprise.

Probabilistic laws were no novelty in ₚphysics—they had been present ever since physicists began to speculate about the motion of atoms. In the kinetic theory of gases, one always spoke of average speeds of atoms, average distances between collisions, without trying to trace the motions of the individual atoms in detail. This probabilistic character merely reflected practical ignorance; it was an acknowledgment of the impossibility of coping precisely with the motion of 10^{23} incredibly tiny atoms as individual objects. No one doubted that the details or the motion were subject to Newton's laws, and if one were given the staggering amount of information required, one could exactly describe the future motion of every atom. What Born seemed to be saying was that there was no way whatsoever to predict the precise future position of even one isolated atom.

Uncertainty

One of Born's younger Göttingen colleagues, groping for a deeper understanding of his mentor's work, was struck by the probability-ignorance connection. Werner Heisenberg realized that the new quantum theory still retained much of the structure of Newton's mechanics. Through the wave-particle duality, it still permitted a description of motion in terms of ordinary concepts like position and momentum. In fact, Heisenberg himself had arrived at his own form of the quantum theory, one that gave many of the predictions of Schrödinger's, without ever mentioning waves. It was hard to see why, after one once knew precisely the position and velocity of a particle, its future could not be determined exactly. Did Born's interpretation imply that something would disturb it, deflect it somehow from the path assigned it by Newton's laws? Thinking in this vein, he had the key insight into the origins of the indeterminacy at the atomic level. He saw that this indeterminacy was indeed the result of ignorance, not merely a practical ignorance, but one of an inherent and unavoidable kind. Its source was *the disturbance of an object by the act of observing it.*

Classical physics had always removed the observer from the phenomenon observed. The flight of a ball is in no way altered by the presence or absence of a witness. It had been recognized that no measurement could be made without in some way disturbing things; even the light falling on the ball alters its path imperceptibly. But it was always assumed that careful experimental procedures could reduce the disturbance to a minimum, or at least enable one to correct for the disturbance. For example, a cold thermometer bulb will cause a small drop in the temperature of a beaker of hot water; but if one knows the original temperature and weight of the bulb, one can calculate the size of the effect and thus obtain the true temperature of the water before the insertion of the thermometer.

But quantum mechanics had changed all that, at least on the atomic scale. No longer could one arbitrarily reduce the disturbance caused by a measurement. At least one quantum of energy must be used to make an observation; and Heisenberg saw that furthermore the effect of this quantum was to disturb the object observed in a quite random and uncontrollable way, so that one could not correct for the disturbance! In purely mathematical terms, the statement reduced to the result that one could not simultaneously measure the position and momentum of an object to any desired accuracy. No matter how good the instruments used or how careful the procedures, there had to be an irreducible error in at least one of the measurements. The quantitative statement of this rule is known as the *uncertainty principle;* it takes the form:

$$\Delta p \, \Delta x \geqslant \hbar \tag{1}$$

Δp and Δx are the errors in measurement of position and momentum, respectively. What the law says is that one has to make a choice: if one measures position accurately, that is to say, if Δx is small, then Δp must be large to make the product of the two larger than $\hbar$. The symbol $\geqslant$ ("greater than or equal to") implies that $\hbar$ is the *best* one can do. In a perfect instrument the product of the errors will be equal to $\hbar$. Any defect in the measuring procedure will make things worse, and the product of the errors will be even greater.

Any error in measurement of momentum, since mass is usually well determined, will lead to an error in velocity. And it is precisely the simultaneous knowledge of position and velocity that is essential to knowing where an object will be in the future. If we know how fast an object is going, but have a poor idea of where it now is, we are just as badly off or worse off when it comes to predicting where it will be at some future time.

Heisenberg derived his law on quite general and abstract grounds. Its true significance becomes apparent only when one shows how it enters into any specific measuring process. This is another *"gedanken* experiment" game, like those we played in the development of relativity. The law works differently in every imaginable measuring process, but it is always there.

As just one example, consider using a microscope to measure the position of a stationary electron. The situation is illustrated in Figure 2. To reduce the disturbance of the electron to a minimum, we use only one photon of light. The error in position comes about because of the wavelength of the light. The image formed by the microscope will give the electron a "size" of about one wavelength. What does "image" mean when we are dealing with a single photon? It means that there is a certain region in which the photon might strike the photographic plate. The actual spot on the film will be as small as the film quality permits; but if the measurement is repeated, the spot will not necessarily be in the same place. No matter how careful we are to place the electron in the same place, we cannot reduce the size of the spot when we make many repeated measurements. The situation is similar to the picture of a Bohr orbit in Figure 1. This illustrates what (at least in this case) Heisenberg means by an *error*. It is not a question of the precision of the measuring instrument; a needle on a dial can be, at least in principle, as accurate as the instrument maker's skill permits. Or, as in this case, the size of a spot on the film depends on the film quality. The real problem is that of repeatability—a repetition of the experiment under conditions the experimenter has done everything possible to make identical will give a spot in a different place on the film.

Now comes the question of the momentum uncertainty, which in this case arises in a quite different way. When the photon rebounds off the electron, the electron must recoil. We have no way of knowing the *exact* direction of the photon when it entered the microscope lens, which must be, for reasons which will be explained below, quite wide. In this case, we can compute the *speed* of the electron after its collision with the photon to considerable accuracy; but if we don't know the *direction* it is heading, we have no idea where it will go.

In this and most other examples, the choice between accuracy in mo-

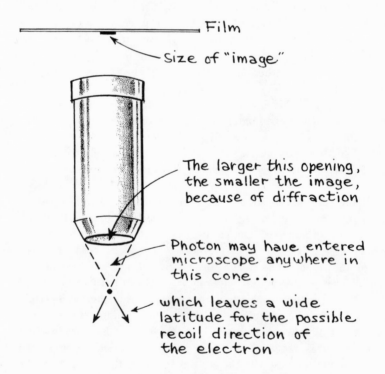

Figure 2   Uncertainty in observation of an electron by means of a microscope.

mentum and position reduces to a choice of wavelength. A long-wavelength photon has a low momentum, and thus the momentum uncertainty is reduced; but the position is less accurately known. A short-wave photon permits a more accurate position measurement, but gives the electron a bigger kick.

At this point it is to be hoped that your mind is searching for a way out of this mess; why not narrow down the lens of the microscope, so we know better where the photon went and therefore the direction of the electron recoil? This suggestion, however, ignores the wave character of light, which the existence of photons in no way negates. A wave passing through a narrow hole is spread out by diffraction; the smaller the hole, the larger the effect. In terms of the photon, just as the de Broglie wave represents the probability of finding an electron, the intensity of the light wave gives the probability of finding a photon. Narrowing the lens will widen the region of the photographic plate in which the photon may hit. The uncertainty principle is inexorable; any move we make that lets us determine the momentum more accurately must turn out to sacrifice accuracy in position. If the measuring instrument is perfect, the gain in accuracy of one variable is exactly offset by a loss in precision in the other.

The "Old Men" Won't Buy It

The shock and outrage of Einstein, Planck, de Broglie, and Schrödinger at these arguments were predictable. They had seen order and continuity restored to the microworld, only to see it snatched away a few short months later by Born and Heisenberg. Einstein in particular simply refused at first to accept the validity of the uncertainty principle, a position summarized in his celebrated remark that "God does not play dice!" His first reaction was to search for counterexamples, gedanken measuring procedures that would be exempt from the principle. But these proved as futile as the similar attempts made earlier against his own relativity theory. The others gradually and reluctantly came to accept the new view. A celebrated visit by Schrödinger to Bohr's institute in the fall of 1926 proved the turning point. After days of debate lasting well into the night, he finally conceded defeat with the outburst: "If one has to stick to this damned quantum jumping, then I regret ever having gotten involved in this thing!" He had started out to eliminate discontinuity from the quantum theory and had seen it instead enthroned in the very heart of the theory, in a way that drastically altered the physicist's traditional "gut feeling" for reality.

Why the Wave Expands

Armed with the uncertainty principle, we can now interpret Schrödinger's expanding wave packet and obtain some insight as to the significance of the wave itself. The size of the wave packet, at the outset, represents the uncertainty in our knowledge of the position of the electron, the Δx. The spread of the wave packet with time arises from the momentum uncertainty; since we don't know exactly how fast the electron is going, the longer we wait, the less certain we are as to where it is. This reveals the "information wave" character of the Schrödinger wave. It represents not the electron itself, but *what we know about the electron at any given time*. A large spread means simply that we can't predict the electron's position with precision. The Schrödinger wave is determined not solely

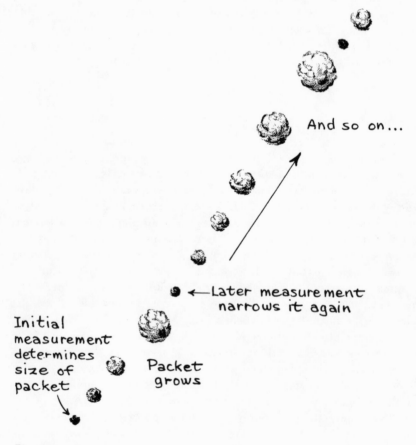

And so on...

←—Later measurement
narrows it again

Initial
measurement
determines
size of
packet

Packet
grows

Figure 3

DOES GOD PLAY DICE? *229*

by the nature of the electron and the forces on it; it also reflects the history of measurements performed on it.

If we make a number of successive observations of the electron, following it along its path, the behavior of the wave (Figure 3) is most peculiar. At each successive observation, the wave contracts. This reflects the fact that just before the observation we weren't quite sure where we'd find the electron. It could have been anywhere in the large area covered by the Schrödinger wave. Once the electron is observed, we can narrow it down to a smaller region, of a size determined by the precision of our measuring process; but the value of this information for future prediction is hampered by the uncertainty in momentum. Our ability to predict gradually deteriorates, until another measurement ties down the electron again.

The purely wave aspects of the spread of the wave packet can also be explained in terms of the uncertainty principle. The uncertainty in momentum corresponds, in the wave picture, to a spread in wavelengths; the wave packet is a *superposition* of waves of varying wavelength. Since, in the case of the Schrödinger wave, waves of different length travel at different speeds, the packet will naturally spread out.

The Problem of Prediction

Since the value of $\hbar$ is very small, the significance of the uncertainty principle depends crucially on the size of the objects involved. This is because it relates uncertainty in position to uncertainty in *momentum,* not velocity. It is the *velocity,* and not the momentum per se, that must be known in order to predict the future position. The more massive the object, the less important the uncertainty in momentum becomes, because it corresponds to a small uncertainty in velocity. This can be expressed mathematically in the form

$$\Delta p = m \, \Delta v \tag{2}$$

Substituting in Equation (1) and dividing by m to obtain an uncertainty relation between Δx and Δv,

$$\Delta x \, \Delta v \geqslant \frac{\hbar}{m} \quad \text{or} \quad \Delta v = \frac{\hbar}{m \, \Delta x} \tag{3}$$

The larger the mass, the smaller the uncertainty. For objects visible to the naked eye, the mass is large, and also it takes a large position uncertainty to be noticeable. Thus, both m and Δx in Equation (3) are much larger than they are for, say, an electron. The uncertainty in velocity becomes completely negligible, and we can use classical physics with full confidence.

This is illustrated quantitatively in Table 1. This table answers the question, "How far in the future can I predict the position of an object to a certain desired level of accuracy?" The answer is obtained in the following fashion. In the first column we choose a level of accuracy we consider appropriate to a given scale of phenomena. In the second, we

TABLE 1

Scale, Δx, cm	Object, mass, g	Δv, cm/sec	Prediction time limit, sec	Remarks
Subatomic 10^{-9}	Electron 10^{-27}	10^{10}	10^{-19}	No continuity. Classical physics essentially of no use.
Atomic 10^{-8}	Atom 10^{-22}	10^4	10^{-12}	Can't describe whole history, but time long enough to describe collision with another atom very roughly.
Biochemical 10^{-6}	Small protein molecule 10^{-18}	0.01	10^{-4}	Long enough for nerve cell to fire. Thus, short-term, functions can be described classically, though uncertainty very significant.
Microscopic 10^{-4}	"Speck" 10^{-12}	10^{-10}	10^6 (about 2 weeks)	A dust mote barely visible in microscope; yet for almost all purposes completely classical.
Macroscopic 10^{-3}	Pea 0.1	10^{-23}	10^{20} (3×10^{12} years)	Age ot universe about 10^{10} years! Can ignore uncertainty completely.

choose the mass of an object that is to that scale. The third column gives the uncertainty in velocity of the object, as calculated from Equation (3), given the mass and Δx from the first two columns. Finally, column 4 tells us how long it will be before the uncertainty in velocity will contribute as much to our lack of knowledge of where the object is as came from the original position error Δx.* After this time, the uncertainty due to our lack of knowledge of velocity will dominate and just get worse with time.

*Mathematically, $t = \Delta x / \Delta v$.

The lesson of the table is clear. Even if we take a fuzzy picture of the atom, that is, only measure position to within about one-tenth the diameter of the first Bohr orbit, we cannot predict with much confidence beyond about 10^{-19} sec—a small fraction of the time it takes an electron to get around its orbit in the older Bohr atomic pictures! Yet on the scale of a small pea, we could wait 300 times the age of the universe before we would encounter a deviation of more than 0.001 cm (finer than a human hair) from Newton's laws.

Thus, the transition from the world of our everyday experience, where Newton's laws are for all practical purposes perfect, to the subatomic level, which is flagrantly "quantum," is a continuous one, governed by the size of h and the masses of the objects involved.

To summarize: the Schrödinger wave gives a perfectly continuous picture of the electron, or for that matter any other object. But the wave is spread out in space, reflecting the impossibility of precise knowledge of the electron's past and therefore of its future. And its relation to the future is determined by a toss of the dice. The situation is suggested in Figure 3. And the whole mess can be thought of as the result of the irreducible interference of the observer with what he is observing.

The Orbit Disappears

One of the more disturbing consequences of the scheme is that it becomes quite difficult to think of the states of electrons in atoms as "orbits" any more, for we cannot observe them moving in their orbits. To do so would imply that we saw the electron at one position, then later at another, and so on, mapping out a path.

But each of these observations again involves the exchange of at least one quantum with the electron. An electron in a hydrogen atom is not free to interact with any old quantum, for it is not free to assume any energy it pleases. The very *least* reaction it can have is to be knocked into some higher energy state. Thus, the orbit can only be observed once; the electron will be knocked clean out of it before we can see it again. We must be reconciled to the fact that, if the electron follows an orderly path in the atom, it will never be within our power to map it out. Under the circumstances, one has little choice but to admit that the word "orbit" is probably not a sensible one for describing an atomic state. Unfortunately, the theory offers no better one. We have learned to understand the structure of the atom only at the cost of giving up the sort of simple descriptive model that physicists are used to.

Even worse, though the electron has no path, it stubbornly retains all the other attributes of motion, momentum, velocity, and so on. In classical terms, to speak of motion without a path seems absurd.   Yet this is what the quantum theory forces on us.

Thus, the quantum revolution is complete.   It began with arbitrary rules that failed to describe all the details of subatomic motion.   It ends with a complete theoretical framework that denies the possibility that man can ever have knowledge of these details!   As we shall see in the next chapter, it led the "Copenhagen school," Niels Bohr and his followers, to deny the very reality of the subatomic motions they originally set out to understand.

18

Whatever Became
of Reality?

The law of chaos is the law of ideas,
of improvisations and seasons of belief.

—WALLACE STEVENS, EXTRACTS FROM ADDRESSES
TO THE ACADEMY OF FINE IDEAS

This chapter will illustrate by example the source of the perplexity that
has plagued physicists since the 1920s. On the surface, the uncertainty
relations might be dismissed as a mere nuisance, the price man has to
pay for being a very large bull in the tiny china shop of the atomic
world. They certainly hamper his attempts to look at the submicroscopic
world, but why should one imagine that they affect in any way the *reality*
of that world? Even if one cannot observe an electron moving from place
to place in an orderly orbit, is there any reason to deny the very existence
of the orbit itself? In short, perhaps the uncertainty relations do no more
than limit what can be *known* in a particular experiment.

But the example discussed in this chapter will show that it is not so easy to separate the questions of knowledge and existence. They have a maddeningly intimate connection. Without this connection, Einstein, with his deeply materialistic beliefs, would hardly have felt compelled to challenge the validity of the uncertainty relations themselves and would have dismissed them as a limit on the precision of atomic experiments, real enough, yet devoid of deeper implications.

Young's Experiment with Electrons

The example chosen is that of Young's experiment, which we shall use as a *gedanken* experiment. It is hardly surprising that this particular experiment should be an apt one for our purposes. After all, it administered the *coup de grâce* to Newton's particle theory of light, and it seems only natural that a theory based on a wave-particle dualism would find it a tough nut to crack.

Young's experiment was introduced in Chapter 8 as a purely wave phenomenon. To emphasize the particle aspects, let us imagine it to be performed with electrons and a phosphorescent screen (such as that on a TV picture tube). Electrons are more tractable in another respect; they carry electric charge, and the forces exerted by this charge make it easy to observe them "in flight." This is not true of photons, which can be created or absorbed, but not observed in flight.

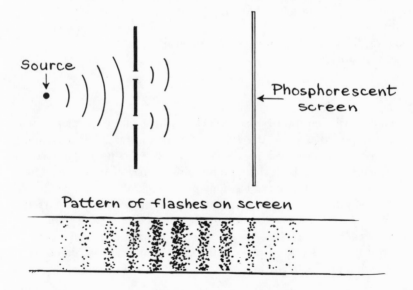

Figure 1 Young's experiment with electrons.

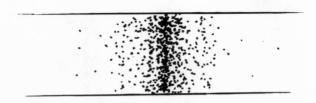

Figure 2   Pattern of flashes from a single slit.

If we view the electron as a wave, the experiment is little changed from Young's original version. On the screen behind the slits, there are places where the distance to the slits is such that waves arrive crest-to-crest; here they are strong, and a bright band is obtained. At others, the waves meet trough-to-crest and cancel; this produces dark bands. The resulting pattern of light and dark bands is shown in Figure 1. The only change introduced by quantum mechanics is that instead of a continuous glow, we will have a series of flashes at individual points on the screen. If there are enough of these in a short time, so that the eye doesn't see the individual flashes, or if we wait long enough for a large number of them to pile up on a photographic plate, we will still obtain the pattern shown.

But from the particle point of view, the result is most perplexing. Surely each electron that produces its flash on the screen must pass through one or another of the holes. It is hard to imagine that the presence or absence of the other hole, the one it *didn't* go through, can affect the motion of the electron. If we were to close one hole, we would get a pattern without light and dark bands. Even conceding enough to the wave picture to admit that a particle is a wave packet, and diffraction will cause the packet to fan out a bit after passing through a small hole, we still expect that a single slit will give the pattern shown in Figure 2, and this proves to be the case. If we were to perform the experiment with each slit closed half the time, we would get a double exposure of Figure 2, as shown in Figure 3. Why don't we get this same pattern when *both* slits are open?

But a host of interference experiments with electrons have been successful. How can we account for this? Does each electron, as it passes through its hole, somehow "know" whether the other hole is open or closed, and accordingly "decide" whether to follow the Figure 1 or the Figure 2 pattern? Indeed, the electron's dilemma is even more complicated: the spacing of dark and light bands in Figure 1 depends on how far apart the holes are, so the electron's behavior may even depend on how far it was from a hole it didn't go through!

The answer, of course, is that it does matter whether both holes are open or not, because *the wave describing each individual particle passes through both.* But at first sight this merely deepens the mystery. What then does this schizophrenic wave have to do with an electron, which mea-

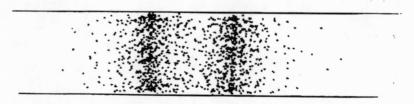

Figure 3   Pattern of flashes from two slits never open at the same
time.

surement shows us to be a very small object?   Could it have somehow
split in two?   It left its source and wound up all in one piece on a screen
where it made one tiny flash as it came to rest.   Surely it must have
come through one hole or the other.   Which one?   We feel the wave
picture must be giving us an incomplete description of what went on.   If
the theory will not answer our question, let us resort to experiment.   Let
us find out which hole each particle goes through, to see whether it indeed
passes through one hole or the other, or whether it somehow splits and
passes through both, like the wave.

The apparatus for this experiment is shown in Figure 4.   It is the
same as before, except we now have some type of particle detector by
each slit to tell us which one the electron went through.   A loop of wire
to sense the electric field of the electron as it passed would do this with
a minimum of disturbance.   Taking a very weak beam of particles, so
that we can observe them one at a time, we find that each time there
is a flash on the screen, one or the other particle detector will register—never

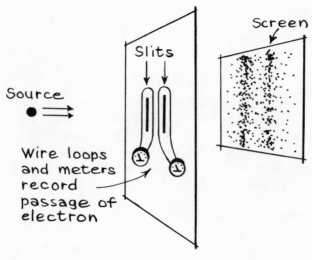

Figure 4

236

both. The particle indeed passes through one hole or the other. But that is not all we discover. *The pattern shown in Figure 1 has vanished!* We instead get the pattern shown in Figure 3.

How can this be? The answer lies in the uncertainty relations. We have added another measurement into the experiment, and the effects of this measurement must be taken into account. To see the passage of an electron, we had to transmit at least one photon to the loop of wire. This changed its momentum, and therefore its wavelength, by an unknown amount, different for every electron. By the time it reaches the screen, the change in wavelength is enough to destroy the synchronization with the wave from the other slit, at which the detector remained silent.

Once again, the uncertainty relations force us to make a choice. We can change to a larger loop of wire, which can detect a "soft" photon, one with low momentum and therefore a long wavelength. This disturbs the electron momentum less, but leaves us more uncertain as to its position. It turns out that if the size of the loop is small enough, and thus the photon is "hard" enough, to tell us the position of the electron to an accuracy much less than the slit separation, so that we can be certain which slit the electron passed through, the pattern is destroyed. If the error in position measurement is larger than the slit separation, the pattern is retained, but then one can't be really certain which slit the electron went through.

This result is not an "either-or" situation; intermediate cases exist. For example, we could use a detector whose accuracy was slightly smaller than the slit separation. This would never tell us for certain which slit the electron went through, but might tell us, for example, that the odds were three to one that it went through one particular slit. A detector like this would only partially destroy the pattern, fuzz it out a bit, producing something intermediate between Figures 1 and 3, as shown in Figure 5.

This example illustrates vividly how the quantum theory faces a choice or at best a poor compromise between irreconcilable opposites. The wave and particle features cannot coexist in their pure form. One must choose between knowing which slit the electron went through (particle picture)

Figure 5 Partial interference pattern seen when an "unreliable" detector is used to tell which slit the electron passed through.

and seeing an interference pattern (wave picture). One can never have both simultaneously. At best one can have an educated guess at where the electron went coexist with a smudged interference pattern. Niels Bohr called this characteristic of the theory *complementarity,* which he felt had deeper philosophical implications. We shall return to them later, after one last attempt to get around the problem.

Can We Outwit the Uncertainty Relations?

The reader has every reason not to give up without at least one more attempt to thwart the uncertainty principle. After all, he is in pretty distinguished company, that of Einstein and others of comparable stature. The experiment shown in Figure 4 isn't necessarily the cleverest one imaginable. In particular, it is beaten from the start because it disturbs the electron in flight. Why not let the electron hit the screen and *then* find out where it came from, by observing its direction? Then the new measurement is carried out *after* the interference pattern has already been formed unalterably. Uncertainty principle or no, surely one can't change things that have already happened!

The apparatus for this ingenious dodge is depicted in Figure 6. Two screens are used, since one by itself won't reveal the direction of the electron

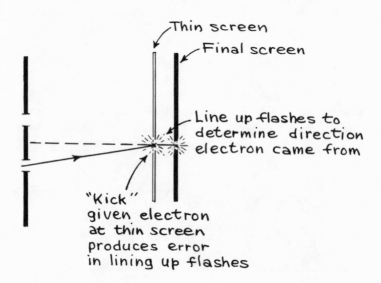

Figure 6   *Apparatus for observing electron direction after pattern is produced.*

that produced the flash. The first is made thin to permit the electron to make a flash, pass through, and make another flash on the second screen. The line joining the flashes surely will point to one screen or the other. We can have our cake and eat it too; so much for complementarity!

But again the uncertainty principle dashes our hopes. The electron can't make a flash without exchanging a quantum of energy with the first screen. This quantum gives the electron a kick, changing its direction. Of course we can use a very *small* quantum, to make the kick very small. But then the position of the electron when it passed through the first screen is poorly known. This means that the flash may come a great distance from where the electron went through. The result is often a flash where they should be a dark band; the interference pattern is unobservable. If we work out the quantitative details, we find the bind is the same one we were in with the arrangement shown in Figure 4. If the kick Δp is small enough to still let us tell for sure which slit the electron passed through, Δx turns out to be larger than the spacing between bands. The result is a pattern like that in Figure 3. Again, a compromise is possible: a Δp that still leaves a partial doubt as to which slit the electron went through will allow us to see an attenuated interference pattern, as in Figure 5. What kind of pattern we see depends on how we choose the properties of our screen.

How frustrating! Quantum mechanics tells us there is a perfectly good interference pattern at the first screen. But if that screen is sharp enough to let us see the pattern of light and dark bands, it can't help but destroy our knowledge of the electron's path. A conspiracy seems to be opposing our efforts.

Games of this sort can (and have) been played ever since 1927. An ingenious experimental setup is proposed that seems to get around the problem of complementarity, to permit a particle to exhibit its full wave and particle characteristics at the same time. So far, all such attempts have failed; it always turns out that the uncertainty relations have been ignored at some step of the argument. It hardly seems likely, after more than 40 years, that this sort of frontal attack will bring down the edifice of the quantum theory.

The Copenhagen Interpretation

If we adopt a purely utilitarian view and make no demands on the quantum theory beyond the successful prediction of experimental results, the discussion could end here. But man undertakes the study of nature not merely to master it, but out of a deep-seated need to clothe his life experience in meaning.   While younger minds were overcoming the formal mathematical problems of quantum mechanics, Niels Bohr struggled to find a deeper message behind the abstract symbols.

From his earliest days, Bohr had been influenced by the writings of Denmark's foremost modern philosopher, Sören Kierkegaard.   A central tenet of the Kierkegaardian view was the belief in an irreconcilable dualism between thought and reality.   Rather than an impartial observer of reality, man was an active participant whose very effort to understand was part of the reality he falsely believed he was objectively contemplating.   Reality understood is reality changed.   The magnificent orderly systems that were the pride of classical physics struck Kierkegaard as narrow, symbolic interpretations of a tiny aspect of the full, rich panoply of reality.

Such dualistic views were popular with the rising empiricist school of philosophers.   The American psychologist-philosopher William James viewed human thought as a conflict between the sensory images that constituted its "reality" and the rational thought processes that strove to organize and connect them.

Bohr found in these dualistic schemes a striking analogy to the wave-particle relation in the quantum theory.   To a puzzled audience at an international conference in the fall of 1928, he announced his principle of complementarity.   Wave and particle were irreconcilable, but both were necessary for the description of the subatomic world.   On this level, complementarity was explored in the preceding section.

But to Bohr the wave-particle duality was merely a reflection, in the language of the old physics, of a deeper conflict between the concepts of *description* and *causality*.   One could describe the world, at any instant, to any desired accuracy, and produce a snapshot, so to speak, showing where everything was.   Yet the uncertainty principle said that this snapshot could only be taken at the cost of foreswearing any connection between it and future snapshots.   The sharper the snapshot, the looser its causal ties with the future.   The uncertainty principle is merely a symbolic statement, in the descriptive language carried over from the old physics, of this deeper conflict.   Man must choose some compromise between an orderly, causal world which he cannot even visualize, and a sharp picture that reflects only the instant when it was taken.   To visualize the atom in terms of concrete models in sheer nonsense.   In Bohr's world there are no atoms; only observations.   The atom is a creation of man's mind, to bring some order into the chaotic pattern of observation.   The paradoxes and conflicts of the atomic world originate in the workings of the human consciousness.

Bohr's younger adherents eagerly welcomed this point of view.   After all, they felt with pride that they had created a new physics.   Now their mentor was telling them that not only had they overthrown the laws of classical physics, but the whole view of reality on which those laws were based. In its place was a new conception in harmony with the positivist and existentialist views so popular among their contemporaries in other fields. The new physics had spawned an equally modern metaphysics.

In their elation, the proponents of this Copenhagen interpretation cast to the winds the traditional caution with which physicists approach philosophy. Young Johann Von Neumann crowed that it was impossible to formulate the laws of physics without direct reference to the human consciousness and proved a theorem which purported to show that the Copenhagen view could never be separated from the quantum theory.

With the principle of complementarity, physics had come full circle from the days of Galileo. By removing man from nature, by making him a disinterested, nonparticipating observer, Galileo and his rationalist contemporaries had hoped to uncover a reality free from the subjective creations of the human mind. Now $3\frac{1}{2}$ centuries later, his intellectual descendants were denying that any such separation was possible.

The Determinists Strike Back

If Einstein and his followers were disturbed by the probability interpretation of the quantum theory, they were outraged by the deeper and more ambitious claims of the Copenhagen interpretation. Abandoning his unsuccessful direct attacks on the uncertainty principle, Einstein challenged the logical consistency of the theory as a whole. Though his arguments took many forms, they concentrated on the contraction of the wave packet that takes place when a particle's position is measured, which was described in the preceding chapter.

When an electron passes through a small hole, diffraction causes its wave packet to fan out rapidly. A short distance away, the packet covers an enormous fluorescent screen. When the electron flashes on the screen, the wave packet instantaneously contracts down to a tiny spot, for we know where the electron is.

The contradiction, in Einstein's view, lay in the word *instantaneously*. In less time than it takes for a signal to cross the screen, a physical event at one point (the flash) causes a disappearance of the wave. A physical influence has been transmitted at a speed exceeding that of light, in violation of relativity.

Yet to Bohr, Einstein's example was not a contradiction but a *proof* of the validity of his point of view. It merely showed that it was forever hopeless to ascribe any physical reality to the wave. The existence of a wave packet covering the entire screen merely reflected the possibility that the electron could strike the screen anywhere. An observer at the point of the flash knew instantly that the wave packet had vanished everywhere else; having seen the electron strike near him, he knew at once that it was no longer possible for it to strike elsewhere. Observers at other points on the screen would have to wait for the news to reach them, at the speed of light, before they realized the wave packet had shrunk. Since observers not in relative motion would disagree in the meantime as to the size of the wave packet, this was the final proof of Bohr's assertion that the wave packet represented not the electron itself, but our *knowledge* of its position. It was Einstein's own search for a "real" interpretation of the wave packet, not Bohr's view of it as an information wave, that violated the principles of relativity.

Though he rephrased his argument many times in increasingly subtle form, Einstein ultimately lost the debate. The Copenhagen view quickly achieved the status of orthodoxy—at least among those heterodox physicists who even trouble their minds about such matters. Einstein regretfully conceded that Bohr's views were at least self-consistent. What he refused to concede was that they were the last word. Someday, he fervently hoped, a new discovery would restore order to the microworld.

The obvious way to fulfill Einstein's dream would be to repeat, in a sense, what he did to Newton's laws: to show they were but an approximation, valid when dealing with speeds much less than that of light. A small but devoted band has taken upon themselves this task. The most celebrated of these, David Bohm, succeeded in 1952 in at least demonstrating that the search is not doomed from the start. He showed by example that it is possible to construct a theory that appears completely indeterminate on the atomic scale, but becomes deterministic on an even smaller scale. On this smaller scale, the Schrödinger equation and the uncertainty relations would be reduced to the status of approximate laws.

If a Bohm-type theory were ultimately to prevail, we would have a strange situation indeed in physics. One would still be unable to predict where the electron would hit the screen. Yet experiments on an even smaller scale would reveal that the exact point at which it would hit was predetermined all along. There would just be no way to make use of this knowledge to predict where it would hit. We would have a curious world in which an artificial but impenetrable indeterminacy on the atomic scale was sandwiched between two deterministic levels of reality. Of course, Bohm has no such theory to offer; he merely maintains that it is not preposterous to imagine one.

To most physicists now living, Bohm's views seem absurd in the extreme. But if the recent history of physics has taught us anything, it is that we should beware of dismissing *any* idea, no matter how much it may offend our sensibilities.

For a physicist deeply committed to his work, hope is to be found not in what is understood, but in the mysteries that remain. Beyond the world of the atom lies the strange world of subnuclear particles. For over two decades, an array of scientific talent unprecedented in the history of physics, backed up by material resources that would have staggered the imagination as recently as the 1930s, has been concentrated on this sub-submicroworld. The mysteries of this world have not yet been resolved; indeed, each new advance in experiment and theory seems only to compound them. Bohr himself shortly before his death presided over a conference in this field and summarized the discussion of a new theory with the remark: "We seem to all agree that the theory is crazy. The question is, is it crazy enough to have a chance of being right? My own feeling is that it is not quite *that* crazy."

An Afterword

To be human is to wonder. Children wonder for a while, before we teach them to be smug about the obvious and to stop asking silly questions. It is easier to pay men to retain a little of the child and do our wondering for us. We then take comfort in the assumption that any man devoted to such esoteric pursuits must be insensitive, perhaps even inhuman. With our artists, we perform the equal disservice of regarding them as too sensitive.

Occasionally we are given a glimpse of the finished product. The baby is displayed behind glass, well-scrubbed, and one need not know about the delivery room (it is soundproofed). Thus we are spared the agony of wonder, which is not unlike love and makes as little (or as much) sense as love. But wonder is just too human to fully repress, and it does turn up elsewhere. Some of us turn to fads for the occult, which, interpreted by our twentieth-century minds, becomes a "pop-art" science. More often, we find ourselves left with nothing to wonder about (or to love) but what remains of ourselves after the loss of yet another portion of our humanity.

I, for one, refuse to believe that nothing can be done about this empty place, or about the more general disease of which it is but a minor symptom. But as long as we are sundered so, let me remain one of the children and wonder.

—R. H. M.

Bibliography

Classical Mechanics

Galilei, Galileo: *Two New Sciences* (Macmillan, New York, 1914, available in Dover paperback). Galileo's dialogues, elegantly translated by Henry Crew and Alfonso De Salvio.

Jammer, Max: *Concepts of Space* (Harper, New York, 1960) and *Concepts of Force* (Harper, New York, 1962). Two sophisticated monographs on the history of the key concepts of mechanics from ancient to modern times.

Mach, Ernst: *The Science of Mechanics* (Open Court, La Salle, Ill., 1960). A historical and philosophical analysis by the leading champion of positivism in physics.

Newton, Isaac: *Principia* (University of California Press, Berkeley, 1962, 2 vols.). Difficult at points because of the archaic style, but the ideas are presented clearly.

Relativity

Bohm, David: *The Special Theory of Relativity* (Benjamin, New York, 1965). A recent text for physics majors, but with considerable emphasis on philosophical aspects.

Eddington, A. S.: *Space, Time, and Gravitation* (Cambridge, New York, 1924). One of the few popularizations of relativity that deals with the general theory.

Einstein, Albert: *Relativity* (Crown, New York, 1931) and *The Meaning of Relativity* (Princeton University Press, Princeton, N.J., 1950). Not the best treatment of relativity for the layman, but refreshingly written and from the horse's mouth. The earlier volume requires less mathematics.

French, A. P.: *Special Relativity* (Norton, New York, 1968). One of the better short treatments of relativity for science majors.

Gardner, Martin: *Relativity for the Millions* (Cardinal, New York, 1965). Perhaps the best popular exposition of relativity.

Lieber, Harry O., and Lillian R.: *Relativity* (Holt, New York, 1945). An amusing but difficult popularization (in blank verse, no less) of both the special and general theory, by a mathematician, with illustrations by her artist husband.

Smith, James P.: *Introduction to Special Relativity* (Benjamin, New York, 1965). Requires quite a bit more math than this text, but one of the most complete short books on relativity.

Taylor, E. F., and J. A. Wheeler: *Spacetime Physics* (Freeman, San Francisco, 1963). *The* text on relativity for physics undergraduates. Though some familiarity with the calculus is required, it is beautifully written and treats a large number of examples.

Quantum Theory

Bohm, David: *Causality and Chance in Modern Physics* (Routledge, London, 1957). A critique of the Copenhagen interpretation of the quantum theory by its most persistent contemporary critic.

Bohr, Niels: *Atomic Physics and Human Knowledge* (Vintage, New York, 1966). Bohr's views on the broader implications of his physical thinking.

Cline, Barbara: *Men Who Made a New Physics* (Signet, New York, 1966). Biographies of all the leading figures in the development of the quantum theory, with some exposition of their ideas.

De Broglie, Louis: *The Revolution in Physics* (Noonday, New York, 1953) and *The Current Interpretation of Wave Mechanics: A Critical Study* (Elsevier, Amsterdam, 1964). Popular expositions of modern physics, with the author's views as to its philosophical implications.

Jammer, Max: *The Conceptual Development of Quantum Mechanics* (McGraw-Hill, New York, 1966). The definitive history of the quantum theory, by an author who is both an able historian and a theoretical physicist. Extremely thorough, difficult for students weak in mathematics, but worth the effort.

Moore, Ruth: *Niels Bohr* (Knopf, New York, 1966). A definitive biography of Bohr, with an excellent exposition of the early quantum theory.

Toulmin, Stephen, and June Goodfield: *The Architecture of Matter* (Harper, New York, 1962). An excellent history of atomism and other ideas related to the structure of matter, from ancient to modern times.

Of General Interest

Arons, A. B., and A. M. Bork, (eds.): *Science and Ideas* (Prentice-Hall, New York, 1964). An excellent selection of short articles on philosophy and history of science and mathematics.

Beiser, Arthur (ed.): *The World of Physics* (McGraw-Hill, New York, 1960). Selections from popular or semipopular writings of noted physicists, with the emphasis on the modern era.

Kuhn, Thomas S.: *The Structure of Scientific Revolutions* (University of Chicago Press, 1962). A modern treatise on philosophy of science that emphasizes historical factors.

Shamos, Henry: *Great Experiments in Physics* (Holt, New York, 1960). Descriptions of some of the key experiments in the history of physics, from Galileo to the present.

Watson, James D.: *The Double Helix* (Signet, New York, 1968). An exciting, personal, and controversial account of what it means to participate in an epoch-making scientific discovery.

Appendix

Chapter 1

The Relation between Speed and Distance

The formula $s = \frac{1}{2}at^2$ gives the relation between *distance* and *time* for uniformly accelerated motion starting from rest. It is sometimes useful to have a formula relating *final speed* to distance. To obtain this, we note that the final speed is the acceleration multiplied by the time:

$$v = at \qquad \text{or} \qquad t = \frac{v}{a}$$

Replacing t in the first formula by this value gives:

$$s = \frac{1}{2}at^2 = \frac{1}{2}a\left(\frac{v}{a}\right)^2 = \frac{v^2}{2a}$$

This formula is useful for answering questions like, "How long a distance does it take a car going X mph to stop?"

Interpreting a Table of Distance versus Time

Measured		Computed	
Time, sec	Distance, m	Speed, m/sec	Acceleration, m/sec²
0	0		
2	10	5	
4	24	7	1
6	42	9	1
8	64	11	1

The table above is an example of one way to study motion. The distance traveled is recorded at equal time intervals.

The average speed is easy to compute for each interval. For example, between 2 and 4 sec, a time interval $\Delta t = 4 - 2 = 2$ sec, and the body traveled $\Delta s = 24 - 10 = 14$ m. By the definition of average speed,

$$\bar{v} = \frac{\Delta s}{\Delta t} = \frac{14}{2} = 7 \text{ m/sec}$$

This operation shows the significance of the Δ notation. It means the values used in the formula were obtained by subtracting the value at the beginning of the interval from that at the end.

The reader is invited to verify that the other entries in the "speed" column are correct.

Moving on to the acceleration, note that the speed increases from 5 to 7 m/sec in the time between the 0- to 2-sec interval and the 2- to 4-sec interval. Since this represents a change of 2 m/sec in a 2-sec interval, the acceleration

$$\bar{a} = \frac{\Delta v}{\Delta t} = 1 \text{ m/sec}^2$$

Since the speed increases by 2 m/sec each time, the acceleration is uniform. In this case, it is easy to relate these average values of speed and acceleration to their instantaneous values. Since the body gains an equal amount of speed in each of the 2 sec of the interval, the average value must represent the speed at the midpoint of the interval; i.e., the instantaneous speeds 5, 7, 9, 11 m/sec were reached at $t = 1, 3, 5, 7$ sec. But the acceleration may not have been constant—indeed the calculation of the acceleration would have been only approximate, since we would not know the exact time interval required for a change in speed.

Of course, we are taking on faith that the acceleration stayed the same throughout each interval.

Questions

1 Cite an example of two objects where the heavier actually falls more slowly than the lighter.

2 As an additional argument against Aristotle, Galileo cited the example of the fall of two identical objects attached by means of a string. Try to concoct such an argument.

3 Invent an example (in addition to that cited in the text) of a common experience which indicates that falling bodies do not acquire speed instantaneously.

4 Cite an example where the concept of derivative could be used *outside of the physical sciences.*

5 Give an argument to show that if an object moves with *increasing* (rather than uniform) acceleration, its average speed is *less than* half its final speed.

Exercises

Note: In this and all subsequent sets of exercises, use the approximate value for the acceleration due to gravity

$$g = 10 \text{ m/sec}^2$$

rather than the more precise 9.8 m/sec², except where specifically directed to use the more precise value. This value saves on arithmetic. In fact, because of differences in altitude, the rotation of the earth, and other local effects, g varies from place to place nearly as much as the difference between the "precise" and approximate values.

1 A fast ocean liner makes the crossing from New York to Southampton, a distance of 3,400 miles, in 4 days 4 hr. What is the average speed of the liner?

2 A fast sprinter can cover 100 m in 10 sec flat.
   (*a*) What is the average speed of the sprinter?
   (*b*) What would be his time for the mile (1,610 m) if he could keep up a sprint pace?

3 A driver covers 600 miles between 8 A.M. and 11 P.M.
   (*a*) What was his average speed?

(*b*) If he stopped a total of 3 hr for meals and refueling, what was his average speed while actually moving?

(*c*) If he had driven 10 mph faster at all times when he was actually moving, at what time would he have reached his destination?

4 A sky diver bails out at an altitude of 3,000 m (about 10,000 ft). Ignoring the first few seconds of the jump, he drops at a constant speed of 40 m/sec until he reaches a height of 200 m, where he opens his parachute, which drops his speed of fall to 10 m/sec.

(*a*) Calculate how long it takes him to reach the ground.

(*b*) Calculate his average speed for the entire time of fall.

(*c*) Comment on whether the calculation in (*b*) is particularly meaningful.

5 A driver plans a trip between two cities. The route includes 10 miles of major city streets, speed limit 30 mph; 105 miles of expressway, speed limit 70 mph; 25 miles of ordinary highway, speed limit 50 mph. What is the minimum time for the trip, without breaking the law?

6 What speed is acquired by a falling body in 5 sec? What is its average speed? At what time is its instantaneous speed the same as this average speed?

7 A sports car can accelerate at 5 m/sec². How long does it take to go from 0 to 30 m/sec (about 70 mph)?

8 A jet plane accelerates at 2 m/sec². It must reach a speed of 80 m/sec to take off. How long a time does it spend on the runway?

9 A car speeds up from 24 m/sec to 30 m/sec in 2 sec. Calculate its acceleration.

10 An object initially moving 20 m/sec experiences a negative acceleration: 2 m/sec² for 3 sec. What is its final speed?

11 What is the final speed of the object in the preceding problem if the acceleration continues for 15 sec?

12 How far does a falling body drop in 5 sec?

13 A plane needs 200 m of runway and takes 10 sec to get off the ground. Calculate the following:

(*a*) Its acceleration

(*b*) Its speed at takeoff, calculated *two ways,* one of which does *not* make use of the answer to (*a*)

14 How long does it take for a heavy object dropped from the top of the Empire State Building (320 m high) to reach the ground?

15   The motion of an object is represented by the following distance-time table:

Time, sec	Distance, m
0	0
2	20
4	50
6	90
8	140
10	200

(*a*) Calculate the average speed for the entire 10-sec interval.
(*b*) Calculate the speed for each of the five 2-sec intervals.
(*c*) Calculate the acceleration, and show it is constant.
(*d*) Show that this motion does *not* obey the formula $s = \frac{1}{2} at^2$.
(*e*) *Why* doesn't the formula apply?   (*Hint:* Try to estimate the speed at $t = 0$.)

16   Make graphs of distance, speed, and acceleration versus time for the object in Exercise 15.

17   Make a graph of distance, speed, and acceleration versus time for a car that decelerates uniformly from 30 m/sec to rest in 6 sec.

(*The following exercises need the formula $s = v^2/2a$*)

18   A car with good brakes and tires can decelerate at about 7 m/sec² in a "panic" stop on dry pavement.   Calculate the distance required to stop for a car going 30 m/sec (about 70 mph).

19   If a car's speed is doubled, the distance required for a panic stop goes up by a factor of _____.

20   A jet plane's engines can give it an acceleration of about 2 m/sec². It needs to get up to 80 m/sec speed to take off.   How long a runway does it need?

21   The jet plane in the preceding problem can be stopped at a deceleration of 3 m/sec² by means of brakes plus reversed engines.   A reasonable safety rule is that airport runways permit a pilot to change his mind any time up to the moment of takeoff and stop the plane.
(*a*) What is the total length of runway required to satisfy this rule?

(*b*) Convert the answer to feet (1 m = 3.3 ft) and compare it with the length of typical jet runways at major airports (9,000 to 11,000 ft).

22   A man with a strong throwing arm can throw a baseball at about 40 m/sec (90 mph). In the act of throwing while holding the ball, his arm moves about 1 m. Calculate the acceleration of the ball.

23   A rubber ball is dropped from a height of 20 m and rebounds. It is indented by 1 millimeter (1 mm = 0.001 m) when it hits the floor.
(*a*) Calculate its speed on reaching the floor.
(*b*) Calculate its acceleration while in contact with the floor.

24   Find the speed acquired by a heavy object dropped from the top of the Empire State Building (320 m high).

25   A drag-racing car can accelerate at 8 m/sec². Calculate its speed 100 m after starting.

26   Galileo's inclined plane was about 4 m long, and it took a ball about 10 sec to roll the full length of the plane. Calculate the acceleration and compare it with that of a freely falling body.

Chapter 2

A Practical Formula for Projectile Range

Equation (2) of Chapter 2, while revealing the physics behind projectile motion, is not of much practical value. This is because one does not ordinarily separately measure the horizontal and vertical components of a projectile's velocity. Ordinarily, one knows the *speed* and the *starting angle*. For example, a gun always fires a bullet at nearly the same speed. To redefine Equation (2) in terms of these new variables, we must make use of a trigonometric relationship, illustrated in the diagram.

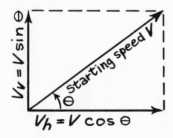

θ is refered to as the *angle of elevation.*   Then the equation becomes

$$R = 2\frac{V_v V_h}{g} = \frac{2(V\cos\theta)(V\sin\theta)}{g}$$

$$= \frac{2V^2\cos\theta\sin\theta}{g}$$

Those with training in trigonometry may remember the identity

$$2\cos\theta\sin\theta = \sin 2\theta$$

Thus the formula becomes

$$R = \frac{V^2\sin 2\theta}{g}$$

From inspection of this formula, two facts about projectiles become apparent:

1   Since the sine of an angle achieves its maximum value (1.0) at 90°, $\sin 2\theta$ is a maximum at 45°.   Thus, a projectile achieves its greatest range for an angle of elevation of 45°.

2   From the fact that $\sin x = \sin(180° - x)$ we can see that $\sin 2\theta = \sin(180° - 2\theta) = \sin[2(90° - \theta)]$.   Thus, a projectile with an angle of elevation of 10° travels the same distance as one with elevation 80°.   Of course, the trajectories look very different in the two cases (see Exercise 15).

Questions

1   Discuss the assertion that "the more education people have, the faster they learn" as evidence for the existence (or nonexistence) of a principle in psychology of learning analogous to the principle of superposition.

2   Propose a law analogous to a conservation law for a field outside the natural sciences.

3   A ball rolls down a wide inclined plane.   Instead of starting from rest, it is given an initial *horizontal* push (perpendicular to the line down which it would otherwise roll).   What path would the ball trace on the plane?   Will the time required to reach the bottom be affected?

4   Cite at least three common everyday experiences that illustrate the operation of momentum conservation.

5   The principle of superposition implies that a bullet fired horizontally from a gun will strike the ground at the same time as one dropped from the level of the muzzle when the gun was fired.   Without knowing the principle, what would you have guessed?   Try the question on 10 friends and see what they guess.

Exercises

(The following exercises on projectile motion do not involve the equation derived in the chapter.)

1   A man on a moving train drops a ball (inside the train). A stationary observer on the ground observes the process through the train window.
(*a*) Sketch the path of the ball, as seen by each observer.
(*b*) Repeat (*a*) for the case where the train is *accelerating*.

2   A car drives off a sheer cliff, moving horizontally at 30 m/sec. It strikes the ground 2 sec later.
(*a*) How far from the base of the cliff does the car land?
(*b*) How high is the cliff?

3   A baseball is hit a distance of 120 m. The highest point on its trajectory is 45 m from the ground.
(*a*) How long is it in flight?
(*b*) What were the horizontal and vertical components of its velocity when it left the bat?
(*c*) What were these components at the top of its trajectory?
(*d*) What were these components at the end of its flight?
(*e*) What was the speed of the ball as it left the bat?

4   A projectile travels a distance of 200 m in 4 sec.
(*a*) What was its horizontal velocity component?
(*b*) What was its vertical velocity component?
(*c*) How high was it at the top of its trajectory?

(The following exercises on projectile motion do involve the formula derived in the chapter.)

5   A ball is thrown with horizontal and vertical components of 25 m/sec, 10 m/sec, respectively.   How far will it travel?

6   A projectile with a horizontal velocity of 50 m/sec travels 400 m. What was its vertical velocity component?

7   The acceleration due to gravity on the moon is one-sixth as great as on the earth.   If a projectile travels 100 m on the earth, how far will an identically thrown projectile travel on the moon?

8   A projectile starts with a horizontal velocity of 40 m/sec and a vertical velocity of 30 m/sec.

(a) How far does it go?

(b) How high would it rise if projected straight up at the same speed?

9 Show that the distance a projectile travels is not changed if we exchange its horizontal and vertical velocity components.

10 A projectile travels farthest if it starts off with equal horizontal and vertical velocity components. Calculate the *speed* of a projectile, fired in this fashion, that travels a total distance of 1,000 m.

(*The following exercises on projectiles involve the use of trigonometric functions.*)

11 A projectile with a speed of 100 m/sec is projected at an angle of 30° up from the horizontal.

(a) How far will it travel?

(b) Show it will travel the same distance if projected at 60°.

(c) What preceding exercise in this section demonstrates why (a) and (b) give the same answer?

12 A cannon fires a projectile with a speed of 400 m/sec.

(a) At what angle up from the horizontal must it be aimed to hit a target 8,000 m away?

(b) How far will the projectile go if the cannon is instead pointed up at a 45° angle?

13 Make a graph showing how projectile range varies as the angle of elevation changes.

14 Find (or estimate) how fast a baseball pitcher can throw a ball. Compute from this the maximum range a baseball can be thrown. Does the result jibe with experience?

15 Show in a sketch the difference between the trajectory of a projectile fired at a 30° elevation and one of the same initial speed fired at 60°.

(*The following are exercises on momentum conservation in collisions.*)

16 A clay ball of mass 3 kg and velocity 16 m/sec strikes a stationary ball of mass 5 kg and sticks to it. What velocity does the combined mass have, after the collision?

17 Two clay balls of equal mass are moving in opposite directions when they collide and stick together. Before the collision one ball is moving 7 m/sec to the right, while the other is moving 3 m/sec to the left. What is the velocity and direction of the combined mass after the collision?

18 A boy of mass 40 kg, running at a speed of 3 m/sec, jumps onto a stationary sled of mass 20 kg. What speed does he slide on the sled?

19 A ball of mass 2 kg and velocity 10 m/sec strikes a stationary ball of mass 1 kg. After the collision, the 2 kg ball is moving at 4 m/sec in its original direction.

  (a) What are the speed and direction of the 1-kg ball after the collision?

  (b) Is this an example of an elastic collision?

20 A ball of mass 5 kg and velocity 7 m/sec collides *elastically* with a stationary ball of mass 2 kg. What are the speeds and directions of both balls after the collision? (This requires solving a pair of simultaneous equations.)

(Other exercises on momentum conservation.)

21 An 80-kg man standing on ice throws a 2-kg ball at a horizontal speed of 20 m/sec to a 58-kg man standing 20 m away, also on the ice.

  (a) How fast does the first man slide after throwing the ball?

  (b) How fast does the man catching the ball slide, after catching the ball?

  (c) Calculate the position of the center of mass of the two men (taking into account the mass of the ball) *before* the ball is thrown and

  (d) one second after it has been caught. [(c) and (d) require some messy arithmetic.]

22 An astronaut (who with his spacesuit has a mass of 100 kg) is attached by a 30-m rope to a 900-kg space capsule out in free space (no gravity). He pulls himself in on the rope to the capsule. How far has the capsule moved when he reaches it?

23 A sealed freight car 40 ft long and weighing 4,000 lb when empty sits on a frictionless track. The car starts to move and finally stops after moving 1 ft.

  (a) Is this sufficient information to conclude that something is moving around inside the car?

  (b) If the motion is due to something moving inside the car, give numerical proof that the motion of one person walking around in the car could account for the motion observed.

Chapter 3

Measuring Acceleration in *g*'s

When dealing with the motion of vehicles (cars, airplanes, spacecraft), it is customary to use the normal acceleration due to gravity, 9.8 m/sec², as the unit of acceleration. Thus, an acceleration of 4.9 m/sec² would be called 0.5g, 20 m/sec² is 2.04g, and so on.   The convenience of this system is that then the acceleration is the ratio of the force to the weight:

$$a = \frac{F}{w} \quad a \text{ in } g\text{'s}$$

This can be derived simply from the second law and the definition of weight:

$$F = ma \qquad w = mg$$

Thus,

$$\frac{F}{w} = \frac{ma}{mg} = \frac{a}{g}$$

which is the definition of "acceleration in g's."

This measure also has intuitive advantages.   Most people have a fair sense of how fast a falling body speeds up, or how strong a force their own weight is.

Terminal Velocity

Newton's laws permit a quantitative analysis of the concept of *terminal velocity* of a falling body, introduced in Chapter 1.   In newtonian terms, the medium has two effects on the fall of a body:

1   There is a *buoyant force* on the body regardless of its motion.   Thus, total force on an object is less than its weight, and even at the start of its fall the acceleration is less than g.
2   There is an additional *drag force* exerted by the medium on a moving object because it must force aside the medium through which it is passing.   This force increases as the body moves faster.

As the body speeds up, a speed is reached at which the sum of the buoyant and drag forces equals its weight.   Then the total force on the body is zero, and thereafter it moves downward with constant speed.

Example: A solid aluminum ball, when placed in water, experiences a buoyant force of 37 percent of its weight.   Thus, the total force on it, starting from rest in water, is

$$F = \text{weight} - \text{buoyant force} = mg - 0.37mg = 0.63mg$$

Thus, its initial acceleration is

$$a = \frac{F}{m} = \frac{0.63mg}{m} = 0.63g$$

As soon as the ball begins to move, a drag force comes into play. Thus, the acceleration becomes less and less. To find the terminal velocity, one must find out the speed at which the drag force becomes $0.63mg$. This could be done experimentally by measuring the force exerted on the ball by a moving stream of water. Experiments of this type have shown that, if the shape of the object is simple and smooth and the speed is not too great, the drag is just proportional to the speed. For example, for an aluminum ball about 1 cm in diameter, the drag would be about 1.25 times its weight in water moving at 1 m/sec. A speed only half this great, 0.5 m/sec, would be sufficient to produce a force 0.63 times its weight. Thus, the terminal velocity will be about 0.5 m/sec.

For a solid body falling in air, the buoyant force is usually very small: less than one-thousandth of its weight. Thus, only the drag force need be considered.

Questions

1 Express Newton's original definition of mass as a mathematical formula.

2 Suppose it were discovered that the mass of a body increases slightly when it is going very fast, but that the amount of increase can be calculated if the speed is known. Comment on how this would affect the validity of Newton's laws.

3 The normal method of comparing masses to a standard is to compare weights on a *balance*. What assumptions must be made in order that this be a valid way of comparing masses?

4 Describe the motion of a falling body which, rather than starting from rest, is given an *initial downward speed* faster than its terminal velocity.

Exercises

1 If a 3-kg mass is observed to be speeding up at a rate of 5 m/sec², how large a force (in newtons) must be acting on it?

2 (*a*) Convert your own mass into kilograms (1 kg = 2.2 lb).
   (*b*) Calculate the force *in newtons* exerted by gravity on your body.

3 A car is being towed by a rope which will break if it transmits a force of more than 5,000 newtons. The mass of the car is 1,000 kg. What is the maximum acceleration that can be given to the car in this way?

4 A car, which can normally accelerate at 4 m/sec², is towing an identical car. What is the greatest acceleration it can achieve?

5 An unknown force produces an acceleration of 12 m/sec² when acting on an unknown mass. What acceleration would it produce if acting on three such masses joined together?

6 If a 2-kg mass is acted on by a force of 6 newtons, what is the resulting acceleration, in m/sec²?

7 Two masses, one of 1 kg and the other unknown, are initially at rest with a compressed spring between them. When the spring is released, the 1-kg mass experiences an acceleration of 5 m/sec² and the unknown mass an acceleration of 1 m/sec².
(*a*) Calculate the unknown mass.
(*b*) What is the strength of the force exerted by the spring, in newtons?
(*c*) Suppose that, instead of measuring the acceleration, only the final speed of each body had been measured, after both had parted fully from the spring. Would this be sufficient information to answer (*a*)? To answer (*b*)? Explain.

8 A body of mass 2 kg is experiencing an acceleration of 3 m/sec². It is doing this because it is interacting with another body of mass 0.5 kg. What is the acceleration of the other body?

9 The engines on a small jet airliner produce a forward thrust of one-fourth the normal takeoff weight of the plane (take $g = 10$ m/sec²).
(*a*) What acceleration is the plane capable of, in g's and in m/sec²?
(*b*) If the plane takes off at a speed of 70 m/sec, how long a runway does it need?

10 The plane in the preceding problem normally takes off with its fuel tanks full. Half its takeoff weight is then fuel. How long a runway would it need to take off with its tanks nearly empty?

11 An object of mass 5 kg accelerates from rest to a speed of 20 m/sec in 5 m. How large a force is acting on it?

(*Exercises on terminal velocity*)

12 A plastic ball experiences a buoyant force of three-fourths its weight when placed in water. What is its initial acceleration, if it falls from rest in water?

13 The ball in the preceding problem has a mass of 0.1 kg, and in a stream moving at 1 m/sec, the drag force on it is 2.5 newtons. What is the terminal velocity of the ball, falling in water?

Chapter 4

Banked Curves

Since a car taking a curve at constant speed is in a form of accelerated motion, it must have a net force acting toward the center of the curve. Ordinarily, this is provided by the sideways friction of the road against the tires; but tires, as any driver knows, slip, with catastrophic results. A safer way to provide this force is to bank the curve. Then, as illustrated in the figure below, the downward force due to the weight of the car and the upward force of the road on the car's tires are no longer in opposite directions: the upward force has a horizontal component that acts toward the inside of the curve. If the curve is taken at just the right speed so that this component of the force provides the required acceleration, there is no sideward force on the tires, and thus no tendency to slip. Even if the curve is taken faster, the presence of the inward component reduces the force that friction must supply and makes the curve safer.

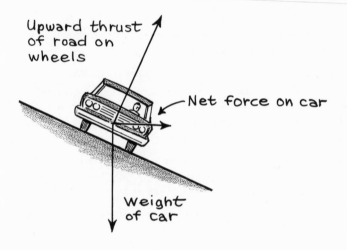

For an airplane, which has no road to grip, the effect is even more significant. It is the horizontal component of the upward force on the wings that makes the turn possible. The angle of bank thus determines how rapidly the plane will turn.

This effect should also be familiar to bicyclists and motorcyclists, who must tilt as they round a curve to avoid toppling, providing their own "bank."

Example: A car rounds a turn of radius 100 m, banked at 26.6°. This angle was chosen for arithmetic simplicity because its tangent is one-half, and thus the force toward the inside of the curve is one-half the car's weight. (Students with trig training are invited to verify, from the figure, that the tangent is the appropriate trig function to use. Remember that the *vertical* component of the force of the road on the car must exactly balance its weight, since there is no vertical motion of the car.) Thus, the force can produce an acceleration of 0.5 g = 5 m/sec².

To find the best speed at which to take the curve, we equate this to the circular acceleration:

$$\frac{V^2}{100 \text{ m}} = 5 \text{ m/sec}^2$$
$$V^2 = 400$$
$$V = 20 \text{ m/sec} \quad \text{(about 45 mph)}$$

Above this speed, the car will pull to the outside of the curve; below, the car will pull to the inside. The difference must be supplied by friction. At exactly 20 m/sec, the car can go through the curve without the driver exerting any force on the steering wheel. It is therefore sometimes called the "hands-off" speed, but the student is advised not to take this term too literally. The formula for the hands-off speed is

$$V^2 = Rg \tan \theta$$

where θ is the angle of bank.

Vector Momentum Conservation

In Chapter 2, we dealt with momentum in "one-dimensional" collisions. As any billiard player knows, colliding balls do not always recoil along the original line of motion. By treating momentum as a *vector*, however, momentum conservation can be applied to these more complex situations, as illustrated in the figure below. Here momentum conservation implies

$$\vec{A} = \vec{B} + \vec{C}$$

If the momentum of the incoming ball $\vec{A}$ and of the recoil $\vec{B}$ are known, the magnitude and direction of the original ball after the collision C can be obtained by the vector operation:

$$\vec{C} = \vec{A} - \vec{B}$$

$\vec{A}$ = original momentum of ball

$\vec{B}$ = momentum after collision of recoil

$\vec{C}$ = momentum of original ball after collision

Questions

1 Cite two examples (other than Newton's second law) where multiplication or division by a scalar is used to go from one kind of vector to another.

2 Automobile racers ordinarily try to take a curve by starting at the outside lane, cutting to the inside, and ending up again at the outside. Explain why they do this.

3 A good airplane pilot can go into a steep turn without spilling a passenger's drink. Explain why.

4 A man swings a bucket of water in a vertical circle. If the motion is sufficiently fast, the water does not spill at the top when the bucket is upside down. Explain why this is possible.

5 A cyclist *must* lean to the inside of a turn on a flat road. Explain why.

Exercises

1 What is the length of a vector formed by adding two vectors, one of length 3 and the other of length 4, at right angles to one another?

2 What is the ground speed of an airplane flying 120 mph with a crosswind of 50 mph at right angles to the direction it is pointing?

3 Solve graphically for the ground speed and direction of an airplane heading north at 300 mph with a wind of 75 mph from the southwest.

4 An airplane cruises at an airspeed of 200 mph, and the pilot wishes to fly due north. There is a wind of 50 mph from the west. By means of a drawing determine:
(*a*) How many degrees west of due north he must point his plane
(*b*) His ground speed

5 Draw a vector diagram that illustrates the relationship $\vec{A} + \vec{B} = \vec{B} + \vec{A}$.

6 Draw a vector diagram that illustrates the relationship $s(\vec{A} + \vec{B}) = s\vec{A} + s\vec{B}$.

7 An object, initially moving at 5 m/sec to the east, changes its direction and speed so that it ends up moving 12 m/sec to the south, 2 sec later. By means of either a vector diagram or computation, find the average acceleration over the 2-sec period.

8   An object travels in a circle of radius 1 m at a constant speed of
1 m/sec.

(*a*) Calculate the time required for one complete revolution.

(*b*) Calculate the average acceleration when the object goes through
one-half revolution.

(*c*) Repeat (*b*) for one-quarter revolution.

(*d*) Compute the instantaneous acceleration from Equation (3) of
Chapter 4 and compare the results with (*b*) and (*c*) above.

9   An object travels in a circle of radius 3.6 m.   What speed must it
have in order to have an acceleration of 1 g?

10   An object of mass 3 kg is held in circular motion in a circle of radius
4 m by a string that will break if a force of more than 75 newtons is
exerted on it.   Calculate the maximum speed the object can travel
without breaking the string.

11   An object of mass 3 kg moving at a speed of 20 m/sec has a force of
12 newtons on it, continually perpendicular to its direction of motion.
What is the radius of the circle in which it moves?

12   Draw a sketch showing the direction of the velocity and acceleration
vectors for a car that is rounding a curve while speeding up.

13   A ball rolls down a track that has a "loop-the-loop" circle of radius
1 m, as shown in the sketch.   What is the minimum speed it must be
moving at the top of the loop, in order to stay on the track?

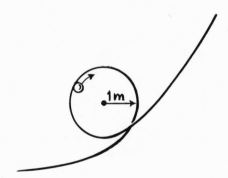

14   Calculate the "hands-off" speed for a curve of radius 90 m banked
at 45°.

15   An airplane that is flying at 100 m/sec goes into a 63.4° bank
(tan 63.4° = 2).

(*a*) What is the radius of the curve it will describe as it turns?

(b) How many times the normal weight of the plane must the wing bear under these conditions?

16 Show that a jet airliner, which flies twice as fast as a propeller plane, will turn in a circle four times as big and take twice as long to complete a turn through a given angle as the propeller plane, at the same angle of bank.

17 An object of mass 2 kg and velocity 4 m/sec strikes a stationary object of mass 10 kg. After the collision, the incoming object is moving perpendicularly to its original path, at a speed of 3 m/sec.

(a) Draw a diagram showing the momentum vectors of the object before and after the collision.

(b) Use this diagram to find the momentum of the 10-kg object after the collision.

(c) Calculate the speed of the 10-kg object after the collision.

Chapter 5

The Mathematical Relation between Kepler's Third Law and Inverse-square Forces

For circular orbits, Kepler's third law relates the length of the year T to the radius R of the orbit:

$$T^2 = \text{const} \times R^3$$

To see the connection with the force, we must see what this law says about the *acceleration* of the planet:

$$a = \frac{V^2}{R}$$

Since V is the circumference of the orbit, $2\pi R$, divided by the length of the year, we have:

$$a = \frac{(2\pi R)^2}{T^2} \frac{1}{R}$$

But $T^2 = \text{const} \times R^3$. Lumping this constant and the factor $4\pi^2$ into a new constant, we have

$$a = \text{const} \times \frac{R^2}{R^3 \times R} = \frac{\text{const}}{R^2}$$

Thus, the acceleration is proportional to the inverse square of the distance. For elliptical orbits the situation is more complex, but Newton was able to show that the same relation holds. (In this case, Kepler's third law replaces the radius by one-half the length of the *major axis,* the long dimension of the ellipse.)

Artificial Satellites

Kepler's third law also applies to the motion of artificial earth satellites. The period of a (hypothetical) satellite at sea level would be 84 minutes. Thus the period, in minutes, of a satellite in an orbit of radius R would be

$$T = 84 \left(\frac{R}{R_e} \right)^{\frac{3}{2}}$$

where R_e is the radius of the earth. Since the radius of the earth is 4,000 miles, and typical manned satellites are usually orbited only a few hundred miles up, R/R_e for these orbits is only slightly greater than 1, and the period is not much greater than 84 min.

Also of interest to the designers of artificial satellites is the orbital speed. This is even easier to calculate. For our hypothetical sea level satellite, we have

$$\frac{V^2}{R_e} = g$$

Using the known values of R_e and g, this gives a result of 7.9 km/sec, or about 18,000 mph. Larger orbits are achieved at smaller speeds. The reader may easily verify for himself the formula

$$V = 7.9 \sqrt{\frac{R_e}{R}}$$

The practical problem of putting an artificial satellite into orbit is easily understood if one takes note of one fact about orbits: they are completely self-repeating. Thus, unless it strikes the atmosphere, a satellite will always return to the point where its rocket burned out, going the same speed and direction.

The figure below illustrates the launch procedure. First, the satellite is fired to the desired orbital altitude. When it reaches that altitude and is moving horizontally, the last stage of the rocket is fired to speed it up to orbital velocity. If too much speed is given by the last stage, little harm results.   The satellite merely goes into a larger orbit.   Since it must return to its starting point, this will become the low point in the orbit (*perigee*).

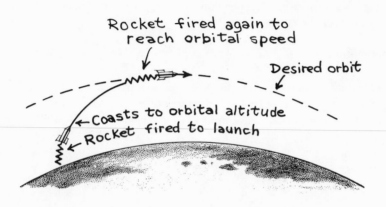

Questions

1   One additional support for Newton's law of universal gravitation was that, in his time, the four largest moons of the planet Jupiter had been discovered, and their motion obeyed Kepler's laws.   Comment on what support this lends to Newton's theory.

2   Angular momentum conservation (Kepler's second law) is used by ballet dancers and figure skaters to produce rapid spin.   The dancer or skater starts the spin with her arms extended, then pulls them in to her side or chest.   Explain why this causes the spin to speed up.

3   Although the gravitational constant was still unknown in Newton's day, and thus the mass of the earth was unknown, one could still make a comparison between the mass of the earth and that of the sun.   Explain how this was possible.

Exercises

Planet	Distance from sun, earth orbit radii	Length of year, earth years
Mercury	0.39	0.24
Venus	0.72	0.61
Earth	1.00	1.00
Mars	1.52	1.9
Jupiter	5.2	12

1 Verify that the planetary data in the table above satisfy Kepler's third law.

2 Prove that, if gravity were constant rather than falling off inversely as the square of distance, Kepler's third law would have been $T^2 = $ const $\times R$, rather than R^3.

3 (*a*) Calculate the acceleration of the earth in its orbit around the sun, using the fact that its orbital velocity is 30,000 m/sec and the orbit radius is 150 billion m.
(*b*) Compare the result to the acceleration due to the earth's own gravity at its surface.
(*c*) Use the result to calculate the ratio of the sun's mass to that of the earth.

(*The following exercises use formulas derived in this section of the Appendix.*)

4 Calculate the period of an earth satellite in an orbit whose radius is four times that of the earth.

5 Calculate the orbit velocity for the satellite in the preceding problem.

6 Halley's celebrated comet has a period of about 70 years, and like all comets it moves in a long narrow orbit. Calculate the length of this orbit, in units of the radius of the earth's orbit.

7 Verify that the formula given in this section for the period of an artificial satellite gives the right length (27 days) for the length of a lunar month (1 day = 1,440 min).

8 Prove that orbit velocity is proportional to the square root of the orbit radius.

9 Verify the calculation of 7.9 km/sec as "sea-level" orbital velocity, using the values $R_e = 6,370,000$ m, $g = 9.8$ m/sec^2. Use the result to verify that the period of a sea-level satellite would be 84 min.

10 It is very useful to launch certain kinds of satellites into orbits with a period of 24 hours. Such a satellite will appear to remain fixed over the same spot on earth. Communications satellites and certain weather satellites have been launched into such orbits, which are called *synchronous orbits*. Calculate the radius, in earth radii, of a synchronous orbit.

11 The radius of the moon is about one-half that of the earth, and the acceleration due to the moon's gravity at its surface is about one-sixth that on earth. Calculate the period of a satellite orbiting the moon, in a low orbit.

(*For the next three exercises you will need the value of the gravitational constant:* $\mathcal{G} = 6.67 \times 10^{-11}$ newton-m^2/kg^2.)

12 Given the above value for $\mathcal{G}$, the fact that the force on a 1-kg object at the earth's surface is 9.8 kg, and the earth's radius $R = 6,400,000$ m, calculate the mass of the earth.

13 Using the data given in and the answer to Exercise 3, calculate the mass of the sun.

14 What is the force between two spheres of gold, each of mass 1 kg, placed with their centers 0.05 m apart? (This is as close together as they can get, since a 1-kg gold sphere has a radius of 2.3 cm. To give you an idea of the difficulty of Cavendish's experiment, the answer is about the weight of a mosquito.)

15 Show that, if a planet is made of material of uniform density, the force of gravity at its surface is proportional to its radius.

Chapter 6

Power

The term *power* in physics refers to the *rate at which work is done,* i.e.,

$$\text{Power} = \frac{\text{work}}{\text{time}} = \frac{dW}{dt}$$

The unit of power is probably familiar to you: it is the *watt,* and 1 watt is 1 joule per second.

The most common form of power in modern society is electrical. Electrical energy is usually sold by the kilowatt-hour (kwhr), i.e., the amount of work done in one hour at a power of 1,000 watts. Since a kilowatt-hour is a unit of power multiplied by a unit of time, it is a unit of energy, not power. Since there are 3,600 sec in 1 hr,

$$1 \text{ kwhr} = 3,600 \text{ sec} \times 1,000 \text{ watts}$$
$$= 3.6 \text{ million joules}$$

Since a kilowatt-hour of electricity costs from 1 to 5 cents, you can see that a joule of energy is very cheap in our society.

As a legacy of the industrial revolution, we have another rather clumsy power unit still in use, the *horsepower.* This unit was originally set up by measuring the work done in a timed period by a real horse. Today it is more prosaically defined as 760 watts.   It has struck the author that the long-forgotten "standard horse" must have had a name; it might have been apt to let the unit bear this name.

Energy in Circular Orbits

For circular orbits subject to an inverse-square force, there is a particularly simple relationship between the kinetic energy and potential energy of the orbiting object.   As was noted at the end of Chapter 6, the potential energy is related to the force by the simple formula:

$$PE = -Fr$$

The kinetic energy also bears a simple relation to the force, because both the acceleration and the kinetic energy depend on v^2:

$$\frac{mv^2}{r} = F$$

Thus,

$$KE = \tfrac{1}{2}mv^2 = \tfrac{1}{2}Fr$$

Thus, the kinetic energy is one-half as large as, and opposite in sign to, the potential energy.   Therefore, to get total energy,

$$E = PE + KE = \tfrac{1}{2}PE = -\tfrac{1}{2}\mathcal{G}\frac{mM}{r}$$

which is equal in magnitude but opposite in sign to the kinetic energy.

Like Kepler's third law, this relation also holds for elliptical orbits, with half the length of the major axis replacing the radius.

This result is very useful in planning orbits of artificial satellites. Although launching a satellite, or changing from one orbit to another, involves changes in both potential energy and kinetic energy, the changes are related and thus need not be computed separately.

Example: Compare the energy required to move a satellite from a low orbit to one twice the radius of the earth with the energy required to launch it in the first place.   Before launching the satellite had no kinetic energy, only potential.   Thus, for the three cases we have:

$$E = -\mathcal{G}\frac{mM}{R_e} \qquad \text{before launch}$$

$$E = -\tfrac{1}{2}\mathcal{G}\frac{mM}{R_e} \qquad \text{low orbit (orbit radius about } R_e\text{)}$$

$$E = -\tfrac{1}{4}\mathcal{G}\frac{mM}{R_e} \qquad \text{orbit of radius } 2R_e$$

Therefore, only one-half as much energy is required to double the orbit size as to launch the satellite in the first place.

This result will be very valuable to us in the section on atomic physics, where we will be considering the energy changes as electrons move from one orbit to another in an atom.

Questions

1   A cannonball is fired in a high trajectory, is slowed by air resistance, and eventually buries itself in the ground. Describe the series of energy changes that take place from the moment the powder is ignited.

2   Invent a conservation law (it need not actually be true) analogous to energy conservation in a field outside the natural sciences.

3   A pendulum consisting of a lead weight on a light flexible string is released from the point shown in the drawing. At the bottom of the pendulum's swing, the string strikes a rigid, immobile peg placed as shown. Assume energy is conserved.

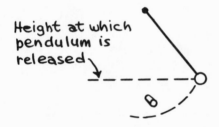

Height at which pendulum is released

(a) Copy the sketch and show where the ball will rise to at the top of its swing to the right.

(b) Show on the same sketch where the peg should be placed if you want the string to wind around the peg.

(c) What statement *about the peg*, made above, assured you that it would not interfere with energy conservation? Explain.

4   Contrast the physical definitions of the words *work, power, force,* and *energy* with their ordinary-language definitions. Do you think the choice of terms was apt or farfetched?

5   Name three situations (other than those cited in the text) where momentum is conserved but mechanical energy is not. In each case state the new form in which the energy appears.

6   Cite two common everyday experiences that are examples of the conversion of mechanical energy to heat.

7 Examine an actual roller coaster at an amusement park and estimate what fraction of the total energy is lost at each rise, from its design.

8 Explain why it takes more work to speed a car from 60 to 70 mph than from 0 to 10 mph.

Exercises

1 How many joules of work must be done to lift a 5-kg object a height of 10 m?

2 A force of 5 newtons pushes on an initially stationary object of mass 4 kg for a distance of 10 m.
(*a*) Calculate the work done.
(*b*) Calculate the final speed of the object.

3 On a 2-kg object initially moving 4 m/sec, 9 joules of work are done. Calculate the change in speed that results.

4 A car of mass 1,000 kg speeds up from 20 m/sec to 30 m/sec in a distance of 200 m.
(*a*) How large a force does this take?
(*b*) What is the acceleration of the car while it is speeding up?

5 Calculate the total energy, in joules, lost in braking a 2,000-kg car to a stop from 20 m/sec. In what form do you think most of this energy appears?

6 A bouncing ball rises to four-ninths its original height if dropped on a hard floor.
(*a*) What fraction of its energy is lost?
(*b*) Assuming the energy was all lost on impact with the floor, calculate the ratio of the speed of the ball just before hitting the floor to the speed just afterward.

7 The first rise of a roller coaster is 20 m from the ground, its first dip is at ground level, and the second rise is 15 m high.
(*a*) Calculate the speed at the first dip.
(*b*) Calculate the speed at the second rise, assuming the roller coaster starts from rest at the first rise.

8 Repeat the preceding problem, assuming the roller coaster tops the first rise at a speed of 10 m/sec. Explain why there is so little increase in the speed at the later points in the motion.

9 A bicyclist approaches a hill, moving 10 m/sec. How far vertically can he coast without pedaling?

10 A car moving 30 m/sec approaches a hill 25 m high. If the car coasts up the hill, what speed will it be moving at the top? If it starts with this speed at the bottom, can it top the hill?

11 It takes 4,120 joules of energy to heat 1 kg of water by 1°C. If all the energy is converted to heat in the water, how large a rise in temperature occurs in water going over a 100-m waterfall?

12 A spring compressed 1 cm will fire a ball 5 m in the air. How much must the spring be compressed to fire the ball 20 m in the air?

13 If the spring in the preceding problem is compressed 1 cm and fires the ball horizontally, how fast will the ball go?

14 An elastic collision, viewed in terms of the energy concept, proves to be one in which both kinetic energy and momentum are conserved. Refer back to the example of an elastic collision in Chapter 2, and verify that kinetic energy is conserved.

15 The brakes of a car parked on a hill fail, and it rolls down 20 m to the bottom of the hill. There it strikes and locks bumpers with a car of the same mass. Assume momentum is conserved in the collision.
   (a) How fast is the combined wreck moving after the collision?
   (b) If there is another hill immediately ahead of the collision point, how high up this next hill can the wreck coast?
   (c) Use this result to show that energy has been lost, and show by computing kinetic energy before and after the collision that this energy was lost in the collision itself.

16 How much power is expended while lifting a 5-kg object 10 m in 4 sec?

17 A crane lifts a 2,000-kg load at a rate of 2 m/sec. How many kilowatts of power are required?

18 A 2,000-kg car is capable of maintaining a speed of 15 m/sec while climbing a street which rises 1 m for every 5 m of length. How many watts of power are required? Convert the result to horsepower.

19 Estimate (or actually measure) how long it would take you to dash up three flights of stairs. Estimate the total height climbed and your mass in kilograms. Calculate your power output in watts. (You will find the result in horsepower somewhat disappointing.)

20 Prove that the power required to maintain a force F on an object moving at a speed V is FV.

21 Show that it takes only twice as much energy to free a rocket from the earth's gravity as to launch it into a low orbit. (*Hint:* remember that escape is possible if the *total* energy is zero or greater.)

Chapter 7

Questions

1 The field concept is most useful for explaining the forces on small charges in the presence of larger ones.   Explain why.

2 Gravity, like electricity, can be interpreted as a field.   Write the formula for the gravitational field strength.   To what physical quantity, mentioned in this text, is gravitational field strength identical?

3 Today we also believe gravity to propagate at the speed of light.   In view of this fact, why was it possible for Newton to overlook this feature and still explain planetary motion?

4 One way of resolving the "nightmare of determinism" is to prove that a calculating machine capable of analyzing the entire universe in this detail would have to be as complex as the universe itself.   Construct an argument to show this is so.   State whether, in your opinion, this resolves the problem.

Chapter 8

Questions

1 Devise instructions for the marching band used as a wave example in Chapter 8 that will enable one to use them to demonstrate the principle of superposition.

2 A guitarist can obtain a very pure tone one octave above the fundamental tone of a string by touching it very lightly at its midpoint.   Explain why this tone should be pure (not mixed with other wavelengths) and why he must use the fingerboard to obtain most other notes.

3 A radio station is required to design an antenna that will avoid transmitting to the south, where another station of the same frequency is located.   The engineer designing the station builds an antenna consisting of two towers one-half wavelength apart, separated along a north-south line.   Explain.

4 Bring your thumb and forefinger together slowly, and observe what you see just before they touch through one eye against a brightly lighted background.   Explain in terms of the wave nature of light.

5 A satisfactory (but rather slow) camera can be made with a pinhole instead of a lens.   As the pinhole is made smaller, at first it tends to make the image sharper. Eventually, however, too small a pinhole will produce a blurred image. Explain.

6 Stringed instruments are tuned by tightening the string to raise the pitch, and the thickest strings sound the lowest notes. What does this indicate about the way in which the thickness and tension in music strings affects the propagation of waves?

7 In the "well tempered" musical scale, there are twelve half-tones to an octave, and the ratio of frequencies of two successive half-tones is exactly the same. Explain why the frets on an instrument such as a guitar get closer together as you move up the neck.

Exercises

1 If a wave of frequency 10 Hz has a wavelength of 100 m, what is the wave velocity?

2 The velocity of light is 3×10^8 m/sec, and the frequency of a typical FM radio station is 10^8 Hz. What is the wavelength of the waves broadcast by this station?

3 The wavelength of red light is about 7×10^{-7} m. What is its frequency?

4 Audible sound waves have frequencies from about 20 to 17,000 Hz, and the speed of sound is 340 m/sec. What are the wavelengths of typical sound waves?

5 Draw the wave pattern that will result from interference of the waves shown in the sketch below, at the instant when the centers of the two wave pulses coincide.

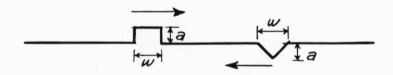

6 Draw a series of pictures showing the reflection of a triangular wave pulse, such as that shown on the right in the figure for Exercise 5, from a fixed point on a string. Show at least five equally spaced intervals, from when the wave first touches the fixed point to when its reflection leaves it.

7 Draw a series of pictures similar to that in Chapter 8, Figure 7, for a standing wave where the string is one wavelength long.

8 What are the wavelengths of the three longest standing waves that can exist on a string of length 3 m?

9 A piano string of length 1 m sounds the A above middle C (frequency 440 Hz) as its fundamental tone (longest wavelength). What is the speed of wave motion on the string?

10 Refer back to Question 7 for the description of the well-tempered musical scale. Show that the ratio between the spacings between two successive frets is the twelfth root of 2. (An octave is a change in frequency of a factor 2.)

11 Two hi-fi speakers, placed 3 m apart, are sounding a note of wavelength 2 m.
(*a*) Show that, if one walks along a line 4 m in front of the speakers, there will be near-silence at the points directly in front of them.
(*b*) In all, at how many points along the line will you hear a maximum of sound intensity?

12 The figure below shows how to find the path difference for waves that meet on a screen whose distance from the slits is much larger than the slit separation. Show that the path difference is $s \sin \theta$, where s is the separation of the slits and θ is the angle at which the waves travel.

Screen far away; thus paths to same point on screen nearly parallel

Path difference

13 Using the result obtained in Exercise 12, calculate how close two slits must be in order to obtain a pattern in which the bright lines near the center are separated by 1 mm (0.001 m), if the screen is 1 m behind the slits and yellow light ($\lambda = 5 \times 10^{-7}$ m) is used.

14 Waves travel around a hoop of circumference L. Devise a formula for the allowed wavelengths of standing waves on the hoop.

Chapter 9

A Useful Approximation

When using the formulas derived in Chapter 9, one frequently deals with situations where v is much less than c. In these cases it is handy to know the following approximate formulas:

$$\sqrt{1 \pm x} \approx 1 \pm \tfrac{1}{2}x$$

$$\frac{1}{1 - x} \approx 1 + x$$

The wiggly equals sign is a reminder that the formula is not exact.

The first approximation is surprisingly good even when x is not much less than 1. For example, we have, using this formula,

$$\sqrt{2} = \sqrt{1 + 1} \approx 1\tfrac{1}{2}$$

which is within 6 percent of the correct answer, 1.414. By the time we get to

$$\sqrt{1.21} = \sqrt{1 + 0.21} \approx 1.105$$

the answer is very close to the true one, 1.100.

Similarly, for the second forumla, we have

$$\frac{1}{0.8} = \frac{1}{1 - 0.2} \approx 1 + 0.2 = 1.2$$

which is not far from the correct answer of 1.25.

Combining the two approximations, we obtain

$$\gamma = \frac{1}{\sqrt{1 - (v/c)^2}} \approx \frac{1}{1 - \tfrac{1}{2}(v/c)^2} \approx 1 + \tfrac{1}{2}(v/c)^2$$

For the Michelson-Morley case, where the expected value of v/c was around 10^{-4}, the formula can be regarded as nearly exact.

Questions

1 Explain why it was necessary to rotate the Michelson-Morley apparatus.

2 Suppose a Michelson interferometer were built to run on sound waves, rather than light, a microphone placed where Michelson's eyepiece was and connected to a speaker. The apparatus is set up outdoors, with a strong wind blowing. Would an effect be observed? What would

one actually hear out of the speaker as the apparatus rotated? What would be the most desirable characteristics for the source of sound?

3 Discuss the reasons why it would be awkward to interpret the Michelson-Morley experiment as evidence that the earth is absolutely at rest.

Exercises

1 An airplane takes a round trip to a point 300 miles away, flying at an air speed of 150 mph. There is a head wind of 50 mph on the trip there, which is a tailwind on the return.
 (a) Calculate the time for the trip out, the trip back, and the round trip in the absence of a wind.
 (b) Calculate the ratio of the time for the round trip with and without the wind, and verify that the answer agrees with the prediction from the formula in Table 1 of Chapter 9.

2 Calculate the time for the round-trip flight listed in Exercise 1, if the same wind blows perpendicular to the flight path. Use Figure 2 of Chapter 9 to save arithmetic.

3 A ferryboat, which can cruise at 13 mph, crosses a river 2.4 miles wide, in which a current of 5 mph is flowing. Calculate the time for the trip.

4 From the approximate formula given at the beginning of this section, calculate values of γ for $v/c = 0.1, 0.2, 0.3 \ldots 0.8$. Make a graph of the results, plotting on the same graph the result from exact arithmetic (Figure 2 of Chapter 9).

5 Suppose the Michelson-Morley experiment is performed with light of wavelength 4×10^{-7} m, on an interferometer that gives a round-trip path length of 12 m in each arm (these figures are close to those for the actual instrument built in Cleveland). How many wavelengths' shift would be expected if the "Aether wind" is 30 km/sec = 10^{-4} c?

6 Using the result of Exercise 5, what is the smallest Aether-wind speed that can be observed if it is possible to detect a fringe shift of $\frac{1}{20}$ of a fringe?

Chapter 10

Questions

1 Devise a method of synchronizing two clocks at opposite ends of a train by means of light (or radio) signals sent from one end to the other. Show that a stationary observer will regard clocks on a moving train synchronized in this manner as being out of time.

2 Construct an argument to show that in a photograph a moving train will appear shortened. (*Hint:* From the point of view of the photographer, did the light that struck the film leave the front and back ends of the train at the same time?)

3 Discuss whether Einstein's argument implies that *gravity,* like electromagnetism, has a finite velocity of propagation.

4 In the case of the identical trains, draw the figure equivalent to Figure 2 of Chapter 10 for the case where observer *A* is at the head of his train and observer *B* at the rear of his, and their watches are synchronized as they pass.

Chapter 11

Relativistic Velocity Addition

At the beginning of Chapter 10, the "paradox" of Einstein's postulate was phrased as follows: "To the man on the train, light behaves like a bullet, while to the man on the ground it behaves like the sound of the shot." The resolution of this paradox was suggested at the end of that chapter, in which it was pointed out that, from the point of view of the man on the ground, the man on the train is using clocks that are slow and unsynchronized to measure motion over a contracted length, and thus gets an exaggerated figure for the speed of the "bullet" with respect to *him.*

Stated quantitatively, relativity says it is not correct to simply add the speed of the bullet relative to the train to the speed of the train relative to the ground to obtain the speed of the bullet relative to the ground. If v is the speed of the train and u the speed of the bullet measured by the moving observer, the observer on the ground finds the bullet moving at the speed

$$\frac{u + v}{1 + uv/c^2}$$

where our commonsense notion would be that the answer is $u + v$.

A little playing with this formula will reveal its significance:

1 If both u and v are small compared to c, the term uv/c^2 is much smaller than 1. Thus, the formula reduces to the commonsense one for ordinary velocities, for the denominator is essentially 1.

2   If *either* u or v is equal to c, the formula gives the answer c, as a small amount of algebra will show:

$$\frac{c + v}{1 + cv/c^2} = \frac{c(1 + v/c)}{1 + v/c} = c$$

This resolves the paradox: By the relativistic rule, c *plus anything is c.* Thus, both the stationary observer and the moving one get the same value for the speed of the bullet, if it is moving at the speed of light.

Questions

1   A spaceship passes a "stationary" observer.   Both he and the spaceship crew are provided with identical timers, which they start at the instant they pass.   Each timer is wired to a light, which it flashes after ten seconds have elapsed.   Which light does the stationary observer believe flashes first?   Which one does the spaceship crew believe flashes first?   Give a nonmathematical argument to explain why their points of view are not inconsistent.

2   The discrepancies between what two observers relatively in motion see arise not from what they actually see, but from their interpretations of their observations, each in his own frame of reference.   Invent an example of such a situation outside the physical sciences.

3   Give your own personal interpretation of or reaction to the concept of space-time.   Does it alter in any way your intuitive notion of time?

Exercises

1   A 1-m rod moving at 0.8c would appear how long to a stationary observer?

2   How much is an actual train 1,000 m long moving at 30 m/sec shortened?   Use the approximate formula given on page 276.

3   How fast would a train have to be moving in order to shorten its length by 2 percent?

4   How much slower does a clock moving at 0.6c run than an identical clock standing still?

5   The fastest-moving large object that can presently be observed for any great length of time is a low-orbiting earth satellite.   The best atomic clocks now available are accurate to about one part in 10^{10} (better than 1 sec in a century!).   If identical clocks of this quality, one riding in a satellite at a speed of 6 km/sec and the other on earth, are com-

pared, can the time dilation be observed? Prove your result numerically.

(*The next four exercises form a set. If worked correctly they will clarify the way in which two relatively moving observers can disagree about time measurements without actually observing anything that looks different.*)

6 Refer to the situation in Question 1, and let the relative speed be $0.6c$.
  (*a*) How much time does the stationary observer feel has elapsed on his own timer when the one on the spaceship flashes?
  (*b*) How much time does the spaceship crew believe has elapsed on the stationary timer when theirs flashes?

7 In Exercise 6, how far apart are the two timers when the one on the spaceship flashes (*a*) according to the stationary observer, and (*b*) according to the spaceship crew? Then calculate how long it takes the light from this flash to reach the stationary observer (*c*) according to him, and (*d*) according to the spaceship crew. *The discrepancy in the answers to* (*c*) *and* (*d*) *is sufficient to explain how each observer can believe his timer flashed first without inconsistency, as will be shown in the next problem.*

8 What does the stationary timer actually read at the time the light flash from the other timer reaches it? Show that the spaceship crew agrees with this result. *Note that the observable quantity, the actual reading of the stationary timer when the flash from the other timer reaches it, is the same for both observers. The disagreements are all in computed quantities, the reading of one timer at the instant the other flashed.* If you have worked this problem set correctly, you will find that 20 sec have elapsed on the stationary clock when the flash from the moving one arrives. To the two observers, these 20 sec divide up as follows:

Observer	Time up to flash	Time of flight of light flash
Stationary	12.5	7.5
Spaceship	8	12

9 To complete the symmetry of this problem set, show that the reading of the timer on the spaceship when the light flash from the stationary one reaches it is the same as the answer to the preceding problem.

10 A train 1,000 m long is moving at $0.9c$. What is the difference in clock readings at the two ends of the train, according to an observer on the ground?

11 A train of rest length 1,000 m moves at 0.6c with respect to an observer.

(*a*) Calculate the length of the train, according to the observer.

(*b*) Calculate the time discrepancy between clocks at the two ends of the train, according to this observer.

(*c*) Reexpress the answer to (*b*) in *light-meters,* i.e., use as the unit of time the time required for light to travel 1 m. (Note how much more convenient it becomes to compare time and space intervals this way.)

(*d*) Show that the answers to (*a*) and (*c*) form a right triangle, the hypotenuse of which is 1,000 m.

12 An observer on a train moving at 0.5c measures the speed of an object moving forward in the train and obtains 0.5c. What speed will the object be moving at, relative to a stationary observer?

13 A train is moving at 0.8c. How fast must an object be moving with respect to the train in order to be moving at 0.9c with respect to the ground?

14 (*a*) Verify that the speed quoted in the example of the twin paradox, at the end of Chapter 11, is sufficient to permit the round trip to be taken in 1 year (ship time).

(*b*) Verify that the time difference between a clock near the star and one on earth would appear to be nearly 25 years, to the astronaut.

15 Prove algebraically that the difference seen in the setting of two clocks at either end of a train by a stationary observer is equal to the difference in *his* estimate and that of an observer on the train of the time required for a light signal to reach the front of the train.

Chapter 12

Kinetic Energy

The approximate formula stated in the Chapter 9 section of the Appendix can be used to show that the definition of kinetic energy as $\frac{1}{2}mv^2$ still works if v is much less than c. In this case we have

$$E = mc^2 = \gamma m_0 c^2 = \left(1 + \frac{1}{2}\frac{v^2}{c^2} \right) m_0 c^2$$

$$= m_0 c^2 + \tfrac{1}{2}m_0 v^2$$

where m_0 is the *rest mass.*

The term m_0c^2 represents the *rest energy* of the object, which it possesses just by existing. The term $\frac{1}{2}m_0v^2$ represents the additional energy due to motion, i.e., the kinetic energy.

Questions

1 State whether there would be a change in mass, and which way the change would go, in each of the following situations:
   (a) An automobile battery is charged.
   (b) A red-hot steel bar is allowed to cool down.
   (c) A rubber band is stretched.
   (d) Hydrogen and oxygen burn to form water inside a sealed, insulated container.
   (e) Same as (d), in a container that allows the heat to escape.
   (f) Two atoms joined together by a force of attraction are pulled apart.

2 Discuss how relativity has modified the law of momentum conservation and the law of energy conservation.

3 Discuss the status of Newton's laws in the post-Einstein era, from the point of view of fundamental validity and from the point of view of utility.

4 Relativity states that there is a greater change of mass required to speed up a slow-moving object than a fast one, for the same total change in speed. It also states that the change in mass is a measure of the change in energy. Does classical physics also state that there is a greater energy change involved in speeding up a fast-moving object than a slow one? Does relativity increase or reduce this effect?

5 State whether two observers in identical spaceships relatively in motion will agree or disagree as to each of the following measurements. Where they disagree, state which way the discrepancy goes:
   (a) their relative speed
   (b) the mass of the other spaceship
   (c) the rate at which a clock is running on the other spaceship
   (d) the length of the other spaceship
   (e) the width (perpendicular to line of relative motion) of the other spaceship
   (f) the velocity of light
   (g) the velocity of a material object moving inside one of the ships, along the line of relative motion
   (h) same as (g), except the motion is perpendicular to the line of relative motion.

Exercises

1 How many times more massive is an object moving at $0.6c$ than the same body at rest?

2 Using the approximate formulas in the Chapter 9 section of the Appendix, calculate the increase in mass of a jet airliner of mass 100,000 kg traveling at its normal cruising speed of 300 m/sec. Is this a measurable effect?

3 How fast must an object be moving in order to have a mass double what it has when it is standing still?

4 How fast must an object be moving to increase its mass by 2 percent over its rest mass? (Use the approximate formula from Chapter 9.)

5 (*a*) Calculate the percentage change in mass of an object from being accelerated from 0 to $0.01c$, using the approximate formula from Chapter 9.

(*b*) Now do the same for an object accelerated from $0.98c$ to $0.99c$. [*Hint:* $(0.98)^2$ is about 0.96; $(0.99)^2$ is about 0.98.]

6 Calculate the work that must be done (i.e., the change in energy) to speed up a body of rest mass m_0 from $0.6c$ to $0.8c$, using (*a*) the relativistic formula $E = mc^2$ and (*b*) the classical formula $E = \frac{1}{2}mv^2$. Express the result in units of m_0c^2.

7 Calculate how many joules of energy would be produced from converting 1 kg of mass to energy.

8 In a nuclear reaction, about one-thousandth of the mass of the fuel consumed is converted to energy. A nuclear power plant is designed to provide 100 million watts of electricity (enough for a city of about 100,000). Assume the power plant delivers as electricity one-third of the energy it produces. How much fuel does it consume in a year of operation? (One year is about 3×10^7 sec.)

9 It takes 2.7 million joules of energy to boil 1 kg of cold water. By what does the mass of the steam produced exceed the mass of the water before boiling? (Hint: Use the answer to Exercise 7, if you worked it.)

10 The yield of a nuclear explosion is measured in *kilotons* or *megatons*, which means, respectively, 1,000 or 1 million tons of TNT. A single 1-megaton weapon can destroy most cities. In physical units, 1 metgaton is 4×10^{15} joules. How many kilograms of mass are converted to energy in a 1-megaton nuclear bomb? (This is about one-thousandth the total mass of explosive material in the bomb.)

Chapter 13

Details of Thomson's Experiment

The forces on charged particles are easy to calculate, once the strength of the electric and magnetic fields are known. In an electric field,

$$F = eE$$

where e is the charge of the particle and E the electric field strength. The force of a magnetic field of strength B on a particle moving with velocity v perpendicular to the field is

$$F = evB$$

Thomson rather cleverly arranged to simultaneously apply electric and magnetic fields that deflected the cathode rays *in opposite directions*. The fields were adjusted until there was no deflection of the beam. Thus, he knew the electric and magnetic forces were exactly equal:

$$eE = evB$$

with the result that, regardless of the size of e, he knew the velocity of the particles:

$$v = \frac{E}{B}$$

Knowing the velocity, he knew how long the particles spent in the field. He then turned off the magnetic field, measuring the deflection of the beam in the electric field alone. The mathematics of this deflection were precisely those of *projectile motion*—the electric force is perpendicular to the original line of flight. From the observed deflection, Thomson could calculate the acceleration due to the electric force. Knowing this, he could find the ratio of charge to mass:

$$F = ma = eE$$

$$\frac{e}{m} = \frac{a}{E}$$

Questions

1 Invent explanations or descriptions in terms of the atomic theory of matter for the following phenomena:
   (*a*) The boiling of a liquid

(*b*) Surface tension in liquids

(*c*) The fact that when a gas is compressed by a piston, it gets hotter

2   If a small drop of oil is placed on a large, smooth surface of water, the oil film will not spread out indefinitely but will spread out to form a circle, the area of which is proportional to the amount of liquid in the drop.   Give an argument using this fact as evidence for the atomic theory of matter and devise a procedure whereby this phenomenon can be used to estimate the size of oil molecules.

3   There is no known substance that remains a gas at absolute zero, and all gases deviate from the simple behavior of Figure 2 in Chapter 13 when they are cooled close to the temperature at which they condense into a liquid.   Do these facts in any way undermine the atomic theory of matter?   Explain.

4   Amplify the argument by which Faraday's law of electrical conduction in liquids was used to conclude that all ions carry the same electric charge.

5   Cite the evidence that the electron is a very light particle carrying the same charge as an ion, rather than an object as heavy as an atom carrying a much larger charge.

6   State in your own words what you consider the most convincing evidence for the atomic nature of matter.

Exercises

1   Using the data on atomic weights given early in Chapter 13, give the "recipe" (ratio of weights) for forming hydrochloric acid (HCl) from hydrogen and chlorine.

2   Carbon forms two kinds of compounds with oxygen (atomic weight 16) —3 parts carbon to 4 parts oxygen, and 3 parts carbon to 8 parts oxygen. Make a consistent guess at the chemical formulas for these compounds and use the data to calculate the atomic weight of carbon.

3   If a gas is compressed to one-tenth its original volume and the temperature is held constant:

(*a*) What happens to its pressure?

(*b*) Explain why it is necessary to insist the temperature be held constant.

4   Room temperature is normally about 20°C.   What is this temperature on the *Kelvin* temperature scale, which is "Celsius degrees above *absolute zero?*"

5 If a closed container holds gas at 0°C, to what temperature must it be heated to double its pressure?

6 To what temperature must the gas in the preceding problem be heated to double the average speed of its molecules?

7 Making use of the fact that gas temperature is proportional to the average kinetic energy of the molecules, and the proportionality is the same for all gases, what is the ratio of *speeds* of hydrogen and oxygen molecules, at the same temperature?   (Each gas forms molecules consisting of two atoms.)

8 Refer back to Question 2 above.   Suppose a droplet of oil of volume 0.001 cm³ (cubic centimeters) spreads out on the surface of a large tank of water to form a circle 40 cm in radius.   Estimate the size of the oil molecules.

9 It is possible, by observing how much energy is required to produce a given rise in temperature in a gas and extrapolating back to absolute zero, to measure the *total energy contained in a known mass of gas*. Devise a mathematical argument that shows that, in this fashion, it is possible to calculate the speed of the molecules *without knowing how massive they actually are!*

Chapter 14

Measuring Nuclear Size

A moment's contemplation should convince you that the alpha particles that come closest to the nucleus in the Geiger-Marsden experiment are those that come straight at a nucleus and recoil backward.   In this case it is very easy to calculate how close the alphas come to the center of the nucleus, for at the point of closest approach the alpha reverses its motion and is, for an instant, standing still.   Thus, all of its kinetic energy has been converted to potential energy.   This kinetic energy was well known by the time the experiment was performed.   Using the formula for potential energy in inverse-square forces derived in Chapter 6, we have

$$\text{Original KE of alphas } E = \frac{qQ}{r}$$

where q and Q are the electric charge on the alpha and gold nucleus, respectively, and r is the center-to-center distance between the alpha and the gold nucleus.   All quantities were known but r; thus it can be solved for

$$r = \frac{qQ}{E}$$

The actual result is computed in the next section.

Electrical Forces on the Atomic Scale

The electrons and nuclei that make up atoms all carry electric charges that are a whole multiple of the electron charge.   To calculate the forces between the components of the atom, it is useful to know the square of the electron charge:

$$e^2 = 2.3 \times 10^{-28} \text{ newton-m}^2$$

To obtain the force, divide this figure by the square of the radius (in meters).   To obtain the potential energy, divide by the radius.   If the charges are opposite in sign, the potential energy is negative.

For nuclei other than hydrogen, one simply multiplies e^2 by the charge on the nucleus, which is the same as its atomic number.   For example, carbon, element 6, carries a charge of $6e$.

Examples: The radius of a hydrogen atom is about 5×10^{-11} m. Thus, the force between the nucleus and an electron at this distance is

$$F = \frac{2.3 \times 10^{-28}}{(5 \times 10^{-11})^2}$$

$$= \frac{2.3 \times 10^{-28}}{2.5 \times 10^{-21}} = \text{about } 10^{-7} \text{ newtons}$$

The force in a carbon atom would be six times greater, in a uranium atom 92 times greater, and so on.

The nuclear size problem in the preceding section can now be solved *by this method*.   The gold nucleus carries a charge of $79e$; the alpha particle $2e$.   Thus, the product of the charges is $2 \times 79e^2$.   We then have

$$r = \frac{2 \times 79e^2}{E} = \frac{\text{about } 160e^2}{E}$$

The energy of the alphas used in the experiment was about 1.3×10^{-12} joules.

$$r = \frac{160 \times 2.3 \times 10^{-28}}{1.3 \times 10^{-12}} = 1.6 \times 2.3 \times 10^{-14}$$

$$= 2.8 \times 10^{-14} \text{ m}$$

The radius of a gold nucleus is about 0.8×10^{-14} m, and that of an alpha particle about 0.2×10^{-14} m; thus, the alphas came fairly close. Lighter nuclei have less repellent charge, but are not much smaller than heavy ones. Therefore, by 1919 Rutherford was able to get alphas to penetrate and disintegrate nitrogen nuclei.

Questions

1 From the behavior of atoms in liquids and solids, it is clear they are pretty much "hard spheres"; that is, once they actually come in contact, there are strong forces of repulsion that tend to keep them from penetrating one another very far. Discuss the problem of explaining this for the plum-pudding atom, in which the positive sphere can be freely penetrated by electrons, and the planetary atom, which is mostly empty space.

2 Invent a picture to show how atoms are held together in molecules, in the plum-pudding model and in the planetary model.

3 There are a number of light sources in ordinary use that produce light in a low-density gas; neon signs and the bluish mercury-vapor lamps used for street lighting are examples. Observe such lights through a glass prism. How many "lines" do you see?

4 Compare Rutherford's use of the Geiger-Marsden data to justify his nuclear atom with Newton's use of Kepler's laws to justify the inverse-square law of gravity.

5 Looking at the data from the Geiger-Marsden experiment, the deviations from Rutherford's prediction do show a slight trend: the points at small angles tend to be a bit higher with respect to the predicted value than those at large angles. It is possible to account for this by admitting that some alphas will be deflected by more than one nucleus. Construct an argument to show why this would enhance the small-angle deflections more than the large-angle ones.

Exercises

(The first two exercises are designed to give a quantitative feeling for the Geiger-Marsden experiment.)

1 The diameter of a gold atom is about 2.5×10^{-10} m. Rutherford's gold foil was about 10^{-6} m thick. About how many gold atoms did each alpha particle that penetrated the foil traverse?

2 In order to come off back of 90°, an alpha particle would have to pass within 10^{-13} m of the nucleus. Imagine each nucleus to be surrounded by a circular "target" of this size. If the alpha comes that close, it will come off back of 90°.

(*a*) In an encounter with a single atom of gold, what are the chances for the alpha to come off back of 90°?

(*b*) Using the result of Exercise 1, about what fraction of the alphas that struck the foil came off back of 90°?

3   The constant in the Balmer formula is about 3.3×10^{15} Hz.

(*a*) Calculate the frequency of the first line ($n = 1$, $m = 2$) in the hydrogen spectrum.

(*b*) Describe how the pattern of lines from a series of such lines (keep $n = 1$, vary m) would appear on a photographic plate.

(The remaining exercises are based' on the section on electrical forces on the atomic scale.)

4   The radius of a hydrogen atom is about 5×10^{-11} m.   Assume that the electron revolves in a circular orbit at about 7×10^{-15} rps.

(*a*) Calculate the speed of the electron.

(*b*) Is it appropriate to use nonrelativistic mechanics to describe its motion?

(*c*) Calculate the acceleration of the electron.

(*d*) Given that the mass of the electron is about 9×10^{-31} kg, show that the force of attraction to the nucleus is about right to account for the acceleration in (*c*).

5   The radius of a nitrogen nucleus is about 3.3×10^{-15} m, and it carries a charge of $7e$.   By scaling down the result obtained for alpha particles on gold, show that the same alphas are sufficiently energetic to penetrate a nitrogen nucleus.

6   Construct an ordinary (nonlogarithmic) graph of the Geiger-Marsden data.   This should convince you of the value of the logarithmic graph.

Chapter 15

Radius and Energy of the First Bohr Orbit

The radius of the orbit is obtained by insisting that the motion of the electron obey Newton's second law; since the force is e^2/r^2, and the acceleration is v^2/r, we have

$$\frac{e^2}{r^2} = m \frac{v^2}{r} \tag{1}$$

The angular momentum rule adopted by Bohr is

$$mvr = \hbar \tag{2}$$

To eliminate the velocity, which we are not interested in, we solve Equation (2) for it:

$$v = \frac{\hbar}{mr}$$

and substitute this value in Equation (1):

$$\frac{e^2}{r^2} = \frac{m}{r}\left(\frac{\hbar}{mr}\right)^2 = \frac{\hbar^2}{mr^3}$$

Multiplying both sides by r^3 gives us

$$e^2 r = \frac{\hbar^2}{m}$$

which gives the desired solution:

$$r = \frac{\hbar^2}{me^2}$$

Using the values $\hbar = 1.05 \times 10^{-34}$ joule-sec, $m = 9.1 \times 10^{-31}$ kg, $e^2 = 2.3 \times 10^{-28}$ newton-m^2, we obtain

$$r = \frac{(1.05 \times 10^{-34})^2}{9.1 \times 10^{-31} \times 2.3 \times 10^{-28}} = \frac{1.1}{9.1 \times 2.3} \times 10^{-9}$$

$$= 5.3 \times 10^{-11} \text{ m}$$

The energy is quite easy to compute, since we have already seen that the total energy is one-half the potential energy:

$$E = \frac{1}{2} \times \left(\frac{e^2}{r}\right) = \frac{e^2}{2(\hbar^2/me^2)}$$

$$= \frac{me^4}{2\hbar^2}$$

the result cited in the text. The constant in the Balmer formula for the frequencies of spectrum lines is obtained from

$$\nu = \frac{E}{h} = \frac{e^2}{2hr} = \frac{e^2}{4\pi\hbar r}$$

$$= \frac{2.3 \times 10^{-28}}{4\pi \times 1.05 \times 10^{-34} \times 5.3 \times 10^{-11}} = 3.3 \times 10^{15} \text{ Hz}$$

The agreement of this number with the one obtained by Balmer was convincing.

Questions

1   It is far easier to demonstrate that electromagnetic radiation is quantized if x-rays or gamma rays are used than with visible light.   Why?

2   One later confirmation of Einstein's analysis of the photoelectric effect involved the following experiment.   The photoelectric effect is produced by using a very faint light and a rapid camera shutter.   The light is so faint that the total energy that should pass through the shutter is less than that required to pull an electron free from the metal.   It is found that, if the shutter is clicked many times, occasionally an electron is ejected from the metal.   What would the classical picture of light predict?   Show how the photon theory can account for the phenomenon.

3   Which two adjoining Bohr orbits are farthest apart in energy?   Explain.

4   Describe how collisions between atoms make it possible for a hot gas to give off light, in terms of the Bohr picture of the atom.

5   List all the physical laws used in the Bohr picture of hydrogen, classifying them as
   (*a*)   carried over from Newton's mechanics
   (*b*)   originating from earlier quantum theory
   (*c*)   Bohr's own contribution

6   If Bohr's model is applied to atoms heavier than hydrogen, with greater positive charge on the nucleus, would you expect the innermost orbit to be smaller or larger than that in hydrogen?   Explain.

Exercises

(*The following exercises involve these constants: Planck's constant, $h = 6.625 \times 10^{-34}$ joule-sec; $\hbar = h/2\pi = 1.05 \times 10^{-34}$ joule-sec.*)

1   Find the energy of a typical visible light quantum (frequency $= 6 \times 10^{14}$ Hz).

2   The energy of a typical medical x-ray photon is about 2×10^{-15} joules.
   (*a*)   Calculate the frequency of such a photon.
   (*b*)   Show that it has a wavelength comparable to the size of typical atoms.

3   In a photoelectric effect experiment, the following results are obtained: the lowest frequency that can produce electrons is 10^{15} Hz; and with light of 3×10^{15} Hz, the electrons have an energy of 12.8×10^{-19}

joules. Use these data to obtain (a) Planck's constant and (b) the energy required to free an electron from the photocathode.

4 Calculate the total energy, in joules, of an electron in the first Bohr orbit of hydrogen, using the Balmer constant and $E = h\nu$.

5 How many times more energy is required to remove an electron completely from the ground state of a hydrogen atom than to move it from the ground state to the next higher?

6 What is the ratio between the energy of a photon given off when an electron falls from the third to the second Bohr orbit, to that given off when it falls from the second to the first?

7 How many times larger is the one-hundredth Bohr orbit than the first?

8 What is the change in angular momentum for an electron moving between two adjoining Bohr orbits, in units of $\hbar$?

9 Draw graphs showing *radius* and *energy* of Bohr orbits versus orbit number.

10 Reexpress the law $E = h\nu$ as a relation between energy and *wavelength*.

11 The visible spectrum goes from frequencies of 4 to 8×10^{14} Hz. Lower frequencies are called *infrared* and are felt as heat. Higher frequencies are called *ultraviolet* and can cause sunburn.
(a) To what part of the spectrum does the photon from the jump from the second to the first Bohr orbit belong?
(b) What is the lowest transition that can produce visible light?

12 The average kinetic energy of hydrogen atoms at room temperature ($300°$ on the absolute scale) is about 4×10^{-21} joules.
(a) Show that this proves hydrogen must be heated to a much higher temperature to give off light.
(b) At about how high an absolute temperature will an *average* hydrogen atom have enough kinetic energy to excite an electron to the second orbit in a collision?

13 There exists a particle in nature called the *mu-meson,* identical to the electron except that it is 200 times heavier. Atoms may be formed consisting of a hydrogen nucleus and a mu-meson.
(a) What is the radius of the first Bohr orbit in such an atom?
(b) Would the energies of photons given off in quantum jumps in such an atom be higher or lower than those from hydrogen, and by what ratio?

14 A helium atom has twice the nuclear charge of hydrogen and has both its two electrons in the smallest orbit. Ignoring the repulsion of the electrons, what should be the size of this orbit?

Chapter 16

Questions

1 As one moves to larger and larger Bohr orbits, do the wavelengths of the electrons get larger or smaller?

2 If a photon and an electron have the same kinetic energy, which has the shorter wavelength?

3 Give an argument to show that atomic orbits of circumference $\frac{1}{2}$, $1\frac{1}{2}$, $2\frac{1}{2}$, . . . wavelengths could not exist.

4 The de Broglie formula implies that the heavier a particle is, the shorter its wavelength. Does this make it easier or harder to account for the absence of wave effects with particles of visible size?

5 Which undesirable features of the Bohr atomic model are eliminated in the wave model? Which remain? What new problems does the wave model introduce?

6 Comment on whether the success of the de Broglie theory makes Planck's constant seem more or less universal in its significance than before the theory was suggested.

7 In the Bohr theory, Planck's constant plays two separate roles: in one it connects the energy states with the frequencies of spectral lines, while in the other it determines the allowed orbits. Explain how the de Broglie theory unifies these roles.

Exercises

1 What is the ratio between the wavelengths of de Broglie waves of electrons in the second and first Bohr orbits? (*Hint:* Do not actually calculate the momentum; just consider the size and wave pattern of each orbit.)

2 Calculate the wavelength of a running man of mass 100 kg at speed of 3 m/sec. Is the result reassuring or disturbing?

3 If the kinetic energy of an electron is quadrupled, what happens to its wavelength?

4 Show that the de Broglie formula gives the correct wavelengths for photons, using the fact that the energy carried by light is its momentum times the speed of light.

5 Electrons (mass 9×10^{-31} kg) in a TV picture tube travel at $0.2c$. Using nonrelativistic formulas,

    (*a*) Calculate their momentum, their kinetic energy, and their wavelength.

(*b*) Compare the wavelength to that of visible light and also to the wavelength of a photon of the same energy.

6 In Davisson's experiment, electrons must have wavelengths about the size of atoms (10^{-10} m). Calculate the velocity of such an electron.

Chapter 17

Questions

1 Show that, in all uses made in this book of Planck's constant, the smaller the constant, the more nearly valid are classical laws.

2 The higher the momentum of a particle, the more pronounced are its particle characteristics and the less pronounced its wave ones. Explain.

3 Show that the uncertainty principle implies that the uncertainty in momentum is large only when the accuracy of position measurement is comparable to the wavelength of the particle.

4 Note that the uncertainty principle makes no direct mention of wave quantities (frequency, wavelength, etc.). Discuss whether this implies a deeper significance for Planck's constant than that implied by the simple de Broglie-Schrödinger theory.

5 Explain why the more massive an object is, the easier it becomes to predict its future position.

6 The velocity of an electron is measured by timing its flight between two viewing screens whose positions are well known, that is, Δx is small and Δp is large. Discuss what the uncertainty principle has to say about our knowledge of
(*a*) The velocity of the electron during its passage between the two screens
(*b*) The velocity of the electron after leaving the second screen
(*c*) The velocity of the electron before striking the first screen
(*d*) The agreement among many measurements of (*a*), if the electrons originate from a source that gives them all the same momentum before striking the first screen.

Exercises

1 (*a*) Calculate the uncertainty in momentum of an object whose position is measured to an accuracy comparable to the size of an atomic nucleus (10^{-14} m).

(*b*) Then calculate the resulting uncertainty in velocity if the object has the mass of a proton $(1.6 \times 10^{-27}$ kg$)$.

2 Verify the entries in the last two columns of Table 1 of Chapter 17.

3 The uncertainty principle can be interpreted as the consequence of the necessity of using at least one photon to measure the position of an object, and the accuracy of such a measurement is about the same as the wavelength of the photon, that is, $\Delta x = \lambda$. Show that the resulting momentum uncertainty Δp is equal to the photon momentum.

4 The electron in the ground state of hydrogen can be anywhere in a region about the size of Bohr's orbit. Thus, Δx is about the Bohr radius for a series of repeated measurements of its position. Calculate the uncertainty in momentum, and show it is about equal to the momentum of Bohr's first-orbit electron.

5 Verify quantitatively the assertion made at the end of Chapter 16 that a free electron wave initially confined to a space the size of an atomic nucleus will expand to fill a space comparable to the Pentagon in one-millionth of a second. Mathematically, the initial situation is $\Delta x = 10^{-14}$ m. (*Hint:* You will find Δp so large that the classical formula $\Delta v = \Delta p / m$ yields a speed much greater than light. This means that the relativistic momentum-velocity relation must be used, and the electron travels close to the speed of light. You need not actually calculate its speed.)

Chapter 18

Quantitative Aspects of the Two-slit Problem

This example will show how the measurement of the position of an electron as it passes through a slit can destroy the interference pattern. The reasoning is that a measurement of sufficient precision Δx to leave one reasonably certain which slit the electron passed through will deflect the electron enough to make it hit in one of the dark places on the screen, rather than a bright one.

The uncertainty principle tells us that if we measure position to an accuracy Δx, the electron will be given a "kick" perpendicular to the line of flight, represented by the momentum uncertainty:

$$\Delta p = \frac{\hbar}{\Delta x}$$

This will cause it to veer through an angle θ whose sine is the ratio of Δp to the total momentum p, as shown in the figure below:

$$\sin \theta = \frac{\Delta p}{p} = \frac{\hbar}{p \, \Delta x}$$

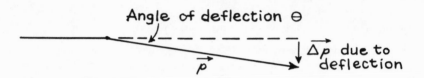

To be reasonably certain which slit the electron went through, let Δx be one-half the distance s between the slits. Then,

$$\sin \theta = \frac{\hbar}{p(\frac{1}{2}s)} = \frac{2\hbar}{ps} \tag{1}$$

We now make use of the formula derived in Exercise 12 of Chapter 7 to tell us where the first "dip" in the interference pattern lies. The formula states that the path difference between rays going through the two slits is given by:

$$\text{Path diff.} = s \sin \theta$$

The first dark region in the interference pattern occurs when the path difference is one-half wavelength. Thus we have

$$s \sin \theta = \tfrac{1}{2}\lambda \tag{2}$$

To compare with Equation (1) above we must reexpress λ in terms of the equivalent momentum, as given by the de Broglie rule:

$$\lambda = \frac{h}{p} = \frac{2\pi\hbar}{p}$$

Substituting this value in (2) gives

$$s \sin \theta = \frac{\pi\hbar}{p}$$

or $$\sin \theta = \frac{\pi\hbar}{ps} \tag{3}$$

Compare this result with that given in Equation (1) above. The angle is not much larger, since the two formulas differ only in the replacement of 2 by π. Thus, an electron originally destined for the center of the central bright line in the interference pattern is deflected almost to the dark band. Some electrons are deflected more than this, others less, for Δp is the average kick. Therefore the interference pattern is almost obliterated. Since some position measurements will be off by more than the average value $\frac{1}{2}s$, it turns out that in this case we will be wrong about which slit the electron went through a few percent of the time. If we reduce Δx to become more certain, Δp gets larger, and thus more smearing occurs.

Questions

1   Criticize the following naïve statement of the wave-particle duality: "The true nature of an electron is intermediate between that of a particle and of a wave."

2   Discuss to what extent the framework of classical physics (conservation laws, Newton's laws, etc.) survives in the quantum theory.

3   Outline the history of modifications in the concept of energy conservation through the following stages:
   (*a*)   As a purely mechanical law
   (*b*)   Nineteenth-century form (many different energy forms)
   (*c*)   Late classical (atoms and fields, but no quantum theory)
   (*d*)   Relativistic
   (*e*)   Quantum theory

4   The quantum theory contains a wave-particle duality, and relativity has a space-time duality. In both cases, it is the *observer* that influences which aspect manifests itself. Discuss the respects in which these two dualities are similar and different.

Exercises

1   Referring to the quantitative treatment of the two-slit problem in this section of the Appendix, show that if the position measurement is made twice as accurate as in the example given, the average deflection exceeds the angle between the central bright line and the adjacent dark line.

2   Do a quantitative analysis to show why the two-screen method of measuring the direction of the electron (see the section of Chapter 18 entitled "Can We Outwit the Uncertainty Relations?") will not succeed in permitting us to observe the interference pattern and also be sure which slit the electron went through.

Index